W9-DGT-398

PSYCHOTHERAPY:
MYTH AND METHOD

By the same author:

TELEPATHY AND MEDICAL PSYCHOLOGY
W. W. Norton and Co. Inc., New York 1948

NEW DIMENSIONS OF DEEP ANALYSIS
Grune and Stratton, New York 1954

FROM MEDICINE MAN TO FREUD
Dell First Edition, New York 1956

NEUROSIS IN THE FAMILY AND PATTERNS OF PSYCHOSOCIAL DEFENSE
Hoeber Medical Division, Harper and Row, New York 1963

PSYCHOTHERAPY: MYTH AND METHOD
An Integrative Approach

JAN EHRENWALD, M.D.

Visiting Consulting Psychiatrist,
The Roosevelt Hospital, New York City

> IT MAY PERHAPS SEEM TO YOU AS THOUGH
> OUR THEORIES ARE A KIND OF MYTHOLOGY,
> AND IN THE PRESENT CASE NOT EVEN AN
> AGREEABLE ONE. BUT DOES NOT EVERY SCI-
> ENCE COME IN THE END TO A KIND OF
> MYTHOLOGY LIKE THIS? CANNOT THE SAME BE
> SAID TODAY OF YOUR OWN PHYSICS?
>
> S. Freud, in a letter to
> A. Einstein, 1932

GRUNE & STRATTON   NEW YORK AND LONDON

WIDENER COLLEGE
WOLFGRAM
LIBRARY
CHESTER, PA.

151170

DISCARDED
WIDENER UNIVERSITY

Copyright © 1966 by Grune & Stratton, Inc., New York City
Library of Congress Catalog Card No. 66–19822
Printed in U.S.A. (G–A)

Contents

Acknowledgments

Grateful acknowledgments for permission to use quotations are due to the following authors, publishers and agents:

from *MAGIC, SCIENCE AND RELIGION* by Bronislaw Malinowski; by permission of The Free Press, New York 10019.

from *MESMERISM* by Gilbert Frankau, by permission of Mrs. Frankau and Macdonald and Co. Ltd., London

from *SHAMANISM* by Mircea Eliade by permission of Bollingen Foundation, New York 10021

from *MEMORIES, DREAMS, REFLECTIONS* by C. G. Jung, edited by A. Jaffé, by permission of Pantheon Books, New York

from *BEING-IN-THE-WORLD* by Ludwig Binswanger, translated by Jacob Needleman, Basic Books Inc., New York

from *THE WORLDS OF EXISTENTIALISM* by Maurice Friedman, by permission of Random House, New York

from *LETTERS OF SIGMUND FREUD* edited by Ernst L. Freud, by permission of Basic Books, Inc., New York 10016, and of Ernst L. Freud, of London.

Other source material referred to in this book has been quoted and duly acknowledged in my historical anthology, *FROM MEDICINE MAN TO FREUD*, Dell Books, New York 1956.

I also wish to thank my wife for her untiring help in preparing the manuscript and to Mrs. Laura Dale for her invaluable editorial assistance and her usual efficiency in preparing the index.

JAN EHRENWALD

Jacket Design by Ben Robinson

Preface

This is a book that tries to find answers to questions which are usually considered impolite in polite society. What is the effective principle in psychotherapy: myth or scientific theories? What is it that kept many prescientific methods of mental healing in business for centuries even though, by present standards, they were largely based on deception and self-deception? In what way are their latter-day successors superior to their present prototypes? What, in the last analysis, accounts for the privileged position of psychoanalysis among contemporary schools of psychotherapy? What about equally ambitious claims of other schools? How are we to account for the fact that despite their conflicting and at times mutually incompatible propositions they all seem to help people and have succeeded in gathering a devoted group of followers—both therapists and patients— into their folds?

In seeking to answer these questions we propose to survey a number of illustrative case histories: the case histories of diverse schools of psychotherapy, scientific and prescientific—not of individual patients treated by their followers. Thus Part I will chiefly be devoted to presenting the case material upon which the discussion of Part II and Part III will be based.

The reader, invited to view in historic perspective the groping attempts of shamans or charlatans, of medicine men or priestly healers, to give solace to the sick in body and mind, will not be surprised to find himself transported into a world of magic and myth. He may note the paradox of the sightless—of the mystic who closes his eyes to the world of reality— trying to help the sighted to cope with emotional crises and calamities, while both know full well that the exigencies of everyday life demand keen vision, skilled hands and time-tested pragmatic know-how. Anthropologists have described the paradox as the dual causality characteristic of primitive man. Perhaps some readers will be surprised to find that civilized man of our time has by no means overcome this dichotomy: that remnants of the principle of dual causality can still be discerned in his superstitious practices, in his religious beliefs, and indeed in some of his most ambitious systems of scientific psychotherapy.

It is true that magic and myth run counter to our modern Western temper. They have been banished from science, repudiated by the psychiatrist, and ridiculed by the man in the street. The techniques of magic have been replaced by the magic of technology. Even theologians are busy demythologizing the Bible. Yet we shall see that both magic and myth stubbornly resist being altogether purged from our mental organization. They continue to cling to life, regardless of their debatable survival value.

We propose to show that one of the reasons for their continued survival, especially in the field of psychotherapy, is that they help to make psychotherapy work. The analyst analyzes; he makes the unconscious conscious. He interprets the meaning of symptoms and dreams, he removes blocks and inhibitions, and he brings about cathartic release. He effects basic changes in the economy of instincts and, hopefully, in the dynamics of personality structure. But it is the therapist's myth—shared with the myth of his patient—which serves as the entering wedge for the therapeutic process. It is true that myth without insight into psychodynamics has to rely on the principle of trial and error. It operates like a surgeon trying to work in the dark. Yet psychodynamics stripped of the therapist's personal impact upon the patient would be like leaving it to the scalpel to perform the operation without a surgeon.

Another major theme pursued in the chapters that follow is an inquiry into the validity of basic psychodynamic principles themselves. We shall note how patients treated by virtually all schools of psychotherapy usually confirm their therapist's propositions. Their productions tend to comply with his unconscious or preconscious wishes and expectations. This is what will be described as doctrinal compliance. This, as we shall see in Part II, is an inexhaustible source of error contaminating virtually all schools of psychotherapeutic thought whose "case histories" are reviewed in Part I. In fact, we will be led to the conclusion that the psychiatrist cannot help but influence the very clinical manifestations which he is supposed to study in a cold, detached and impersonal manner—much in the same way that the physicist observing molecules, atoms or electrons in his laboratory, is bound to modify their behavior by the very act of observing them. The physicist's theories, like those of the behavioral scientist, are the joint products of the observer and of the object observed. As Freud noted, they are closely akin to the myths made by the psychoanalyst.

But there is an important difference between myths spawned by the physical as opposed to the behavioral sciences. Mesmer's myth of animal magnetism proved to be effective for more than half a century regardless of its truth value. Like some earlier and later theories in the field of mental healing, Mesmer's myth had the power of self-fulfillment. False theories proposed by the physicist have a much shorter lease on unchallenged scientific life. He cannot impose his will on the Brownian movements of molecules or make electrons perform minuets to fall in line with his theoretical expectations. The difference is apt to give inferiority feelings to the psychoanalyst or behavioral scientist. But the clear realization and systematic exploitation of the factors responsible for the difference may turn the liability into an asset. Many of our cherished theories of psychotherapy, psychoanalytic or otherwise, may be vitiated by doctrinal compliance. They

may be embroidered by myth, and their practices shot through with vestiges of magic. However, the therapist capable of manipulating both his
myths and scientific concepts, of effecting what will be described as the
existential shift from magic to science—and if need be, back from science
to magic and myth—may find that his patients will do more than merely
comply with his doctrine. They may indeed be helped by his motivation to
help, and unless he is deceived by his own myth, he may even come closer
to knowing how and why myths (or theories) happen to be therapeutically
effective.

However, such deeper insight into the psychodynamics of cure can only
be attained by the unmasking of remnants of magic and myth surviving in
the therapist's mind, much in the same way that effective psychoanalysis is
contingent, among other things, upon the analyst's success in making the
patient's unconscious conscious. Paradoxically, in some of his analytic
friends, the present writer's attempt in this direction was met with the
familiar signs of resistance. It is hoped that such resistance will not impede
the objective scrutiny of his thesis. The analyst certainly does not cure by
myth alone, but the integration of myth with the analytic approach may
well help in the process. More than that: myth, masked or unmasked,
seems to be the common element in the diverse schools of psychotherapy,
and its proper appreciation may pave the way for the comparative study of
their rationale, including the cross-validation of their basic propositions,
theoretical concepts and therapeutic claims. To do this, we cannot be satisfied with taking their own programatic statements and psychodynamic
formulations at their face value. We must extend our inquiry into some of
their tacitly implied presuppositions, unstated premises and, if possible,
into unconscious determinants that have been at the back of the minds of
their originators. We have to study what will be described as the *metadynamics* of their "latent contents."

The concluding chapters are meant to take a few tentative steps in that
direction. A synoptic table included in the text draws the outlines of four
major models of psychotherapy: (1) primitive healing, based on magic
and myth; (2) treatment by rational guidance, persuasion and reeducation,
based on learning theory; (3) various schools of analytic psychotherapy,
including orthodox analysis, based on psychodynamic principles. It will be
noted that all models, except primitive healing, ignore or "repress" magic
and myth but, overtly or covertly, apply methods derived from learning
theory.

Inevitably the author has his own axe to grind. He advocates a revised
and expanded version of psychoanalysis as the fourth model. This model
makes proper allowance for myth and myth-induced existential shifts in the
therapeutic process. At the same time it utilizes familiar psychodynamic

principles coupled with those of learning theory. This is how it seeks to arrive at an integration and reconciliation of the conflicting approaches to psychotherapy. Above all, the fourth model is concerned with helping the patient to reconcile his conflicting instinctual drives with his own values, with cultural and societal demands, and to integrate them in more successful patterns of living.

This, I submit, cannot be accomplished by ignoring or explaining away the part played by surviving vestiges of magic and myth in our mental equipment and sociocultural organization. Nor can it be done, however, by falling back on myth alone. The power of myth is akin to such forces of nature as the winds and the tides. It cannot be made to work to order. But an experienced sailor knows how to rig his sail and to steer his craft so as to make the winds and the tides subservient to his purpose. The mobilization of myth in scientific psychotherapy requires similar experience, know-how and command of analytic technique. Unless the writer is being carried away by his personal myth, the necessary skills and techniques can be conceptualized, spelled out in articles, taught in seminars, and even written up in books like the present volume.

J. E.

New York, Spring 1965

Part One

Primitive Healing: Myth without Rationale

—I—

What Is Myth?

Myth has many meanings. To modern man it has become well-nigh synonymous with lie. We speak of the mythical nature of ideologies which we dislike, of beliefs which we reject, and of scientific theories found to be wanting or proven to be wrong. We speak of myths in the Old or New Testament if we are agnostics, in Jung's analytic psychology if we are Freudians, of the mythological element in Freud's teachings if we are anti-Freudians, and of the mythological roots of scientific concepts in general if we happen to side with the skeptical philosophers and relativistic thinkers of our day.

Occasionally, however, we may be prepared to take time off from an un-compromisngly rational position, to close our eyes to the known, to the obvious, to the commonplace, and to open our mind to the unknown or supposedly unknowable; to be persuaded by allegory, to surrender to the power of symbol, myth and metaphor.

These swings of the pendulum from defamation to exaltation are not confined to classroom or cocktail party discussions, nor to the columns of popular magazine articles. They can be traced in the history of our culture as far back as we want to go. The pioneers of the modern scientific approach to primitive mentality, to animism, magic and myth, were emphatic in their condemnation of all the "monstrous farrago"[1,2] collected in their travels through time and space, from the Paleolithic to the Victorian age; from the Sacred Grove of Nemi in the Albany Hills of Italy to the Gilyak hunters in Eastern Siberia. Myths, Sir James Frazer declared, "being founded on ignorance and misapprehension, are always false, for were they true, they would cease to be myths."

Magic, this lowly handmaiden of mythology, was a favorite target of their censure. Viewed from their exalted vantage point at Trinity College in Cambridge or at the University Museum in Oxford, Sir James Frazer, Sir E. B. Tylor and their fellow Victorians had no difficulties in exposing the teller of tales and the dispenser of magic, the shaman or the medicine man as superstitious savages, frauds or montebanks whose ignorance was exceeded by that of their clients only. It was this margin of superstition and ignorance, they held, which assured their dominance in the tribe and was used to enhance their status and reputation. Seen in this light, the mythical stories told for the edification of their fellow tribesmen were the reflection of the shaman or medicine man's crude, untutored mind. At best they were groping attempts to bring order into the universe by explaining the forces of nature in metaphorical terms. Andrew Lang considered savage mythology the equivalent of savage science whose main function was supposed to be to answer questions.[3]

The advent, at the beginning of this century, of the functional school of anthropology,[4,5] brought a gradual change of this attitude towards primitive mentality. Myths and the magic art were now credited with playing a significant role in the life of the community. They preserved the identity, the historic continuity and social coherence of the tribe. They had a specific social function as "a charter of ritual belief, ethics and social organization." They were the repositories of cultural tradition, the guardians of law and order, the forerunners of a moral code of behavior, as well as of the polarity of the religious and scientific outlook of modern man. The existentialist point of view went further than that. Myths were seen as holding the key for a deeper understanding of man's place in nature. In symbolic or allegorical terms, they were thought to express truths which could not be spelled out in the discursive, causal-reductionistic languages of Western man. Instead of being brushed aside as the mutterings of ignorant savages of a past era, or of a few anthropological fossils surviving in the New World or in the Old, they were now supposed to be samples of the ultimate wisdom attainable to *homo sapiens*—provided he was prepared to forego his pride of scientific mastery, of technical know-how and that he was ready to go back to the origins of his early awareness of himself and the world, relieved of the dichotomies of object and subject, of I and Thou. The Noble Savage of Jean Jacques Rousseau had died, a victim of the inclement climate of 19th century rationalism. The middle of the 20th century seemed to be willing to bestow his mantle on his latter-day descendant: the Noble Mystic.

By contrast to the wild-eyed wizard or medicine man of Sir James Frazer, the Noble Mystic of the Zen worshippers and cocktail party existentialists is the personification of all the virtues lost by modern man. Unencumbered by the legacy of rationalistic philosophy and science, the Noble Mystic is imbued with the transcendent wisdom of a mythical age. Though he may be living in the present, he views the world with his eyes fixed on the existential validity of myths. He is at one with nature, yet he has attained the highest degree of selfhood and individuation. He communes with the clouds in the sky and the lilies in the field without falling victim to the empathic fallacy. He speaks and understands the language of the birds and the bees without having studied the works of von Frisch, Konrad Lorentz or Tinbergen. He has the wisdom of Laotzu, Suzuki, Heidegger and Binswanger at his fingertips without having taken courses in modern existential philosophy. He seems to know all the answers, but he likes to shroud their meaning in the ambiguity of Chinese ideograms or the

Delphic oracle. Generally of a friendly and placid disposition, he is wary of plumbing, barber shops, TV, radio and other mass media. Yet his power over the minds of his fellow men compares favorably with the highest Nielsen ratings of contemporary TV personalities. Professor Jung would no doubt readily recognize him as a classical example of the archetype of the sage or the wise old man. Others may merely see in him a modernized version of the culture hero of mythical times; in any case, one who would take a dim view of the technological department of C. P. Snow's Two Cultures.

✽   ✽   ✽

What then is the nature of myth, and what is to account for the wide divergencies of opinion as to its nature? H. A. Murray,[6] in a wide ranging anthology, distinguishes between eight classes or aspects of myths, each class comprising several subgroups or clusters of myths. He quotes definitions suggested by various authors trying to do justice to each item on his list and points to the difficulties of calibrating one definition against the other.

Instead of trying to wrap up the problem in a neatly packaged definition of my own, I submit that there are three principal reasons for the existing disagreements. One reason is the specific vantage point of the observer from which he happens to be viewing myth. He may be a 20th century western anthropologist studying the cosmology of Navajo Indians as it can be gleaned from the tales told or the sand paintings made by one of their surviving medicine men. The observer may be a southern Fundamentalist insisting on the indisputable authority of the story of Creation as it is laid down in Genesis. Or else, a mythical theme may be enacted on an Athenian stage before an audience of the fifth century B.C., ready to take the time-honored story of King Oedipus at its face value and to be carried away by its high drama and cathartic denouement. Lastly, the observer may be a modern psychoanalyst, Freudian, Jungian or existentialist, who discerns in the fable a symbolic message to suit his particular school of thought—one transcending the meaning it held (or still holds) to the uninitiated. He may view myths as collective daydreams dreamed by primitive societies and may arrive at their latent meaning by probing beneath the manifest content of a mythical narrative. Myth, in this view, would parallel the psychodynamic function of dreams in that it too serves as a "compensation for disowned psychic realities."[7,7a] It turns the gratification of repressed instinctual drives into superhuman deeds and elevates the perpetrators of incest or patricide to the status of heroes or demigods. At the same time such mechanisms of defense as distortion, projection or displacement should permit the listener to enjoy the mythical story with impunity, help master primordial fears and meet his dependency needs.

Or else one may view myth as a product of the collective unconscious. One may look for its numenous, archetypal core, hidden under culturally determined surface appearances.[8] Such an approach will, in any case, focus on altogether different layers of a mythological theme than that of the naive observer, the historian, the theologian or the anthropologist. Clearly their respective concepts of myth will vary with their cultural background, their religious persuasion, with their degree of learning and sophistication, and with the particular bias of their scientific orientation.

A second major obstacle in the way of arriving at a consensus as to the nature of myth is the fact that myth, like any other manifestation of life, has a life cycle of its own. Speaking of myth, we have to state which phase of its life cycle we have in mind. Failing this, we may find ourselves in the position of a zoologist discoursing about an exotic insect without telling us whether he is focusing attention on its larval or caterpillar stage; on the full-grown specimen, or on its fossil remains encased in a block of amber.

Myths, in the beginning of their life cycle, are the first articulate responses of man facing the mysteries of the universe around him, including the mysteries within himself. They are, at this stage, groping attempts to organize, to bring into coherent patterns his perception of self and of the outer world in order to attain a modicum of control over it. This is how myths of creation and myths of emergence shade into myths of the eternal return; myths of polarity,[6] of the culture hero, as well as others. Gradually they assume more than merely projective, descriptive or explanatory functions and come to serve as purveyors and guardians of dimly perceived—or confidently proclaimed—laws governing the affairs of man and his gods. This is how they become repositories of an elementary code of social behavior, of an elaborate system of rites and observances, regulating man's relationships to his fellow men and to the universe at large.

It will be noted that this function goes far beyond that of compensatory wish-fulfillment or collective daydreaming postulated by O. Rank, H. Sachs and other psychoanalysts. It is a social, or psychosocial, function of vital significance to the tribe, helping to determine its behavior both in everyday life and in spiritual crises, providing it with the quality of the sacred as opposed to the profane.[9] It is this aspect of myth which theologians have described as its "effectiveness," comparable to the power of faith which the faithful believe to be capable of moving mountains and which certainly is capable of moving the human heart.[10]

From this point on, myth—or what has up to now been more or less readily identifiable as myth—tends to fork into two seemingly antithetical prongs, one religious, the other scientific, or prescientific.

The vicissitudes of the religious branch lead from magic observances, sacred rites and ceremonials to an elaborate liturgy, buttressed by the claim of divine revelation and the promise of salvation in the hereafter. It reaches its high point with the advent of a charismatic mythical personality: a Buddha, a Messiah or a Christ Savior. Ultimately it may petrify in dogma presided over by authoritarian ecclesiastic institutions.

Of particular interest in the present context are recent attempts by Protestant theologians to reverse this trend, at least as far as the Judeo-Christian heritage is concerned. Paul Tillich[11] called for a reinterpretation of Christian symbolism in the language of our time. Rudolf Bultman,[12] presumably taking his cue from the old controversy that resulted in the dedogmatizing and ultimate dissolution of dogma, went further than that. He proceeded to strip Christianity of the last remnants of its pagan, magico-mythical tradition: to demythologize the Old and the New Testament. Yet it is also interesting to note that such an attempt was bound to empty myth of its most highly charged ingredients and to shift the burden of its spiritual power and effectiveness to an expurgated and resanctified religious sphere.

A parallel process of increasing demythologization and secularization can be seen in the prescientific, or would-be scientific, branch of the fork. Myth, stripped of its religious underpinnings and claim of sanctity, is exposed as a discredited welter of unwarranted or frankly misleading beliefs. Even recourse to the pragmatic test of effectiveness can no longer persuade the skeptic. He may point to the bizarre covenant of Aztec religion requiring the faithful to burn all their worldly possessions every 52nd year of their calendar because the world was supposed to come to an end on that date. Myth, in this case, was certainly effective. But it may well have contributed to the mysterious disappearance of several tribes espousing such myths from the stage of recorded history. The time honored sacredness of India's sacred cows, giving rise to their virtually unchecked propagation, with the attending waste of valuable pasture land and consecutive famines, is another case in point. A more recent example is the pathetic story of the rebellious Lumpa sect in Rhodesia. They were led to their deaths by their prophetess, Alice Lenshina, who promised to turn to water the machine gun bullets used against them to put down their rebellion.

The apparent positive survival value of other myths obviously evolved by the principle of trial and error. Myths meeting the needs for preservation and coherence of the tribe were handed down from one generation to the next, thus making sure that there were always enough tribesmen left to "tell the tale." According to the diffusion theory, some myths of this order served their purpose so well that they were taken over by more and more neighboring tribes. If, in addition, they were associated with anxiety reducing, reassuring or otherwise socially beneficial customs, rites and observances, they were given the stamp of religious approval to buttress their authority. Alternatively, they were subjected to the process of gradual demythologization and rationalization till they graduated from primitive fertility rites, hunting, fishing or healing magic, to become forerunners of diverse branches of empirical science, stripped of its cruder magico-mythical ingredients.

This is how what is left of myth has been subjected to Western man's growing rationalistic trend. We may be ready to pay occasional homage to Parmenides' prophetic vision anticipating some of the concepts of evo-lutionary theory. We may even nod, somewhat condescendingly, approval of the ancient rite of circumcision or of some of the Jewish or Mohammedan dietary laws. More often than not, however, we are giving short shrift to the purported truth value or attempted reinterpretations of a mythical narrative. We cannot reasonably be persuaded that the world was created in six or seven days, and we regard the wide variety of rival cosmologies that have come down to us from other cultures as imaginative creations of the primitive mind, archetypal or otherwise, but apart from Jung's more zealous followers, we are not likely to look in them for verifiable factual information as to the nature and origin of matter and mind.

The fact is that since Aristotle, Herodotus and the Sophists—to say noth-ing of the Humanistic Revolution and 18th century Enlightenment—myths have been thoroughly discredited, deflated and debunked. At best, they are relegated into the realm of fable or fairy tale. Modern man may view them as intriguing anthropological oddities but rarely stops to think of them as human documents of deeper significance. They have become historically obsolescent or defunct.

Psychoanalysts have called attention to another factor. The gradual ero-sion of the intellectual message—of the manifest content—of myths exposes more of their latent means than we can take. This, in turn, results in the mobilization of much the same emotional resistances and defenses as can be seen in dreams featuring suppressed or thinly veiled incestuous or sadomasochistic motifs. They become collective nightmares, disturbing the sleep of mankind.

Myth, then, may be repudiated on several counts. Deprived of its sacred connotation, of its numenous quality, it may face opprobrium as a fad of the vulgar and illiterate crowd. Stripped of its purported truth value, it may be exposed as a concatenation of deception on the grand historic scale. The very symbolic truths to which it may happen to allude only add to its potential nuisance value. This is how, in the end, the very term myth may become synonymous with lie.

✿   ✿   ✿

This condensed account of the typical life cycle of myth would be in-complete without reference to what in the view of some authorities is an important exception to the rule. Indeed, they hold that it is the short-lived, ephemeral, garden variety of myth—such as will be discussed in the first part of this book—which is the exception and that Myth, writ large, is basically timeless, infallible and outside the reach of cold scientific scrutiny.

The deeper, archetypal dimensions of such myths, we are told by Jung, places them in one class with other manifestations of the evolutionary process. They are of the same parentage as our bone and marrow, our erect posture, our propensity to sleep and "perchance to dream." Joseph Campbell, in his brilliant attempt at bringing myth into an all-embracing psychobiological frame of reference, uses the ideas of Bastian, Thomas Mann, C. G. Jung, Konrad Lorentz and Tinbergen as his stepping stones. He regards myth as a function of man's "internal release mechanism"[13] touching off his "deepest centers of motivation" and in turn evoking "super-normal cues" that feed into his quest for ever higher goals of self-expression and self-actualization. In the last analysis mythological motifs develop "from the imprints of the sociologized biology of human growth," from infancy to childhood, maturity and old age. It is this quality, Campbell suggests, which accounts for the recurrence of the same mythological themes in a wide variety of cultures in widely separated geographical locations. His argument thus amounts to a restatement of Bastian's theory of elementary ideas, universal to all mankind, modified by ethnic influence and the imprints of local sentiments.

Viewing myth in this light, few will remain impervious to the grandeur of the vistas opened up to the spectator. Some of the myths handed down to us from the past seem to be ageless, bigger than life-size, transcending the categories of time and space. In any case, they have stood up remarkably well to rationalistic scrutiny and to attempts at secularization and demythologization. But this should not detract from the fact that minor mythological themes—and local variants—have not.

Be that as it may, the enduring, archetypal quality of a limited number of major mythological motifs is a third factor to make any sweeping generalizations as to their nature precarious. Other reasons, as stated above, are the diverse culturally determined vantage points of the observer, and his changing focus on various levels and consecutive reference points in the life cycle of the myth.

These then are the reasons for existing disagreements and seemingly irreconcilable pronouncements as to the nature of myth. Paraphrasing an old adage, it could be stated: one man's myth is another man's religion, yet another man's science, self-deception or outright lie.

✻   ✻   ✻

What then is the relevance of these general considerations to our issue? Evidently the postulated functional significance of myth, its power over man's minds, its *effectiveness* will vary at various points in its life cycle. In its germinal stage—before it is shared by a growing number of people— it may be fervently believed in and accepted as the gospel truth by the few; but it does not, as yet, qualify as myth. Gradually, however, such a system of beliefs may be reinforced by a process of circular feedback and consensual validation by an increasing number of believers and followers. This is how it graduates to the status of myth of growing momentum, social significance and effectiveness. On the other hand it is readily understood that its potency is bound to decline with the growing critical scrutiny to which it is subjected by successive generations: Its effectiveness becomes inversely proportional to the degree of its secularization and demythologization. At the beginning there was myth, lacking the authority and credentials of science. In the end we may be left with science stripped of the power and arcana of myth.

REFERENCES

1. FRAZER, J. G.: The Golden Bough, abridged ed. New York: Macmillan, 1947.
2. TYLOR, E. B.: Primitive Culture. London: J. Murray, 1871.
3. LANG, A.: Custom and Myth, London: published 1901.
4. MALINOWSKI, B.: Sex, Culture and Myth. New York: Harcourt, Brace and World, 1962.
5. RADCLIFFE-BROWN, A. R.: The Andaman Islanders, address Cambridge Univ. Press. 1933.
6. MURRAY, H. A.: Myth and Mythmaking. New York: Braziller, 1960.
7. RANK, O.: The Myth of the Birth of the Hero. New York: Robert Brunner, 1952.
   ——— and SACHS, H.: The Significance of Psychoanalysis for the Humanities. Amer. Imago 21, 1-2, 1964.
8. JUNG, C. G.: Contributions to Analytical Psychology, New York: Harcourt, Brace, and World, 1928.
9. ELIADE, MIRCEA: The Sacred and the Profane. New York: Harper, 1961.
10. WIEMANN, H. N.: Myth, in: Encyclopedia of Religion, ed. by V. Ferm. New York: Philosophical Library, 1945.
11. TILLICH, P.: The Protestant Era. Chicago: Univ. of Chicago Press, 1948.
12. BULTMAN, R.: Kerygma and Myth, ed. by H. W. Bartsch. New York: Harper, 1961.
13. CAMPBELL, J.: The Masks of God. Primitive Mythology. New York: Viking, 1959.

—II—

Psychotherapy and the Decline of Magic

Viewed against the triple canvas of myth, magic and religion, where does psychotherapy come in? We shall see that it comes in at the end of the life cycle of myth, when magic has been eroded by the critical scrutiny of reason, and religion, emptied of its meaning, has become a formalized institution, a repository of magic rituals and observances. It is this characteristic sequence of events which is also responsible for the ambiguous position of psychotherapy today. Its stated objective is to cure psychological ills by psychological means. Its techniques are designed to meet the standards of the scientific method, and its values are those of the pragmatic scientist. But it is becoming increasingly clear that the needs psychotherapy is called upon to meet transcend the naturalistic frame of reference to which it has been confined in the first place by the downfall of its forerunners.

Psychotherapy is thus saddled with the ambiguities of man's changing role in the historic process, subject to its underlying deterministic forces, carried along by their currents and undercurrents. But at the same time it is bent on understanding the forces that shape the destinies of the individual and his society, determined to take a hand in changing them at will. At times modern man sees himself in the image of a machine, of an electronic computer, programmed, as it were, by his biological makeup and by his inexorable phylogenetic past. But at other times he sees himself in the image of God: as the chooser and decision maker, as the programmer of his own brain; as the master of his destiny. Thus his self-image is shifting and wavering, like a reversible picture in the textbooks of psychology or a double exposure on a photographic plate, with now one, now the other take gaining the upper hand. It is the picture of man alienated from himself, the plaything of the forces of nature—or else man who has learned to play the game himself—according to rules laid down in his newly discovered theory of games.

Yet most of the time his self-image is that of the achiever and doer of things. He sees himself as the splitter of atoms, the conqueror of outer space, and the harnesser of nuclear energy. Even when he is engaged in more pedestrian pursuits, satisfied with stepping on a gas pedal, pushing buttons or using a basement full of gadgets made by others for his convenience, he tells himself—or is being told—that, apart from the federal income tax and troubles in far away countries, all is well in the world as it is today. Automation has taken much of the drudgery out of his work.

Improved means of communication give him a sense of mastery over time and space. New Deals or Fair Deals, Marxist or anti-Marxist formulas promise ultimate victory over financial insecurity, poverty and racial unrest. Medicine is increasingly successful in taking the sting out of physical disease. Striking new discoveries in the natural sciences are reducing the margin of mystery in the universe to the vanishing point. Man's growing insight into the forces of nature seems to hold the promise of ultimate mastery over them. Confident that he will attain his goals with the aid of science and technology, he has turned away from myth and religion and no longer strives for omnipotence through magical means.

The fact is that the heritage of magic, together with memories of his early childhood, are all but forgotten and repressed. Their surviving remnants have become thoroughly discredited, relegated to the lunatic fringe of our culture or subjected to ridicule. They are no longer compatible with the self-image of modern man.

There are moments, however, when the other side of the reversible picture emerges again, and primitive mentality, playfully or in earnest, reasserts its primacy over rational thought. The story goes that one day one of Professor Bohr's students paid a visit to his house in Copenhagen. To the visitor's amazement a big horseshoe hung prominently on the professor's entrance door. "Don't tell me you are superstitious," the young man exclaimed. "No, of course not," retorted the famous scientist. "I only keep it there for good luck."

The story of the pioneer of quantum mechanics subscribing to what anthropologists call the principle of dual causality may be fictitious. However, accounts of jet pilots in World War II carrying mascots in their cockpits and investment counsellors consulting palmists about their business affairs, is not. Hotel managers still hesitate to have the number 13 painted on room doors and job seekers still avoid asking for interviews on Fridays. On the other hand, even the most superstitious cab driver will keep a firm hand on the wheel, instead of knocking wood three times, when driving past the site of a bad accident. The Admiralty may invite the Governor's Lady to break a bottle of champagne on the bow of a new battleship. Still, Navy men place more reliance on the shipbuilder's skill than on magic ritual. Soldiers of all ages did take time out praise the Lord before going to battle. But they also made sure to pass the ammunition.

Nonetheless, if modern man has learned to place his chief reliance on pragmatic experience, the difference between him and his primitive forerunner is largely one of degree. For obvious reasons, primitive man's area of control over the universe was infinitely smaller than that of his modern counterpart; his need for magic proportionately larger. Primitive man, cowering in his cave, listening to the howling of wind, threatened by floods, ice floes or wild beasts, resorted to a variety of rites and observances to avert danger and to better his lot. The hunter drew an effigy of his prey on the rock wall, hoping this would extend his power over the beast. The planter or food gatherer resorted to human sacrifice or to symbolic offerings to propitiate the god or goddess of fertility. Alternately, he would make stone carvings of women with bulging bellies, protruding buttocks and breasts to bolster the fertility of the tribe.

Bronislav Malinowski has reminded us, however, that even primitive man by no means lived by magic alone.[1] In his much quoted study of the Trobriand Islanders, he notes that when going on a fishing expedition in the island lagoon they would rely on their customary routine of preparing the bait, checking their canoe, navigating the narrows, etc. But when setting out for the dangers of the open sea, they combined their seafaring skills with elaborate magic rituals that were considered just as important for the success of their venture. They had what amounts to a dualistic orientation in the world: one pragmatic, one magical. This is what Evans-Pritchard[2] described as the philosophy of *dual causality*. Primitive man, in effect, is only a part-time primitive, much in the same way that modern man is never his full-time civilized counterpart. He, too, subscribes to the principle of dual causality. Magic, Lynn Thorndike has pointed out, is still part of his potential mental equipment,[3] however rudimentary it may be.

❖   ❖   ❖

The survival of myth and magic in modern man's mental organization has by no means gone unchallenged. Like the appendices in people's anatomies, they may have lost much of their physiological function and psychological significance, but they continue to give rise to occasional untoward or even violent reactions. A cursory glance at the history of Western civilization testifies to the vehemence of the struggle between the surviving remnants of the internalized past, and the forces of cultural repression directed against them. Indeed, the repudiation and repression of magic and myth seems to be characteristic of all cultures coming close to their high-water marks. We shall see that it is the eventual success of this crusade which prepared the ground for the advent of psychotherapy in our culture. Psychotherapy was called upon to fill the void left by the demise of the discredited creeds and by the secularization of religion. Yet at the same time psychotherapy has become the inheritor of both their virtues and weaknesses. It is perhaps these disconcerting historical ties which are responsible for some of the unreasonable attacks which have, until recently, been levelled against the new science.

We hinted, however, that the attacks directed against the magicians and mythmakers of the past, both oriental and occidental, were by no means confined to scholarly debate. Classical Confucian doctrine has been equally vehement in condemning the nefarious practices of magicians and sorcerers as the Buddhist systems of Mahayana and Hinayana. The burning of widows may have been a sacred rite in ancient India, but it was a treatment also accorded to witches, male and female, regardless of their marital status. The magic practices of Tantric Buddhism have met with the same opprobium by the orthodoxy as have various Neoplatonic and gnostic cults by the early Christian church. Likewise, the iconoclastic zeal of Moses and the lesser prophets has been merely the prelude of Judeo-Christian intolerance of idolatry that has lasted to our day. The prophet Jeremiah is on record demanding the stoning of the witch "who is in your midst." The Talmud has shown the same impatience with the survival of oriental mysticism among Jews in the diaspora as has the Roman Catholic Church of the 18th and 19th centuries with the Rosicrucians, Swedenborgians, and spiritualists of modern times. In orthodox Judaism, demonological lore, mystic belief and the thaumaturgic practices of the Hasidim were just as odious as the occult rituals of the Black Mass were to medieval ecclesiastic authorities.

The revulsion against the heritage of magic reached a tragic climax in the excesses of medieval and early Renaissance Inquisition that sent thousands of innocent (and often mentally disturbed) women to their deaths. Yet the paradoxical fact is that the Inquisition did so with the avowed purpose of purging the Christian world of the last vestiges of magic and superstition. The Dominican monks Kramer and Sprenger,[4] the most articulate spokesmen of their ilk, considered themselves as crusaders for Christian rationality and enlightenment, bent on healing the sores of superstition and heresy in the bodies and minds of their victims.

It was an added paradox that the new Protestant movement, pitted against the Roman Church, helped to fan the flames lit by the Catholic witch hunters. Luther and his followers found themselves in perfect agreement with their theological adversaries on the need to eradicate the scourge of magic and sorcery from the Western world. In this respect they were on common ground with the pioneers of the new humanistic creed, committed as it was to progress and enlightenment in its own right.

Unfortunately, the witch hunters and inquisitors fought their battle against the "enormities of superstition" with superstition of equal, if not greater, enormity. They met the delusions of their victims on the level of the deluded and it is a matter of historic record that at times they themselves fell victim to the demons they were supposed to exorcise. A third paradox, perhaps more tragic than the other two, was the fact that the real target of the witch hunters, both Catholic and Protestant, was not the witch or sorcerer whom they happened to drag before the ecclesiastical court. It was the ancient heritage of magic refusing to die, and indeed threatening to stage a comeback to the well-ordered Christian Universe of their time.

Yet the war waged by the waning Middle Ages and early Renaissance was by no means the last action taken by Western civilization against the archenemy of reason and the scientific temper. It is true that belief in magic retreated from the limelight of modern man's religious conscience and cultural preoccupations. Its manifestation became more subtle than before and the struggle against it shifted to the field of impassioned debate or learned controversy. Johannes Weyer, the first physician approaching the problem of witch hunting as a sober psychiatric observer, pleaded for understanding and Christian compassion with the plight of the pitiful "little women" falsely accused of magic practices. Cornelius Agrippa, his older contemporary, though himself once a believer in magic and astrology, wrote a famous pamphlet against the "ludicrous vanity of the occult sciences" and risked his life defending a young woman accused of witchcraft. Another great Renaissance physician, Paracelsus von Hohenheim, raised his voice for the same cause, charging that "there is more superstition in the Catholic Church than in all these witches and women."

Paracelsus was among the first users of mercury in the treatment of syphilis. He may also have introduced the opiate laudanum into medical practice. Yet at the same time, he was an ardent advocate of the notorious Weapon Salve, that was supposed to cure injuries when applied to the weapon that caused the injury—instead of applying it to the wound itself. His writings are replete with references to magic lore and alchemistic practices.

In a similar vein, his great contemporary, Johann Kepler, one of the founders of the modern heliocentric concept of the universe, remained committed to a strange mixture of medieval mysticism and magic belief. The same attitude can be traced in the letters and scientific writings of one of the pioneers of the scientific method, Isaac Newton. These great figures of the Renaissance, however diverse their respective backgrounds and personalities, had one thing in common: they all subscribed to the philosophy of dual causality, supposedly characteristic of primitive man.

Shifting attention to another aspect of the time, it is common knowledge that virtually all medieval and Renaissance art was imbued with remnants of the surviving—or resuscitated—pagan tradition. Its madonnas, angels and other holy figures wore unmistakable features of ancient Greek gods and goddesses. Its iconography was replete with symbolism rooted in myth and magic. Some of it barely concealed the proverbial cloven hoof—itself a historical allusion to the cult of the Horned God and his coterie of centaurs and satyrs.

In a similar vein, liturgical dramas and mystery plays gave prominent place to the struggle between the old and the new creeds. It is the main theme of Dante's *Divina Commedia*. Similar themes appear time and again on the stained glass windows of the cathedrals of Rouen, Chartres, Exeter, and Milan. Their gargoyles have rightly been described as portrayals of deposed pagan idols of the past. Likewise, the bizarre symbolism of Hieronymus Bosch's canvases, though commissioned by the Catholic Church, are said to conceal the painter's secret allegiance to a heretic Christian sect.[5] At the same time the very pageantry and ritual of the church, the mystery of the Holy Communion and other sacraments; the miraculous powers attributed to the relics of the saints, are in many ways reminiscent of ancient magic beliefs and practices. It is at these points of confluence between the paraphernalia of pagan tradition and medieval mysticism that the lines of demarcation between religion and magic, between dogma and myth, become blurred. One is reminded of L. Thorndike's[3] dictum that it is in effect "the discarded cult, now practiced only privately and covertly by a minority" which is stigmatized as magic; or of Professor Ducasse's succint definition of magic as "inverted religion."[6]

✡   ✡   ✡

Call it religion, magic, or a hybrid blend of the two, modern man has become wary of both. He would presumably even resent the suggestion of secretly adhering to Evans-Pritchard's principle of double causality. To the inheritors of Edison's or Ford's accomplishments, magic is encased in a miniaturized transistor radio, miracles are made in computerized research laboratories, and myths are disproved scientific theories. God, they may be willing to grant, was good at making trees; but man is nearly as good at making machines. A "Prime Mover" may have been needed to get the whole "works" going. But from then on He had become an "unnecessary hypothesis."

According to legend, more than two thousand years ago a voice calling across the waves of the Mediterranean balefully announced that the Great God Pan was dead. His demise was followed by that of the rest of the gods of classical antiquity. At the turn of the 19th century Nietzsche proclaimed the death of their Judeo-Christian successors, and in the decades that followed millions had taken up the cry and spread the news of the Twilight of the Gods. The world, once sanctified by faith, sustained by myth or at least kept in line by dogma, became a spiritual wasteland, the battleground of socioeconomic forces, of power blocks and clashing political ideologies. Time and space, emptied of the dimension of the sacred, became reduced to mathematical concepts; houses of worship to crumbling masonry or tax-exempt real estate. The gargoyles and carved figures of saints still kept their toehold under the vaulted arches of the old cathedrals, but they were drained of symbolic meaning and gradually corroded by air pollution, much in the same way that the Holy Stones and Trees of antiquity had been transmuted into dead mineral or vegetable matter. Indeed, God himself is dead, we are told by the new theologians.

At long last modern man seemed to have come of age. He had disassociated himself from the falsehoods masquerading as myth. He rid himself of the "monstrous farrago" of primitive magic. He had vanquished the "enormity of superstition" and ignorance of a past era. The *mysterium tremendum* of a divine—or demonic—universe no longer held a threat to him.

However, when modern man is brought face to face with his personal limitations, with suffering and ill health, and forced to deal with inner conflicts and frustrations reflecting the inexorable demands of society and his conscience, he is apt to lose his cocksureness and find little solace in scientific and technological achievements. This is when a seemingly forgotten or repressed aspect of his personality comes to the fore. It is the aspect of the child frightened in the dark, of his Paleolithic ancestor cowering in the unlit cave, of modern man cast into a universe emptied of value, purpose and meaning. This is when the agnostic tends to fall back on religion; the unsophisticated on magic and myth; the skeptic (and would-be believer) on the medicated solace of psychotherapy—psychoanalytic, existential, or otherwise.

✲   ✲   ✲

Psychotherapy, then, has to come in as a stopgap to fill a spiritual void, to meet unmet metaphyscial needs, and to help man to cope with his emotional conflicts, irrational fears and existential anxieties. It tries to do all this without recourse to mythical ideologies or magic ritual.

The revolutionary nature of such a venture goes without saying. Psychotherapy, by definition, aims at treating psychological ills by purely psychological means. This involves the manipulation by the therapist of a system of verbal cues and related symbols while deliberately abstaining from trying to influence the patient's bodily functions with drugs or other physical means of treatment. Yet at the present stage the leverage of the therapist's symbolic manipulations and interventions is still far from predictable. We shall see in the concluding chapters that the leverage varies with the nature of the existing pathology, with the authenticity of the therapist's motivations, with the trust placed by the patient in their mutual relationship, and with the potency of their common beliefs and expectations in general.

It will also be noted that the difficulties inherent in such an approach are in striking contrast to the situation of the engineer or physicist trying to manipulate levers, pulleys or electrons in his laboratory. The physicist is in far better position than the psychotherapist to test, retest and ultimately to predict the leverage of his actions. Resorting to horseshoes and other charms—including those of the Governor's Lady—may be nothing but a playful gesture or a left-handed homage to primitive man's principle of dual causality. But the scientific psychotherapist of our day, in the face of his limitations, may easily be led to take the line of lesser resistance and to fall into the footsteps of his prescientific precursors. His avowed scientific purpose to the contrary, he may smuggle the archaic contraband of myth and magic into his approach. The question is, how big is the cleavage between him and his professional predecessors and to what extent can his ministrations meet his patients' needs? Before trying to answer this question we have to turn our attention to his primitive forerunners in person.

REFERENCES

1. MALINOWSKI, B.: The Argonauts of the Western Pacific. New York: Dutton, 1932.
2. EVANS-PRITCHARD: Witchcraft, Oracles and Magic among the Azande. Oxford: Clarendon Press, 1937.
3. THORNDIKE, L.: History of Magic and Experimental Science, Columbia Univ. Press, Macmillan, New York 1923-1958.
4. KRAMER, H. and SPRENGER, J.: Malleus Maleficarum, London: Pushkin Press, 1951.
5. FRANGER, W.: The Millennium of Hieronymus Bosch, Chicago: Univ. of Chicago Press, 1951.
6. DUCASSE, C. J.: A Philosophical Scrutiny of Religion, New York: Ronald, 1953.

— III —

The Medicine Man in Action and the Effective Myth

What then are the characteristics of the primitive medicine man, and of his surviving latter-day prototype, as compared with the practitioner of modern psychotherapy? On trying to discover family resemblances that may exist between the two, we have to realize that our notion of the magician, the witch doctor, the shaman, or priestly healer is distilled from many cultures and cultural periods. It is a composite picture that fails to make allowance for the distinction between tribal chief, witch doctor and religious functionary, nor for the personal union of these functions seen in many primitive cultures. Also it glosses over the lack of a sharp line of demarcation between white and black magic; between the healing and the nefarious practices of the magician. Yet apart from these strictures, the Navajo wizard, the Melanesian "head-shrinker," the Asclepiad of ancient Greece, and even the psychotherapist of our time, all have one thing in common: the motivation to come to their patients' aid and the mandate given to them by their society to minister to their needs. The common denominator is the dual pattern of a would-be helper confronted with a seeker of help: the reciprocity of supply and demand on the spiritual plane. The reciprocal quality of this pattern is indeed inescapable. A helping hand is predicated on a hand reaching out for it, and a hand reaching out for help, even in empty space, is likely to end up in a prayerful gesture seeking help from a benevolent divinity.

In the last analysis the pattern is derived from man's slow pace of maturation, with his attending prolonged dependence on an all-powerful parent figure. Hence its transcultural, virtually ubiquitous, occurrence. It will be recalled that Freud sought to trace back the concept of God himself to this inevitable early childhood experience, while Jung saw in it the roots of a universal archetype: the archetype of the king, the sage, the healer, or the wise old man.

Yet despite this common denominator, our implied juxtaposition of widely divergent and culturally disparate functionaries of the healing arts is in need of justification. The sociocultural gap between the primitive prototype and its modern counterpart is too wide to be lightly brushed aside. It is as wide as the gap between magic and science, between myth and empirically testable theories, or between the tribal organization of preliterate peoples and modern industrial societies.

We hinted that in many primitive cultures the medicine man was the magical healer, tribal chief and priestly king rolled into one. His specializing

18

as a witch doctor comes at a later stage. Even then his role may include both beneficial and nefarious practices, control of both health and disease; protection from evil and infliction of evil; his trade is black and white magic at the same time.

The tools of his trade range from the mask, the drum, the bone dart and the magic effigy to the poisoned arrow and the obsidian knife; and his practices include spells and incantations, the ritual dance, rainmaking ceremonies and ecstatic trance. We have to assume that relying as he did on this armamentarium, his therapeutic influence upon his clients must have been largely based on trial and error. It resulted from accident rather than design, aided by what today would be attributed to suggestion or autosuggestion. It may have been an example of what in modern terms would be described as a placebo effect: the psychological effect of a medically inert drug or procedure.

The witch doctor's functions have to be contrasted with those of the priestly healer or the thaumaturge in primitive religions, called upon to mediate between the faithful and the divinity. Avowedly, the priest's mandate comes from above, not from below, and he exercises his miraculous powers as an agent of the gods. Yet here again, the pattern of reciprocity and functional interdependence between healer and sufferer is unmistakable. Like the medicine man and his tribe, they form a dovetailing dynamic or psychological unit of their own, even though they may be functioning on a plane of higher complexity and sophistication.

The modern psychotherapist and his society operate on an even higher plane. In this case, science has taken over from magic and made a clean sweep of myth and primitive religion. The only discernible common element in scientific psychotherapy and primitive healing is the pattern of reciprocity between healer and sufferer, between the would-be helper and the would-be helped. Irrespective of cultural differences, they represent an elementary psychosocial unit in their own right, meeting the same needs and serving the same purpose. Despite divergencies in sophistication, in method and rationale, they are variations on the identical theme of fears, frustrations and suffering—and of their alleviation by essentially psychological means.

Thus our juxtaposition of the medicine man, witch doctor, shaman and psychotherapist should by no means be taken as an oblique slight against a venerable profession. It does not suggest that one can be reduced to the level of the other. What we propose to do in the pages that follow is to trace diverse methods of mental healing back to their elementary prototype so as to arrive at better understanding of the modern psychotherapeutic approach, viewed against the background of its historic, if not prehistoric, past.

❖   ❖   ❖

Our first illustrative example is taken from the celebrated *Papyrus Ebers,* discovered in 1874. It is a compilation of Egyptian healing magic dated approximately 1500 B.C. but may go back to even earlier times.[1] Its introductory passages are as follows:

> Here begins the book of the preparation of medicines for all parts of the body of a person. I was born in Heliopolis with the priests of Het-Aat, the lords of protection, the kings of eternity and of salvation. I have my origin in Sais with the maternal godddesses who have protected me. The Lord of All has given me words to drive away the diseases of all the gods and mortal sufferings of every kind. There are chapters for this my head, for this my neck, for this my arms, for this my flesh, and for these my limbs, so that (disease) enters unto this my flesh, placing a spell on these my limbs, whenever Ra has taken mercy and has said "I protect him against his enemies." It is his guide Hermes who gave him the word, who created the books and gave glory to those who know everything and to the physicians who follow him to decipher that which is dark. He whom the god loves is made alive; I am the one whom the god loves, me he makes alive, to pronounce words in the preparation of medicine for all parts of the body of a person who is sick. As it should be a thousand times. This is the book of the healing of all diseases.

There are two points in this remarkable document which are of interest in the present context. First, the author wants to make his professional identity perfectly clear "to whom it may concern." Born in Heliopolis and presum- ably brought up in Sais, he traces his ancestry to venerated priests and maternal goddesses who were his patrons and had "protected" him. Though we cannot properly evaluate the weight carried by such patronage, we may take it for granted that his *curriculum vitae* is meant to convey the credentials of his qualifications as a priestly healer. It is an attempt to establish his personal myth, much in the same way that a psychiatrist may let it be known that he was educated in Vienna, analyzed by Dr. So-and-So, or had his postgraduate training at the Shrine of Topeka, Kansas, at the Washington School of Psychiatry, or at the New York Psychoanalytic Institute.

A second point of interest is the author's pronouncement that the "Lord of All" had given him the powers of words to drive away diseases and mortal suffering of every kind. It is this declaration by which he stakes out his claim to the field proper of psychotherapy. The assumed power of words literally marks the beginning of man's career as a symbol-making animal. Genesis credits Adam with naming the names of plants and animals as the first step in assuming his role as lord of creation. The same principle is reflected in the Gospel of St. John stating: "In the beginning was the *Word.*" Words, like mathematics, are in effect, a man-made universe, and as Ernst Cassirer pointed out, only man has formed a universe of which symbols, language and myth are the most important constituents.[2] By the same token, man is confident that skillful manipulation of symbols is the functional equivalent of manipulating the things designated by them. This precisely is the expedient he resorts to in times of trouble. Unable to pit his will against the hard and stubborn facts of physical reality, he tries his hand—or rather his prehensile mind—at their symbolic representations. The primitive healer is the first specialist in this field of endeavor—and his patients seem to put their trust in his ministrations.

The same principle is illustrated by the following passages from an Assyrian tablet dating from about 2500 B.C.[3]

> Sickness of the head, of the teeth, of the heart, heartache;
> Sickness of the eye, fever, poison;
> Evil-spirits, evil-demons, evil-ghost, evil-devil, evil-god, evil-friend;
> Hag, demon, ghoul, robber sprite;
> Phantom of night, night wraith, handmaid of the phantoms;
> Evil pestilence, noisome fever, baneful sickness;
> Pain, sorcery or any evil,
> Headache, shivering.

> Evil spell, witchcraft, sorcery,
> Enchantment and all evil:
> Drive from the house, go forth, unto the man, the son of his god, come
>   not into,
> Get thee hence.

Another tablet contains a prayer addressed to the Babylonian god Ea, the Lord of the Deep:
(To be said over a sick man:)

> He that stilleth all to rest, that pacifieth all,
> By whose incantation everything is at peace
> He is the great Lord Ea.
> By whose incantation everything is at peace,
> When I draw nigh unto the sick man
> All shall be assuaged.
> I am the magician born of Eridu
> Begotten in Eridu and Subari
> When I draw nigh unto the sick man
> May Ea, King of the Deep, safeguard me.

(Then the magician is thus to address the deity sought:)
> O Ea, King of the Deep, see
> I am the magician, am thy slave.
> March thou on my right hand,
> Assist (me) on my left,

Add thy pure spell to mine;
Vouchsafe (to me) pure words
Make fortunate the utterances of my mouth,
Ordain that my decisions may be happy,
Let me be blest where'er I tread,
Let the man whom I now touch be blessed.

It is as though man, having discovered the power of words, was confident
that their knowledge assures his mastery over them. To make assurance
doubly sure, both the Egyptian and the Babylonian scribes drew up
comprehensive lists of names covering virtually all areas of human anatomy
known to them and all conceivable afflictions that may befall them. Using
this encyclopedic technique, in conjuction with invoking the name of the
proper deity, was apparently the best the priestly healer of the time could
do for his patients.

The same belief in the power of words is reflected by the following
passage from an Anglo-Saxon or Celtic document dating from the 8th
century A.D. It is known as the *Lorica of Gildas*, i.e., a magic coat supposed
to protect the Christian believer from the influence of demons and evil
spirits.[4]

> Oh God, with thy inscrutable saving power defend all my parts, deliver
> the whole trunk of my body with thine own protecting shield that foul
> demons may not hurl, as is their wont, their darts at my flanks, skull, head
> with hair and eyes, forehead, tongue, teeth and nose, neck, breast, side and
> reins, thighs, under-rump and two hands. To my head, with hair on top of
> it, be a helmet of protection, to forehead, eyes and triformed brain, to nose,
> lip, face and temple, to chin, beard, eyebrows, ears, cheeks, lips, internasal
> septum and nares, to the round pupils, eyelids, and eyelashes, gums, breath,
> jaws, fauces, to the teeth, tongue, mouth and throat, uvula, larynx and
> frenum of the tongue, to head-pan, brain and gristly, and to my neck be
> thou a protector in thy mercy; I beseech thee, O Lord Jesus Christ, for the
> nine orders of holy angels. Be thou a secure lorica both to my members and
> to my viscera. So that thou turn back from me the invisible points of the
> shafts which transfix the abhorred. Cover me then, O God, Thou strong
> lorica, as to my shoulders, arms and forearms. Cover arms with elbows and
> hands, fists, palms, fingers with nails. Cover the spine and ribs with their
> joints, the rear and back with nerves and bones. Cover skin, blood with
> kidneys, haunches and rump with thighs. Cover hams, calves and thigh
> parts with knuckle-bones, poplites and knees. Cover the tenfold branches
> (of the feet) with toes and their twice five nails. Cover ankles with shanks
> and heels, legs, feet, soles with insteps. Cover breast, peritoneum and breast
> bone, mammae, stomach and navel. Cover belly, groin, genital parts and
> paunch and vital parts of the heart. Cover the trifid liver and ilia, scrotum,
> kidneys, intestines and rete mirabile. Cover tonsils, thorax with lung,
> vessels, sinews, gall with pericardium. Cover flesh, groin with marrow,
> spleen with tortuous intestines. Cover bladder fat and all the innumerable
> sorts of structures. Cover hairs and the other members the names of which

I have perchance omitted. Cover all of me with my five senses, and with the ten doors that were contrived (for their use), that from the soles to the top of the head in no member, without or within, may I be sick; that there may not thrust the life from my body neither pest nor fever nor langour nor pain, while by God's grace I may reach old age and may wipe out my sins with good deeds, and leaving the flesh I may be blameless and may be worthy to pass on high and by God's pity I may rise happy to the refreshing ether of the kingdom. Amen. Amen.

The similarity of this quotation with the passages taken from the Egyptian papyrus and the Babylonian tablets is unmistakable. So much so that their authors, had they known about the incantation composed by Gildas the Briton in a faraway land some 2,000 or 3,000 years after their demise, might well have accused him of plagiarism. There are, however, countless similar examples in the history of medicine, widely separated in time and place, testifying to the universality of archaic man's belief in the healing magic of words. Evidently, under the pressure of circumstances hopelessly beyond his control, he switches his attempts at control and mastery from objects in the outside world to their symbolic representation in the mental sphere. Once he had made this shift, he was apt to belabor the point in ceaseless efforts to make it work. It apparently is this channelling of frustrated or aim-inhibited action into language which accounts for the proliferation of magic spells, chants, and incantations under primitive conditions. On the other hand, it may be the inevitable frustration attending such aim-inhibited action which is responsible for their characteristic tendency to perseveration and their obsessive-compulsive quality.

Channelling into words was not the only recourse open to the primitive healer. Another was the magic rite and ritual. Indeed, it was an outlet carrying in its current the flotsam and jetsam of once empirically purposeful, goal-directed activities that had since lost their usefulness. Here, again, it may be their ultimate failure which accounts for their interminable repetition and their obsessive-compulsive quality pointed out by Freud.

A graphic example of magic ritual can be found in Malinowski's classical description of the behavior of a Melanesian Medicine Man:[5]

> Let us have a look at a typical act of magic, and choose one which is well-known and generally regarded as a standard performance—an act of black magic. Among the several types which we meet in savagery, witchcraft by the act of pointing the magical dart is, perhaps, the most widespread of all. A pointed bone or a stick, an arrow or the spine of some animal, is ritually, in a mimic fashion, thrust, thrown, or pointed in the direction of the man to be killed by sorcery. We have innumerable recipes in the oriental and ancient books of magic, in ethnographic descriptions and tales of travelers, of how such a rite is performed. But the emotional setting, the gestures and expressions of the sorcerer during the performance, have been but seldom described. Yet these are of the greatest importance.

If a spectator were suddenly transported to some part of Melanesia and could observe the sorcerer at work, not perhaps knowing exactly what he was looking at, he might think that he had either to do with a lunatic or else he would guess that here was a man acting under the sway of uncontrolled anger. For the sorcerer has, as an essential part of the ritual performance, not merely to point the bone dart at his victim, but with an intense expression of fury and hatred he has to thrust it in the air, turn and twist it as if to bore it in the wound, then pull it back with a sudden jerk. Thus not only is the act of violence, or stabbing, reproduced, but the passion of violence has to be enacted . . . Or when in love magic the performer has really or symbolically to grasp, stroke, fondle the beloved person or some object representing her, he produces the behavior of a heartsick lover who has lost his common sense and is overwhelmed by passion.

Freud has suggested that such behavior is an expression of the magician's implicit belief in the omnipotence of thought. Yet in his heart of hearts the medicine man may find himself on the opposite pole of such assurance. The very frenzy and overacting of his part betrays his lingering doubt. Like Hamlet's mother, he protests too much. If he felt really secure in his purported omnipotence, he would presumably be satisfied with sitting cross-legged under a lotus tree, his arms folded over his chest, with a Bohdissatva's archaic smile on his face, performing miracles and curing the sick without moving his little finger.

The fact is that staging a highly colored pantomime of sympathetic or imitative magic may be one of the medicine man's standard procedures. Sir James Frazer's *The Golden Bough*[6] is replete with anecdotal accounts of this order. One of his examples is the wizard of the Natchez Indians of North American, trying to make rain. After a requisite period of fasting, he would engage in a ritual dance, with pipes filled with water in his mouth. "The pipes were perforated like the nozzle of a watering can and the rain maker blew the water towards that part of the sky where the clouds hung heaviest. But if fair weather was wanted he mounted the roof of his hut and with extended arms, blowing with all his might. he beckoned the clouds to pass by."

In other rainmaking rituals most of the magician's activities may be channelled into interminable dancing movements of growing intensity, ably assisted by the participation of the whole tribe. Frazer adds, however, that "sometimes, when drought has lasted a long time, people drop the usual hocus-pocus of imitative magic altogether, and being far too angry to waste their breath in prayer, they seek by threats and curses or even downright physical force, to extort the waters of heaven from the supernatural beings who so to say cut them off at the main."

One is reminded of the story of the pious Jew in the synagogue who, on the Day of Atonement, desperately beat his chest with his fist, his body swaying in fervent prayer. His fellow worshipper sitting next to him in the pew shook his head in friendly admonition: "Take it easy, Sam, violence won't get you there."

The healing magic performed by the shamans of Eastern Siberia and Central Asia is a combination of ecstatic trance and magic ritual. According to Mircea Eliade,[7] the shaman is the religious version of the primitive medicine man or witch doctor. He is the manipulator of the sacred *par excellence*, and has developed special techniques to bring him in touch with the supernatural. One of the techniques is the trance in which the shaman is believed to be capable of leaving his body and of either flying up into the sky or descending into the netherworld. An important part of the performance is the ceremonial search for the lost or stolen soul of the patient. Eliade describes a Kazak-Kirgiz séance called *baqca* as follows:

> The séance begins with an invocation to Allah and the Moslem saints, and continues with an appeal to the jinni and threats to the evil spirits. The baqca sings on and on. At a certain moment the spirits take possession of him, and during this trance he "walks barefoot over red-hot iron" and several times introduces a light wick into his mouth. He touches the red-hot iron with his tongue and "with his knife, sharp as a razor, strikes at his face, leaving no visible mark." After these shamanic exploits he again invokes Allah: "O God, bestow happiness! Oh, deign to look on my tears! I implore thy help!"

> Among the Yenisei Ostyak healing requires two ecstatic journeys. The first is more of a rapid survey; it is during the second, which ends in trance, that the shaman enters deep into the beyond. The séance begins, as usual, with invoking the spirits and putting them in the drum one after the other. During all this time the shaman sings and dances. When the spirits have come he begins to leap; this means that he has left the earth and is rising toward the clouds. At a certain moment he cries: "I am high in the air, I see the Yenisei a hundred versts away." On his way he meets other spirits and tells the audience whatever he sees. Then addressing the spirit helper who is carrying him through the air, he cries: "O my little fly, rise still higher, I want to see farther! . . ." Soon afterward he returns to the yurt, surrounded by his spirits. It seems that he has not found the patient's soul, or he has seen it at a great distance, in the land of the dead. To reach it, he begins dancing again, until trance supervenes. Still carried by his spirits, he leaves his body and enters the beyond, from which he finally returns with the patient's soul.

Shaman ceremonies among the Yacut include various convulsive and tic-like manifestations in the trance, piercing cries, ecstatic dancing to the accompaniment of frenzied music and drum beats. All this is to invoke various spirits to help the shaman perform his exorcism. Finally "he flings himself into the air, sometimes as high as four feet. He cries out wildly . . . then in a low voice he intones a solemn hymn . . ." In the end "he goes to the patient and summons the cause of the illness to depart . . . or he lays hold of the trouble, carries it to the middle of the room and never stopping his imprecations, chases it away, spits it from his mouth, kicks it, drives it with his hands and breath."

The proverbial dance of the dervishes is an example of sheer physical violence and passion channelled into exotic whirling and leaping, accompanied by the frantic repetition of sacred phrases and chanting in unison, leaving the participants exhausted or all but collapsed at the end of the performance. The Rifa-is, or howling dervishes, the most fanatic fraternity of them all, cut themselves with knives, handle red-hot irons, devour serpents and claim supernatural healing powers issuing from their labors.

In this instance the magic quest for omnipotence reaches its culmination in uncontrolled and well-nigh amorphous muscular discharge, with most of its message and symbolic meaning lost in the shuffle. S. Ferenczi,[8] elaborating on Freud's thesis, has suggested that the infant's uncoordinated discharge movements by which he tries to force his will upon his parents, is likewise predicated on the belief in the "omnipotence of movement." Unfortunately, both the infant's and his fellow magician's lot—as that of Gilbert and Sullivan's policeman—"is not an easy one." More often than not their trust in omnipotence, in symbiotic control, is sorely disappointed.

❋   ❋   ❋

The quest for personal power and magic self-enhancement is not, however, the last expedient by which man sought to conquer the forces of nature and to find salvation from evil. The way of the mystic, both Western and Eastern style, was another means to reach these objectives.

The mystic does not merely close his eyes to external reality. He surrenders his will, his strivings, his whole self to the divinity, and in return expects to be absorbed by divinity itself. A classical case in point is the Buddhist's renunciation of worldly desires with the goal of total self-denial and self-effacement. The sacred writings of the East are replete with detailed instructions and prescriptions of how to achieve this end. But it is the various systems of Yoga which claim to have developed specific spiritual disciplines and physiological methods of training to realize it in practice.[9] Put in Yoga terms, the goal is to merge Atman, the individual Self, with Brahman, the cosmic principle, the all-encompassing divine soul. By doing so, the Yogi is to attain total mastery over his own body and mind, and ultimately over the world at large. The cultivation of the powers of spiritual healing is more or less a by-product of Yoga discipline designed, as it is, to provide the ultimate remedy for anxiety and suffering. In the last analysis, the Yogi's quest for salvation also reached out for the illusion of omnipotence—by proxy, as it were. Paradoxically, in his case, its attainment is predicated on total self-effacement and self-renunciation.

The officiating priests in the ancient Asklepian shrine of Epidaurus invoked the power of myth in its purest form to perform their miraculous cures, here and now. To be sure, their failures have remained unsung and unrecorded. But their successes have come down to posterity, engraved in the memorial tablets of the temple. One of the tablets tells the story of a patient suffering from paralysis of four fingers of his hand. Although a skeptic by both ancient and modern standards, he was promptly cured by the god:

> A man, whose fingers, with the exception of one, were paralyzed, came as a suppliant to the god. While looking at the Tablets in the temple, he expressed incredulity regarding the cures and scoffed at the inscriptions. But in his sleep he saw a vision. It seemed to him that he was playing at dice below the Temple, and was about to cast the dice, (when) the god appeared, sprang upon his hand, and stretched out his (the patient's) fingers. When the god had stepped aside it seemed to the patient that he could bend his hand and (he) stretched out all his fingers one by one. When he had straightened them all the god asked him if he would still be incredulous of the inscriptions on the tablets in the Temple. He answered that he would not, (and the god said to him): "Since, then, formerly you did not believe in the cures, though they were not incredible, for the future your name shall be "Incredulous."" When day dawned, he walked out sound.[10]

Needless to say that the permanency of the alleged cure is open to doubt. But the tablets found in the temple of Epidaurus, and in scores of similar shrines, testify to the effectiveness of the myth regardless of actual therapeutic results or the truth value of the myth.

❀   ❀   ❀

In the face of all this perseverance and prodigious expenditure of effort and imagination, much of it wasted by modern standards, the Western observer may well ask what it is that kept the primitive medicine man, the mystic or the priestly healer in business over the centuries, if not millennia?

A flippant answer may point to a major advantage they held over their contemporary counterparts: they were not expected to subject results to the test of repeatable experiments or statistical evaluation. On the other hand, there can be no doubt that they were operating against infinitely greater odds than those confronting the modern medical practitioner or psychotherapist. Their chances with physical disease, both curable and incurable, were very slim indeed, to say nothing of droughts, floods, famines, and other calamities. Still, their failures do not seem to have discredited them in the eyes of their community. At least they were not blatant enough to put them altogether out of business.

But the question is whether the point made by the Western observer is at all applicable to the primitive healer. Did the Navajo medicine man's fellow tribesmen really insist on being cured of an existing ailment? Did the Natchez wizard have a contractual agreement with his customers to make rain? Did the Sufi dervish dance to the point of exhaustion in order to deliver the spiritual goods expected from him or face a "money-back" alternative in case of nonperformance? All the available evidence indicates that this was not the case.

Ari Kiev's richly documented studies in primitive psychiatry,[11] published when the manuscript of the present book was all but completed, point in the same direction. They suggest that untutored healers, working in preliterate societies of our day, likewise obtain striking therapeutic results. Here, again, actual improvements are difficult to evaluate. But their accomplishments have to be viewed in a broader cultural context. Obviously, the performance of the magician, the priestly healer, the dancing dervish or the Yogi served an end transcending its avowed purpose. It was not utilitarian in terms of achieving the material welfare of their respective groups. The goal was to meet existential crises and emergencies, both tribal and individual, and to do—or seem to be doing—something about them. The writings of modern anthropologists from Malinowski and Radcliffe-Brown to R. Boas, A. Koerber and Margaret Mead, make the vital necessity of such spiritual ministrations abundantly clear. Spells and incantations, fertility rites and rituals of rainmaking or healing magic are needed not because they "work," which they usually don't, but because their solemn, or not quite solemn, performance is an assertion and reassertion of the individual's and the group's will to survive, maintain their social identity and to preserve their trust in a universe ruled by sacred or demonic—yet, in any case, meaningful and intelligible—forces.

The same is true for myth. Its significance does not lie in its doubtful validity as an explanatory hypothesis or as a garbled account of alleged historic or cosmological events. It is derived from its time-tested sociological and spiritual function. Myth, we have stated, tends to be effective, regardless of its truth value. Hence its importance as a therapeutic tool.

REFERENCES

1. PAPYRUS EBERS, quoted from Ehrenwald, J.: From Medicine Man to Freud, An Annotated Anthology. New York: Dell, 1956.
2. CASSIRER, E.: Language and Myth. New York: Dover Publications, 1946.
3. ASSYRIAN TABLETS, cf. (1).
4. Lorica of Gildas (ibid.).
5. MALINOWSKI, B.: Magic, Science and Religion. New York: Doubleday, 1954.
6. FRAZER, J. G.: cf. Chapter I (1).
7. ELIADE, MIRCEA: Shamanism. New York: Pantheon, 1964.
8. FERENCZI, S.: Stages in the Development of the Sense of Reality, Contrib. to Psychoanalysis, Boston: R. C. Badger, 1916.
9. BEHANAN, KOVOOR T.: Yoga, A Scientific Evaluation. New York: Macmillan, 1937.
10. VEITH, I.: The Infancy of Psychiatry, Bull. Menninger Clinic, 28.4. 1964.
11. KIEV, A.: Magic, Faith and Healing, Studies in Primitive Psychiatry Today. New York: Free Press of Glencoe, 1964.

A 17th Century Placebo and the Truncated Myth: Sir Kenelm Digby's Powder of Sympathy

The preceding chapters may have made one of the major objectives of this book sufficiently clear: to follow the vicissitudes of man's stubborn belief in the existence of spiritual powers fashioned after his own image, matched by his equally stubborn belief that, by pleading or persuasion, by art or artifice, he should be capable of coaxing or coercing them to bend to his will and to do his bidding. We have seen that the conquest of suffering, ill health and other human frailties are prominent parts of the quest.

The Paleolithic artist tried to achieve his goal by picture magic covering the walls of the cave of Lascaux; the shaman by his ecstatic trances and rituals; the teller of mythical tales by stringing together beads of collective daydreams shared by generations of his people over the centuries. Modern man, unwilling to settle for mere adaptation and survival, stakes out his claim for higher goals. Not satisfied with what is possible, he reaches out for the impossible and tries to persuade himself that there is no such thing as that. This is the pride—the *hybris*—of ancient Greek tragedy that led to the hero's undoing, whether his name was Hercules, Oedipus or Prometheus. Examples of *hybris*, Christian style, and of censure, social ostracism and more severe retaliatory measures brought into play against it, were reviewed in Chapter II. *Hybris* in the Christian world was not only the temerity to steal fire from heaven, but rather to rebel against the one and only God, and to usurp His powers, His omnipotence and omniscience. This is why magic and sorcery were condemned as heresy, as attempts to reinstate the repudiated pagan creed.

From Akhnaton and Moses to Theodosius the Great and Savonarola or Hus uncounted graven images were destroyed and books written by heretics and idolatrists burned. But the ancient belief in magic, denounced with equal fervor by science and religion, survived. It vanished from sight like an underground stream, but after passing through hidden caverns and crevices it reemerged time and again at unexpected places.

Paracelsus, the great Renaissance physician, hailed by his admirers as the spiritual heir of classical Hippocratic tradition and as the pacemaker of the modern experimental method in medicine, continued to use a variety of magic procedures based on essentially mythical concepts. His writings abound with references to nymphs, sylphs, pgymies and other supernatural beings, peacefully coexisting with ordinary mortals, but capable of exerting decisive influence upon human affairs in both health and disease. He believed in the secret powers or arcana attached to various herbs and plants, each of which was supposed to act according to its signature, that is, according to the particular remedial properties assigned to it by the Creator. Steeped as he was in the tradition of astrological and alchemistic "correspondences," he ascribed similar properties to the stars, to various minerals and metals, and conceived of man's betterment and spiritual transformation in terms of the transmutation of lead into ever purer potencies of gold. One of his magical remedies was the notorious Weapon Salve, an ointment which, he claimed, was capable of healing wounds at a distance, even when the injured person was "20,000 leagues away." Paracelsus' authorship of such stories has been questioned. But the Weapon Salve remained closely associated with his name, and so has the tradition of magic.

Yet a significant change in the technique of the magic art has to be noted at this point. In the hands of more sophisticated practitioners magic gradually dispensed with its traditional spells and incantations, rites and rituals. Its underlying myth may not have undergone any radical change, but the magician increasingly abstained from the "monstrous farrago" of uninhibited acting out, frantic gesturing or dramatic pantomime. He placed his reliance on words rather than on deeds; his ministrations became increasingly those of the spiritual healer, and his motivations increasingly directed into psychotherapeutic channels. Before long, growing restraint on the part of the healer and progressive narrowing of his target range, with the main focus on his patient's expectations—and on the tacitly implied myth shared with his patient—became the hallmarks of the new approach. This, incidentally, is in striking contrast to the "poly-pragmatic" techniques of the old-fashioned "general practitioner" of magic, of the rainmaker or witch doctor, called upon to heal; to perform black magic, fertility rites, or to influence other processes of nature, as the case may be.

Even so, in the wake of the Humanistic Revolution, magic had to find new disguises to hold its own. Disclaiming its historic ties with astrological and alchemistic lore, it sought to masquerade as science, or at least as what Francis Bacon called "Natural Magick." We shall see that the new trend set the pace for subsequent developments in the healing arts up to our day.

The story of Sir Kenelm Digby and his *Powder of Sympathy* is a characteristic example to illustrate our point. Sir Kenelm (1603-1665), author, adventurer, seafarer and courtier, was a protegé of King James I of England. He wrote poetry and philosophical treatises, lectured on botany and is said to have been a friend of Descartes. Discretely glossing over Paracelsus' Weapon Salve and other precursors of his remedy, he described the Powder of Sympathy as a concoction of copper sulfate and other ingredients prepared according to an old alchemistic or astrological formula.

Nevertheless he insisted that it had nothing in common with magic and demonology and was based on sound, scientific principles. Yet, like Paracelsus' panacea, it too was supposed to be capable of healing wounds at a distance. Digby recounts that the formula of the powder was handed down to him by a Carmelite monk who had brought it to the West "from Persia or India." In an address given to a SOLEMNE ASSEMBLY OF NOTABLES AND LEARNED MEN AT MONTPELLIER, FRANCE, he offers to provide information on *"How to Make Said Powder, Whereby Many Other Secrets of Nature Are Unfolded."*

The following is an excerpt from his discourse, translated into English by Robert White in 1658.[1]

> Touching the Cure of Wounds by the Powder of Sympathy. . . . I should be very sorry, that having done my uttermost to make it clear, how the Powder which they call the Powder of Sympathy, doth naturally, and without any magick, cure wounds without handling them, yea, without seeing of the patient; I say I should be very sorry that it should be doubted, whether such a cure may effectually be performed or no. . . . But they who have not seen such experiences, ought to referre themselves to the Narrations, and authority of such, who have seen such things; I could produce divers, whereof I was an ocular witness . . . . All the circumstances were examined, and sounded to the bottom, by one of the greatest, and most knowing Kings of his time, viz. King *James*, of *England*, who had a particular talent, and marvellous sagacity, to discuss natural things, and penetrate them to the very bottom; as also by his Son, the late King *Charles*, and the late Duke of *Buckingham*, their prime Minister. And in fine, all was registered among the observations of the great *Chancelor Bacon*, to be added by way of Appendix, unto his Naturall History. And I believe, Sirs, when you shall have understood this History, you will not accuse me of vanity, if I attribute unto my self the introducing into this Quarter of the World this way of curing. Now the business was thus.
>
> Mr. *James Howel*, (well known in *France*, by his Writings, and particularly by his *Dendrologia*, translated into French by *Monsieur Baudoin*) coming by chance as two of his best friends were fighting in Duel, he did his endeavour to part them, and putting himself between them, seized with his left hand upon the hilt of the sword of one of the Combatants, while with his right hand he laid hold of the blade of the other; they being transported with fury one against the other, strugled to rid themselves of the hindrance their friend made that they should not kill one another; and one of them roughly drawing the blade of his sword, cuts to the very bone the nerves, and muscles, and tendons of Mr. *Howels* hand; and then the other disingaging his hilts, gave a crosse blow on his adversaries head, which glanced towards his friend, who heaving up his sore hand to save the blow, he was wounded on the back of his hand, as he had been before within. It seems some strange Constellation reigned then against him, that he should lose so much blood by parting two such dear friends, who had they been them-

selves, would have hazarded both their lives to have preserved his: but this unvoluntary effusion of bloud by them, prevented that which they should have drawn one from the other: For they seeing Mr. *Howels* face besmeared with blood, by heaving up his wounded hand, they both ran to embrace him; and having searched his hurts, they bound up his hand with one of his garters, to close the veines which were cut, and bled abundantly. They brought him home, and sent for a Surgeon. But this being heard at Court, the King sent one of his own Surgeons, for his Majesty much affected the said Mr *Howel*.

It was my chance to be lodged hard by him; and four or five dayes after, as I was making my self ready, he came to my House, and prayed me to view his wounds, for I understand, said he, that you have extraordinary remedies upon such occasions, and my Surgeons apprehend some fear, that it may grow to a Gangrene, and so the hand must be cut off. In effect, his countenance discovered that he was in much pain, which he said was unsupportable, in regard of the extream inflammation: I told him that I would willingly serve him, but if haply he knew the manner how I would cure him, without touching or seeing him, it may be he would not expose himself to my manner of curing, because he would think it peradventure either ineffectual, or superstitious: he replied, "That the wounderful things which many have related unto me, of your way of curing, makes me nothing doubt at all of its efficacy; and all that I have to say unto you, is comprehended in the *Spanish* Proverb, *Hagafe el milagro, y hagalo* Mahoma, Let the miracle be done though *Mahomet* do it."

I asked him then for any thing that had the blood upon it, so he presently sent for his Garter, wherewith his hand was first bound: and having called for a Bason of water, as if I would wash my hands; I took a handfull of Powder of Vitrol, which I had in my study, and presently dissolved it. As soon as the bloody garter was brought me, I put it within the Bason, observing in the interim what *Mr. Howel* did, who stood talking with a Gentleman in a corner of my Chamber, not regarding at all what I was doing: but he started suddenly, as if he had found some strange alteration in himself; I asked him what he ailed? I know not what ailes me, but I find that I feel no more pain, methinks that a pleasing kind of freshnesse, as it were a wet cold Napkin did spread over my hand, which hath taken away the inflamation that tormented me before; I replved, since that you feel already so good an effect of my medicament, I advise you to cast away all your playsters onely keep the wound clean, and in a moderate temper twixt heat and cold. This was presently reported to the Duke of *Buckingham,* and a little after to the King, who were both very curious to know the issue of the businesse, which was, that after dinner I took the garter out of the water, and put it to dry before a great fire; it was scarce dry, but Mr. *Howels* servant came running, and told me, that his Master felt as much burning as ever he had done, if not more, for the heat was such, as if his hand were twixt coales of fire: I answered, that although that had happened at present, yet he should find ease in a short time; for I knew the reason of this new accident, and I would provide accordingly, for his Master should be free from that inflammation, it may be, before he could possibly return unto him: but in case he found no ease, I wished him to come presently back again, otherwise, he might forbear coming. Thereupon he went, and at the instant I did put again the garter into the water;

thereupon he found his Master without any pain at all. To be brief, there was no sense of pain afterward; but within five or six dayes the wounds were cicatrized, and entirely healed. King *James* required a punctuall information of what had passed touching this cure: and after it was done and perfected, his Majesty would needs know of me how it was done, having drolled with me first (which he could do with a very good grace) about a Magician and a Sorcerer. . . .

Behold now, Sirs, the Genealogie of the Powder of Sympathy in this part of the World, with a notable History of a cure performed by it. It is time now to come to the discussion, which is, to know how it is made. It must be avowed that it is a marvellous thing, that the hurt of a wounded person should be cured by the application of a remedy put to a rag of cloth, or a weapon, at a great distance. And it is not to be doubted, if after a long and profound speculation of all the oeconomy and concatenation of naturall Causes, which may be adjudged capable to produce such effects, one may fall at last upon the true causes which must have subtill resorts and means to act. Hitherto they have been wrapped up in darknesse, and adjudged so inaccessible, that they who have undertaken to speak or write of them, (at least those whom I saw) have been contented to speak of some ingenious gentilenesse, without diving into the bottom, endeavouring rather to show the vivacity of their spirit, and the force of their eloquence, than to satisfie their Readers and Auditors how the thing is really to be done. They would have us take for ready mony some terms which we understand not, nor know what they signifie. They would pay us with conveniences, with resemblances, with Sympathies, with Magnetical virtues, and such terms, without explicating what these terms mean. They think they have done enough, if they feebly perswade any body that the businesse may be performed by a naturall way, without having any recourse to the intervention of Daemons and spirits: but they pretend not in any sort to have found out the convincing reasons, to demonstrate how the thing is done. . . .

On comparing this report with some of the early historic documents of healing magic reviewed in Chapter II, several interesting points of resemblance—and difference—can be found. First, Sir Kenelm Digby, like his Egyptian or Babylonian forerunners, makes sure to impress his audience with his credentials. However, this time they are derived from mundane, not supramundane authorities. His account, he tells us, is verified by "the greatest and most knowing king of his time"; by his son, Prince Charles; by the Duke of Buckingham; by the Chancellor Bacon, and other prominent personages. Secondly, he implores his audience to realize that the effects of his remedy are based on thoroughly scientific principles and not on magic and sorcery. Thirdly, he seeks to secure their sympathy both for himself and the two chief protagonists of his story by depicting in glowing colors the injured man's gallantry and nobility of heart, and the worthy purpose for which he had suffered his injury.

But while going out of his way to invoke the authority of worldly dignitaries, he also enlists the prestige of the Carmelite monk, that is, of the Roman Catholic Church, in his behalf. In case this should not be sufficient to bolster his case, he also stresses the mythical origin of his Powder from the "mysterious east." It is as though the makers of a modern antibiotic tried to base the reputation of their product on the fame of Sir John Fleming, the authority of the Food and Drug Administration, and on the assurance that its liquid base was imported directly from the holy fountain of Lourdes.

Yet in keeping with the prevailing scientific temper of his time, Sir Kenelm is scornful of amateurish attempts to explain the marvelous properties of his Powder by reference to "Sympathies, Magnetical Currents and such terms, without explicating what these terms mean."

His own explanation? A mysterious omnipresent *effluvium*, activated by the effects of sunlight, aided by a no less mysterious filtration effect "going to gaine the heart of the party" and supposed to "return back to its principles and so leaves the party well recovered." At the end of the discourse he invokes yet another principle. "In time of common contagion, they used to carry about the powder of a toad . . . which draws unto it the contagious air which otherwise would infect the party . . . Or else they carry Arsenick, or some other venomous substance . . . and the same powder of a toad draws onto it the poyson of a plague-sore . . ." In short, he echoes some of the medical concepts based on the principle of *similia similibus curantur* widely held by his contemporaries, while at the same time he anticipates some of the theories of magnetopathic and homeopathic medicine which were to become the fads of the 18th and 19th centuries.

Yet the very description of his remedy as the *Powder of Sympathy* should make its roots in the age-old tradition of magic—in effect of what Frazer described as sympathetic magic—abundantly clear. It is not surprising, after all, that both his therapeutic claims and his attempts at explaining them were met with skepticism on the part of the medical profession of his time, and gave rise to acrimonious controversy.

Nevertheless, Robert Amadou, his French biographer,[2] assures us that Digby's colorful personality, his suave manners and fanatical faith in his remedy earned him a considerable reputation in France, England, Italy and Spain. Soon the use of the Powder became a craze all over western Europe "till there was no village barber left who did not know about it." The debate persisted long after Digby's death. His remedy was denounced as pure superstition, or praised as "the sweet effect of divine magic." Madame de Sevigné was one of its admirers, although she doubted its capacity to heal wounds at a distance.

But by the middle of the 18th century the Powder of Sympathy seems to have reached the end of its career. Demoted from its position as a nostrum for wounds and wound infections, it was now used as a popular sudorific. Thus the story of its miraculous effects turned out to be a minor myth, with a life cycle of less than 100 years. It may not be quite by chance that the time it passed into oblivion coincided with the advent of a no less striking medical discovery: Anton Mesmer's animal magnetism.

✿   ✿   ✿

Here, again, as in the case of the primitive medicine man, one may wonder about the reasons for the remarkable success story and durable popularity of a totally ineffectual physical agent. Explaining it in terms of trickery by an unscrupulous charlatan, as a result of the gullibility of his dupes, or as a product of dishonest reporting avoids the real issue. More relevant is the fact that the fad—or the myth—started by Sir Kenelm's hocus-pocus did succeed in acquiring a vast number of followers and in mobilizing in thousands of sufferers an expectancy of help that compared favorably with similar expectancies—or "patient attitudes"—encountered under modern conditions. Put in contemporary terms, whatever results he achieved were due to suggestion and autosuggestion centered about the so-called *placebo effect*.

A placebo has been defined as a medication or therapeutic procedure "which is objectively without specific activity for the condition being treated."[3] A. K. Shapiro, in a careful study of the subject, emphasizes that placebos have been used from time immemorial by witch doctors and medicine men. In fact, Shapiro goes so far as to suggest that "the whole history of medicinal treatment until relatively recent time is the history of the placebo effect."

S. Lesse[4] distinguishes between "pure placebos," that is, chemicals or procedures that are in themselves physiologically inert or inactive, from "impure placebos," that is, placebos that have some measure of activity, chemical or otherwise, but which have no direct effect upon the patient's symptoms. He also makes a distinction between planned and unplanned placebos, that is, between drugs or procedures used deliberately by the therapist, for research purposes, knowing full well that they are in fact ineffectual, and placebos used by the practitioner without being aware of their lack of specific effectiveness. If so, both patient and therapist are held to be victims of deception or self-deception.

Viewed against the background of modern placebo research, Paracelsus' Weapon Salve or Digby's Powder of Sympathy are models of pure, unadulterated and unplanned placebos. They were so much so that their hypothetical effect upon the patient was brought to bear by remote control only.

There is no way of telling to what extent the psychological effect of these remedies actually helped to alleviate symptoms. Judging from what we know today about the powerful effects of placebos in general, they may well account for the extraordinary claims made for the Powder of Sympathy. But while modern research has afforded abundant proof of the efficacy of the placebo, we know much less about the way in which its effects are brought to bear upon the patient.

Extensive studies by J. D. Frank and his co-workers,[5] and the critical analysis of the literature by A. K. Shapiro, S. Lesse, and others, provide at least a few hints on that score. They suggest that the key factor is the doctor-patient relationship, in particular a positive transference upon the therapist. They stress, furthermore, the part played by the doctor's faith in the drug (or procedure) used, and the expectations with which the patient enters into the treatment situation in the first place. Other factors mentioned are the patient's suggestibility, his anxious, compliant attitude, and his dependency needs. On the other hand, it was found that the doctor's (or the nurse's) negative attitude toward the placebo may considerably reduce its effectiveness. In short, here again, positive expectations of those involved in the prescription and administration of the placebo, including positive expectations on the part of the patient, are of decisive importance.

In trying to evaluate these clinical and experimental investigations we must realize that, for obvious reasons, they have to be based on methodological variables that are not amenable to simple operational definitions, measurements and statistical treatment. This is why, in spite of the wealth of available data, the ultimate reasons underlying both the patient's and the therapist's faith and expectations in the respective placebo are still left in the dark.

Sir Kenelm's case of an unplanned and unintended placebo throws light on precisely these aspects of the placebo effect. It shows that here, for once, a placebo, standing entirely on its own feet, derived its power from a cluster of myths shared in equal proportions, as it were, by healer and sufferer. We have seen that their myths had served as a rationale for thinly veiled magical concepts that were still rooted in the spirit of the time. The myth maker, we stated, sought to play both sides of the field at the same time. He drew his inspiration from both magic and science, and turned for added support to more mundane, princely authorities as well.

Yet here, again, it may be the reciprocal nature of the psychological give-and-take involved in Digby's myth which accounts for part of its effectiveness. Faith in its efficacy was shared by therapist and patient. This was reinforced by a circular feedback from the individual to his subculture and from his subculture to the individual. We shall see on a later page that much the same considerations account for the efficacy of a wide variety of latter-day myths, from animal magnetism, phrenology and phrenomagnetism, to James Graham's "Celestial Bed," Wilhelm Reich's "Orgone Box," and various semimythical assumptions underlying some contemporary schools of psychotherapy.

Yet there is one important point of difference. As compared with Digby's Powder of Sympathy, the methods used by modern placebo research are necessarily devoid of one half of the mythical dimension. The experimenter, working as he does, with a "planned" or "deliberate" placebo, cannot help being aware of the fact that he is, in effect, deceiving his patient. He does not minister to his patient's need by offering him bona fide magic. He knows that in an appreciable number of his "samples" all the patient gets is distilled water or a tablet of lactose. He does not share the patient's faith, illusions or expectations. As a result, the patient is shortchanged of what under scientifically less stringent conditions, might have been the therapist's naive, unconscious, and certainly unplanned contribution to the placebo effect. All he can offer in addition to his placebo is the therapist's cold scientific curiosity, coupled with the augur's smile. His ministrations amount to make-believe magic, supported by a truncated myth. By contrast, the bona fide magician and mythmaker may at least be credited with deceiving not only his patient but also himself. Put in more positive terms: he shares his patient's faith, illusions and expectations. He offers him a placebo activated by living myth, not its dehydrated, dissected or truncated version.

❖   ❖   ❖

There is one more intriguing aspect of the Powder of Sympathy that calls for comment: its claimed action at a distance. The concept was made popular in the 17th century by Newton's theory of gravitation, but applied to human behavior, it certainly ran counter to generally accepted laws of nature. It will be recalled that the pain and inflammation in the injured man's hand subsided the moment an object drenched with his blood was immersed in a basin located in another room or even much further away. Conversely, the pain returned the moment the object was removed from the basin. This purported observation is wholly in the tradition of sympathetic magic. It thus goes back to Frazer's or Malinowski's primitive witch doctor, if not to Paleolithic times with their magic images in the cave of Lascaux and the protruding bellies of the fertility goddesses of Moellendorf or Lespuges.

In the last analysis, assumed action at a distance is derived from a primary inner experience. It is the projection of an intrapsychic state of "felt energy" into the outside world. It stems from the externalization of human volition into the world outside, unencumbered by spatial limitations and intervening objects. Belief in action at a distance is in effect one of the general "structural psychic determinants" of (primitive) mythic compositions as H. A. Murray put it.[6]

Yet such an assumption was apparently less paradoxical to man of the 17th century than it is to us. Seventeenth century science was still imbued with the notion of Plato's *anima mundi*. Henry More, the English philosopher, proclaimed the "Spirit of Nature" or the "universal soul of the world" to be the ultimate metaphysical principle, the manifestation of a divine

presence which did not leave "the least minute space void."[7] William
Gilbert, "the father of scientific magnetism,"[8] described it in terms of a
"magnetic soul" capable of actions at a distance and attributed its
power to an effluvium emitted by the lodestone. Robert Boyle, Newton's
older contemporary, shared with him the notion of an all-pervading ethereal
medium. Likewise, Newton's concept of gravitation necessarily implied
action at a distance, though he emphasized that this could not possibly take
place "through a vacuum without the mediation of anything else."[9] Even
William Harvey, the discoverer of the circulation of blood, felt it necessary
to assume the action of "ethereal spirits" to account for "the passage of heat
and nourishment from the sun to the heart and blood of living creatures."[10]

Thus Sir Kenelm Digby's attempts to explain the effects of his remedy
may not have sounded quite so absurd to his contemporaries as they do to
us. But this still leaves the question open as to why he or, for that matter,
Paracelsus before him, should have chosen to strain the credulity of their
public with extraordinary claims bordering on sympathetic magic. Presumably, the answer lies in the mythical aspect of their placebos.

Belief in man's capacity to transcend the categories of time, space and
causality seems to be deeply rooted in our mental organization. It is a belief
which is impervious to practical experience and reality testing. If man's
evolutionary history, his racial and individual development have severed
his original ties with the rest of the universe, animate and inanimate, his
unconscious seems to have preserved some memory traces of this lost unity.
This may be the meaning of some of our most ancient myths: of the
myth of emergence from a primordial matrix common to all creation; of the
myths of the Golden Age; of the Garden of Eden; of Paradise Lost; of an
all-embracing "Cosmic Spirit" or "World Soul." The notion of a ubiquitous
healing principle called forth by a miracle man, witch doctor or charlatan
is a desacralized derivative of such myths. It bridges the gap between
person and person; between the individual and his physical environment.
It conjures up the illusion of a protective and beneficial parental presence,
the spiritual counterpart of the amniotic fluid, as it were.

It may well be that it is the survival of emotionally charged archaic beliefs
and expectations of this order which account for the powerful appeal of the
panaceas or placebos reviewed here. We shall see on a later page that
Mesmer's animal magnetism or von Reichenbach's *Od* belong in the same
class. Nor is our enlightened 20th century medicine quite immune to the
blandishments of such beliefs, even though they may be couched in a
scientifically more sophisticated language.

Another, paradoxical, reason for the initial success of Sir Kenelm Digby's
Powder of Sympathy may have been the very absurdity, the exaggerated
nature and the attending shock value of his claims. Recent political history

has witnessed the effectiveness of the "big lie." Modern hard-sell advertising techniques may well be responsible for the effectiveness of both major and minor myths. Indeed the myth which is satisfied with all the hallmarks of reality and credibility on its side is not a myth. It may be firmly rooted in the soil, but unless its head and shoulders reach high into the clouds and into the sky beyond them, it is nothing but a tall story. It may well be that the miraculous effect of a claimed miracle is largely based on the magnitude of the claim itself. It appeals to man's secret belief in magic, while its shock value silences the voice of reason and numbs his critical faculties. Like the medieval devotee, he may bow his head in awe of the unexpected and unbelievable and, in case he had the benefits of classical education, mutter to himself: *"Credo quia absurdum est."*

REFERENCES

1. DIGBY, KENELM: A Late Discourse, transl. by R. White. London: 1658.
2. AMADOU, R.: La Poudre de Sympathie. Paris: Gerard Nizet, 1953.
3. SHAPIRO, A. K.: The Placebo Effect in the History of Medical Treatment. Am. Journ. Psychiatry 116, 298-304, 1959.
4. LESSE, S.: Placebo Reactions and Spontaneous Rhythms. Am. Journ. Psychotherapy, XVIII, Supplem. 1, 1964.
5. FRANK, J. D.: Persuasion and Healing. New York: Schocken, 1963.
6. MURRAY, H. A.: cf. Chapter I (6).
7. MORE, H.: quoted from Burtt, E. A.: The Metaphysical Foundations of Modern Science. New York: Doubleday, 1954.
8. GILBERT, WILLIAM (ibid.).
9. NEWTON, ISAAC (ibid.).
10. HARVEY, WILLIAM (ibid.).

— V —

Mythmakers and Mental Healers
1. Mesmer and His Myth

Anton Mesmer, the discoverer of animal magnetism; his disciple, the Marquis de Puységur; James Braid, the pioneer investigator of hypnotic phenomena; the Portuguese Mesmerist, Abbé Faria; and Mary Baker Eddy, the founder of the Christian Science Movement, have variously been classed as cranks, cultists, promoters of unintentional placebos, or as systematizers and builders of imaginative theories of prescientific psychotherapy. By the same token, they could be described as latter-day mythmakers: as makers of *effective* myths. Such a designation, it should be noted, is more than a matter of semantics. Nor is it merely a footnote to the history of psychiatry at best deserving small print at the bottom of the page. Their description as makers of effective myths is meant to go to the heart of the matter and to bring out a major trend in the unfolding of the healing arts from the medicine man to Freud.

Myths, in spiritual healing and perhaps in the field of psychotherapy in general, are the vehicles of a circular process of feedback in which belief generates cures and cures generate, and reinforce, belief. To the believer it makes little difference whether or not the cures are corroborated by statistical methods. What counts is the deepening and self-perpetuating conviction that his suffering has been or is going to be relieved. More often than not this conviction is vindicated by the established fact that more than half the cases of mental or psychosomatic disorder tend to improve anyway—with or without treatment. They have, and apparently always have had, the tendency to spontaneous remission. Thus the skeptic may well claim that both healer and sufferer have a better than even chance of success in their joint venture. Yet we indicated that neither today's nor yesterday's patients are primarily interested in scientifically validated cures, as opposed to mere suggestion, autosuggestion or placebo effects. They may be satisfied with the illusion of cure, provided that it is supplemented by the experience of a supportive parent figure, a charismatic healer or mediator with the divinity. The ministrations of the Tibetan monk preparing the dying for his 40 days in limbo and for his subsequent reincarnation in afterlife are usually followed by the demise of their clients. So are, in most cases, the last sacraments given to the Catholic believer. Yet the age old tradition of these sacred rites testifies to the reality of the spiritual needs they meet, even though they have yet to prove their power to bring about the promised salvation, Eastern or Western style, at the appointed deadline.

But the process of circular feedback does not always operate in favor of the myth. We have seen that the fad of the Powder of Sympathy was relatively short-lived. After going strong for nearly half a century the disbelief and disappointment of the "other half"—of those whose wounds failed to heal and whose suffering did not subside—gave rise to increasing doubts as to its efficacy. Their growing tide of disbelief and disappointment in turn led to its degradation and ultimate eclipse.

In Digby's case one can only speculate as to the reasons for this turn of events. One reason may have been the increasingly critical temper of his time which found it more and more difficult to go along with the claimed magical action of the powder. Another reason, anticipated by no less an authority than Descartes, may have been the slow but steady progress made by the medical profession which had freed itself from the tradition of the medieval dirt pharmacy and no longer condoned the contamination of wounds with such remedies as cows' dung or dried powder of toads. As a result, legitimate surgical procedures were no longer at a disadvantage over an otherwise ineffectual sympathetic agent which at least had the virtue of keeping the patient's wounds out of harm's way. It may well be that it is the growing margin of difference between surgical competence and the chances of spontaneous recovery of Digby's patients—left as they were to their own resources—which is responsible for the beginning of the downhill trend of his remedy.

＊　　＊　　＊

In the case of Mesmer's animal magnetism, the available evidence is more substantial. His writings provide an explicit formulation of his theories. His clinical case histories, though fragmentary, permit at least an educated guess as to what has transpired between him and his patients. The reactions of his numerous admirers and followers, of his equally numerous critics and detractors and of the public at large have become a matter of recorded history. Indeed, the literature covering the life cycle of his myth is so vast that it is not possible (nor necessary) to go over it in the present context.[1,2,3] Its interest to our issue stems from the fact that Mesmer's myth—and its mesmerizing effect upon his contemporaries—can serve as an example of an effective myth whose origins can be traced back to the remote past, whose years of glory were witnessed by our forefathers barely more than four or five generations ago and whose last repercussions can still be discerned on the contemporary scene.

Mesmer's theories follow in the footsteps of Paracelsus' or Van Helmont's "magnetic healing," of Fludd's magnetic philosophy, or of Digby's dabbling with sympathetic magic and astrological notions. One of his earliest spiritual ancestors may have been Empedocles who held that the universe was kept together by the all-pervading forces of Love and Strife. Mesmer may not have been familiar with the writings of Gilbert and Boyle, mentioned in the preceding chapter. It is more likely that he had been influenced by their contemporary, the versatile friar Athanasius Kircher, who had expressed similar thoughts to explain the forces of attraction and repulsion emanating from the lodestone. Another indirect influence may have been the great English physician, Sydenham, who tried to account for convulsions and disturbed functions of the organism by reference to "Animal Spirits" which accumulated in, or were displaced from, one place of the body to another, depending on the nature of the existing ailment.

But Mesmer's view of these forces was colored by the flamboyant, romantic outlook of his time. To him the world was filled to the brim with a vibrating, all-pervading cosmic principle linking all things together in heaven and earth. It was a principle shared by human beings, animals, plants, rocks, mountains and the Seven Seas alike, subject to the ebb and flow of the tides which were in turn controlled by the celestial bodies.

When the Jesuit priest, Father Hell, shared with Mesmer his observations of supposedly curative effects obtained with the lodestone Mesmer immediately decided to investigate the matter further. It soon dawned on him that the priest was mistaken when he attributed his results to the magnet as such, or to the shapes to which the magnetized pieces had been molded. Mesmer discovered that the effective principle was by no means confined to inert matter and that the magnetic effluvia could readily be transmitted from the magnet to whatever object, animate or inanimate, the magnetizer happened to lay hands on. He has therefore modified his original magnetic hypothesis and attributed results to the operation of a mysterious fluid or animal magnetism emanating from his person, and potentially from every living being. The crucial point, in his view, was the contention that animal magnetism was a principle *sui generis*, closely resembling the behavior of electric "fluids"—what today would be described as an electric charge or, for that matter, as psychoanalytic cathexis.

That Mesmer's theoretical explanations were just as wrong as those of Father Hell is another matter. To the bitter end Mesmer remained unaware of the psychological origin of his purported animal magnetism. Nor could he have any inkling of its similarity with the primitive Polynesian concepts of mana and taboo, thought to be residing in the person of a tribal chief or medicine man and claimed to possess powers equally awesome and volatile as the mysterious effluvium emanating from the person of the learned Viennese doctor of the late 18th century.

These are some of the 27 propositions laid down by Mesmer to account for his experiments:[4]

"(1) There exists a mutual influence between the Heavenly Bodies, the Earth and Animate Bodies.

(2) A universally distributed and continuous fluid, which is quite without vacuum and of an incomparably rarefied nature, and which by its nature is capable of receiving, propagating and communicating all the impressions of movement, is the means of this influence.

(3) This reciprocal action is subordinated to mechanical laws that are hitherto unknown . . .

(6) It is by this operation (the most universal of those presented by Nature) that the activity ratios are set up between the heavenly bodies, the earth and its component parts.

(7) The properties of Matter and the Organic Body depend on this operation.

(8) The animal body sustains the alternate effects of this agent, which by insinuating itself into the substance of the nerves, affects them at once.

(9) It is particularly manifest in the human body that the agent has properties similar to those of the magnet; different and opposite poles may likewise be distinguished, which can be changed, communicated, destroyed and strengthened; even the phenomenon of dipping is observed.

(10) This property of the animal body, which being under the influence of the heavenly bodies and the reciprocal action of those surrounding it, as shown by its analogy with the Magnet, induced me to term it Animal Magnetism.

(11) The action and properties of Animal Magnetism, thus defined, may be communicated to other animate and inanimate bodies. Both are more or less susceptible to it.

(12) This action and properties may be strengthened and propagated by the same bodies.

(13) Experiments show the passage of a substance whose rarefied nature enables it to penetrate all bodies without appreciable loss of activity.

(14) Its action is exerted at a distance, without the aid of an intermediate body . . ."

It is interesting to note Mesmer's 18th proposition, which leaves a loophole open to account for cases in which his animal magnetism failed to take effect:

"(18) I have said that all animate bodies are not equally susceptible; there are some, although very few, whose properties are so opposed that their very presence destroys all the effects of magnetism in other bodies."

Feeling that this reservation, reminiscent of Freud's concept of negative transference, should suffice to silence his critics in case his method failed to live up to their expectations, he goes on to say:

"(25) By making known my method, I shall show by a new theory of illnesses that universal utility of the principle I bring to bear on them.

(26) With this knowledge, the physician will determine reliably the origin, nature and progress of illnesses, even the most complicated; he will prevent them without ever exposing the patient to dangerous effects or unfortunate consequences, whatever his age, temperament and sex. Women, even in pregnancy and childbirth, will enjoy the same advantage.

(27) In conclusion, this doctrine will enable the physician to determine the state of each individual's health and safeguard him from the maladies to which he might otherwise be subject. The art of healing will thus reach its final stage of perfection."

After making these ambitious claims, Mesmer adds by way of an afterthought:

"Although there is not one of these assertions regarding which my constant observation over a period of twelve years leaves me in uncertainty, I quite realize that compared with old-established principles and knowledge, my system may contain as much illusion as truth."

The few case histories Mesmer left behind to substantiate his claims do just that. They reflect the striking tendency of the neurotic patient to comply with the therapist's emotionally charged preconceived ideas regarding the validity of his theories. This is what on a later page will be described as *doctrinal compliance*. Doctrinal compliance may already have been foreshadowed by Father Hell's observation that the efficacy of his magnetic passes on the patient was determined by the varying shapes of the magnetic pieces used in assorted ailments. It is interesting to note that Mesmer himself was aware of the pitfalls inherent in such responses—at least as far as other people were concerned. Although first acknowledging his indebtedness to the Jesuit priest, he was soon embroiled with him in controversy and ridiculed his observations. This is how Father Hell, according to Mesmer, had expressed himself:

"I have discovered in these shapes, which agree with the magnetic vortex, a perfection on which depends their specific virtue in cases of illness; it is owing to the lack of this perfection that the tests carried out in England and France have met with no success."

It is needless to say that Mesmer attributed Father Hell's failure to convince the experts to the priest's confusion of the magnetized shapes with his own discovery, that is, with the effects of Mesmer's animal magnetism.

The fact is that Mesmer's first patient, Miss Oesterline, obliged in a manner altogether different from the priest's observations. When Mesmer applied the magnetized pieces to her stomach and both legs "she felt inside her some painful currents of a subtle material which, after different attempts at taking direction, made their way towards the lower part," that is, the genital area. The reader will not be surprised to find that "the current of subtle material" mentioned by the patient provides a perfect confirmation of the experimenter's theories.

These are fragments from Mesmer's account of the Oesterline case:

"It was chiefly in the years 1773 and 1774 that I undertook in my house the treatment of a young lady aged twenty-nine named Oesterline, who for several years had been subject to a convulsive malady, the most troublesome symptoms of which were that the blood rushed to her head and there set up the most cruel toothache and earache, followed by delirium, rage, vomiting and swooning. For me it was a highly favourable occasion for observing accurately that type of ebb and flow to which ANIMAL MAG-NETISM subjects the human body. The patient often had beneficial crises, followed by a remarkable degree of alleviation; however, the enjoyment was always momentary and imperfect.

The desire to ascertain the cause of this imperfection and my own unin-terrupted observations brought me time and time again to the point of recognising Nature's handiwork and of penetrating it sufficiently to forecast and assert, without hesitation, the different stages of the illness. En-couraged by this first success, I no longer had any doubts as to the possi-bility of bringing it to perfection, if I were able to discover the existence, among the substances of which our globe is made, of an action that is also reciprocal and similar to that of the heavenly bodies, by means of which I could imitate artificially the periodic revolutions of the ebb and flow just referred to."

Summing up his observations at this point of the treatment he declares:

"All bodies were, like the magnet, capable of communicating this mag-netic principle; this fluid penetrated everything and could be stored up and concentrated, like the electric fluid; . . . it acted at a distance . . .

(Basically) animate bodies were divided into two classes, one being susceptible to this magnetism and the other to an opposite quality that suppresses its action . . ."

One day in 1775, a British physician called on Mesmer to witness his treatment of Miss Oesterline. Unconvinced, he pleaded with Mesmer to refrain from publishing his method and in the ensuing controversy went so far as to charging Mesmer with prearranged fraud. Unfortunately Miss Oesterline was informed of the English physician's attack upon her doctor. According to Mesmer, she was

"so affronted at finding herself thus compromised that she relapsed into her former state, which was aggravated by a nervous fever."

And he goes on to say:

"Miss Oesterline's condition claimed the whole of my attention for a fortnight. In these circumstances, by continuing my research, I was for-tunate in overcoming the difficulties which stood in the way of my progress and of giving my theory the desired perfection. The cure of this young lady represented the first fruits of my success, and I had the satisfaction of seeing her henceforth in excellent health. She married and had some children."

His report on a second patient, Miss Paradis, is interspersed with an ac-count of his feud with his critics and detractors that sent him out of the country in search of a more favorable scientific climate. This is how he describes her case:

"After returning to Vienna, I persisted until the end of that year in undertaking no further work; neither would I have altered my mind if my friends had not been unanimous in opposing my decision. Their insistences, together with my desire to see the truth prevail, aroused in me the hope of accomplishing this by means of fresh successes, particularly through some striking cure. With this end in view, among other patients I undertook the treatment of Miss Paradis, aged eighteen, whose parents were well known; she herself was known to Her Majesty the Queen-Empress, through whose bounty she received a pension, being quite blind since the age of four. It was a perfect amaurosis, with convulsions in the eyes. She was moreover a prey to melancholia, accompanied by stoppages in the spleen and liver, which often brought on accesses of delirium and rage so that she was convinced she was out of her mind . . .

The father and mother of Miss Paradis, who witnessed her cure and the progress she was making in the use of her eyesight, hastened to make this occurrence known and how pleased they were. Crowds flocked to my house to make sure for themselves, and each one, after putting the patient to some kind of test, withdrew greatly astonished, with the most flattering remarks to myself.

The two Presidents of the Faculty, at the head of a deputation of their corps, came to see me at the repeated instances of Mr. Paradis; and, after examining the young lady, added their tribute to that of the public. Mr. de Stoerck, one of the gentlemen who knew this young person particularly well, having treated her for ten years without the slightest success, expressed to me his satisfaction at so interesting a cure and his regret at having so far deferred his acknowledgment of the importance of my discovery. A number of physicians, each for himself, followed the example set by our leaders and paid the same tribute to truth.

After such authentic recognition, Mr. Paradis was kind enough to express his gratitude in his writings, which went all over Europe. It was he who afterwards published the interesting details of his daughter's recovery in the newspapers."

Unfortunately, here again, Mesmer had to contend with a typical 18th century plot of his enemies. In the end they persuaded the patient's father, Mr. Paradis, to withdraw his daughter from Mesmer's care—with the expected deleterious results. Miss Paradis, her eyes "still being in an imperfect state," relapsed. Both her father and mother insisted with increasing heat on taking her home from Mesmer's mansion and on discontinuing her treatment. Ultimately Mesmer was ready to let the patient go, but declared that "if fresh incidents were the result, she could not count on my help."

What followed had the qualities of a *grand finale* in an 18th century *commedia del l'arte*.

"These words were overheard by the girl, who was so overcome that she went into a fit . . . Her mother, who heard her cries, left me abruptly and seized her daughter angrily from the hands of the person who was assisting her, saying: 'Wretched girl, you too are hand in glove with the people of this house!' as she flung her in a fury head-first against the wall.

Immediately all the troubles of that unfortunate girl recommenced. I hastened towards her to give her assistance, but her mother, still livid with rage, hurled herself upon me to prevent me from doing so, while she heaped insults on me. I had the mother removed by certain members of my household and went up to the girl to assist her. While I was so engaged, I heard more angry shouts and repeated attempts to open and shut the door of the room where I was.

It was Mr. Paradis who, having been warned by one of his wife's servants, now invaded my house sword in hand with the intention of entering the room where I was, while my servant was trying to remove him by guarding the door. The madman was at last disarmed, and he left my house breathing imprecations on myself and my household.

Meanwhile, his wife had swooned away. I had her given the necessary attention, and she left some hours afterwards, but the unhappy girl was suffering from attacks of vomiting, fits and rages, which the slightest noise, especially the sound of bells, accentuated. She had even relapsed into her previous blind state through the violence of the blow given her by her mother, and I had some fears for the state of her brain."

There is reason to believe that, unknown to him, Mesmer was not just one of the leading actors in the play. It looks as though he had been its stage director and indeed the writer of its scenario as well. The machinations of his enemies, including those of the patient's parents, always snatched victory from him when it was almost in his grasp, thus providing an alibi for his theories and an excuse for his failures. Ultimately he resumed the blind girl's treatment on condition that neither her father nor her mother would ever again enter his house. Again the outcome was a draw. Although Mesmer asserts that 15 days' treatment had "cured the blindness and restored the eye to its condition prior to the incident," the patient's family saw no improvement and continued to plot against the man "who had showered them with kindness."

In the end a bitter and disappointed Mesmer, "wearied by 12 consecutive years of labor" and by the intrigues and animosities of his foes, left Vienna again, this time for an extended stay in Paris. Once there, he established himself again and rose to fame once more. His treatment en masse of patients seated around the *Baquet*, an oak tub filled with "magnetized" water, became the craze of the town. Soft background music, attendants pointing iron rods to the diseased parts, "squeezing and massaging" them; crises and convulsions produced by the patients—all this presided over by Mesmer clad in a lilac robe, enhanced the effects of the procedure. This is how members of a commission sent by the French Academy of Medicine in 1784 described the scene:

"The tableaux presented by the patients is one of extreme diversity. Some are calm, composed, and feel nothing; others cough, spit, have slight pains, feel a glow locally or all over the body, accompanied by perspiration; others are shaken and tormented by convulsions. These convulsions are remarkable in their frequency, their duration, and their intensity. As soon as one attack begins others make their appearance . . . They are accompanied by expectorations of a viscous matter, torn from the chest by the violence of the attack. Sometimes there are traces of blood in the expectoration. The convulsions are characterised by involuntary spasmodic movements of the limbs and of the whole body, by contractions of the throat, by spasms of the hypochondriac and epigastric regions; the eyes are wandering and distracted; there are piercing cries, tears, hiccoughs, and extravagant laughter.

The convulsions are preceded and followed by a state of languor and reverie, by exhaustion and drowsiness. Any sudden noise causes the patients to start, and even a change in the music played on the piano has an effect— a lively tune agitates them afresh and renews the convulsions."[1]

The maladies for which cures were claimed by this early version of group therapy included chorea, asthma, colics, fever and blood spitting. Unfortunately here, again, Mesmer's days of glory were numbered. Several committees appointed by the French Academy of Medicine passed devastating verdicts on the claims made by him and by his champion, Charles Deslon, Doctor Regent of the Faculty of Paris. The committee convened in 1784 included such names as Jean Silvain Bailly, Benjamin Franklin and Dr. Guillotin. They found that his results were essentially based on the patient's imagination or due to mechanical friction, imitation, or the like and had nothing to do with magnetic effluvia.

But the learned committee failed to realize one important fact. Mesmerism, although it was founded on thoroughly unscientific premises, was in effect a new method of psychotherapy. They saw only the erroneous aspects of Mesmer's myth and failed to give credit to its effectiveness. They passed on his mistakes as a scientist and ignored his occasional successes as a healer.

The fact is that the cleavage between the rationalistic aspirations and the still lingering astrological and mystical beliefs characteristic of his age run right through his own personality. He was torn between the austere scientific standards set by his profession and his inability to explain his personal impact upon his patients in professionally satisfactory terms. The result was a poorly organized, rambling presentation of his thesis, coupled with his tendency to answer critics in terms of ill-tempered controversy and petty personal invective.

Mesmer was undoubtedly right in his claim of having hit upon a major medical discovery, but like Christopher Columbus, he remained unaware that his discovery had in effect opened up a new world—a hitherto unknown continent of psychological treatment—which had little to do with the discredited magical and astrological concepts of a past era. It was for generations of psychologists and psychiatrists who came after Mesmer to discover what his discovery was really all about. In so doing they did one more thing: they destroyed what was left of the efficacy of his lingering myth.

REFERENCES

1. PODMORE, F.: Mesmerism to Christian Science. London: Methuen & Co., 1909.
2. ZWEIG, S., Mental Healers, transl. by Edw. Paul. Garden City, Doubleday, 1931.
3. Encyclopedia Britannica, Vol. 7, 1954.
4. MESMER, A.: in Mesmerism, ed. by Gilbert Frankau. London: McDonald, 1948.

— VI —

Mythmakers and Mental Healers
2. Mesmer and His Aftermath

The vicissitudes of Mesmer's personal myth follow with striking fidelity the pattern outlined in the introductory chapter. Short-lived as it was, its popular success and its mesmeric powers were superior to the fad initiated by Sir Kenelm Digby's Powder of Sympathy. Viewed in historic perspective, it was in effect more than a personal myth. It was a myth reincarnated, as it were, in the person of the 18th century Viennese doctor. Thus, it was clothed in the romantic costume of his time and shared, as all myths are, with a waxing and waning multitude of fans and followers. We shall see that in another respect too it was running true to form: it showed an unmistakable tendency to branching into two separate prongs of the fork, one scientific and one religious.

Following the meanderings of what was to become the scientific offshoot of the myth, we can see the more temperate effects elicited in the subjects of Mesmer's most articulate and scholarly disciple, the Marquis de Puységur. Less prone to falling into spectacular crises and convulsions, the Marquis' patients showed a preference for passing into so-called somnambulistic states in which they became particularly amenable to unconscious suggestions emanating from their magnetizer.[1]

Some of Puységur's subjects claimed to possess clairvoyant or prophetic faculties during the trance. They diagnosed their own illnesses, or those of other persons, and prescribed their treatments, or else they predicted the exact time and circumstances under which an internal abscess would discharge, nose bleeding would occur or fevers would subside. Other astounding feats attributed to the somnambulistic state were the subject's capacity to respond to the mesmerist's will at a distance; to "see" with the pit of his stomach, with his fingers or toes.

Although the Marquis had paid Mesmer 100 louis d'or for his instruction and tried to keep faith with "orthodox" Mesmerism as long as possible, he moved beyond the notion of a magnetic fluid being responsible for the phenomena. He emphasized the part played by a psychological rapport between subject and experimenter and asserted that belief and will are the key factors in the production of the trance state.

The picture changes again when we turn to the observations recorded by another of Mesmer's followers, the Portuguese Abbé Faria. Faria's approach was colored by his theological background, notably his neo-Platonic,

49

Thomistic ideas. His subjects produced what he described as the "lucid sleep." In this state they displayed extraordinary powers of memory and intuition, exceeding those seen in Puységur's somnambulists. Faria ascribed these manifestations to their freedom from the fallacies of ordinary sense perception and to a compensatory capacity to recapture "lost faculties of the soul."

In effect his subjects may have produced a new version of what in the previous chapter was described as doctrinal compliance. Their productions bore the imprints of Faria's personality; no longer those of the cantankerous Viennese doctor. They seem to be written in a different musical key, less dramatic and spectacular than the tortured utterances of the Misses Paradis and Oesterline, or of the group of hysterics crowded around Mesmer's *Baquet.* If the trance state seen in Mesmer's subjects at times had a Dionysian quality, those of the Portuguese Abbé's seemed to be more of an Appolonian cast, reflecting, as it were, a different "mode of existence." Their possession was, to use a term coined by Professor Tillich, possession from above, not from below. It foreshadowed a major change in the myth bequeathed by Mesmer, a change harking back to an age-old religious and even older classical tradition.

❊   ❊   ❊

The claims of extraordinary faculties called forth by the somnambulistic state were in part the outgrowth of a growing disillusionment and dissatisfaction with the wide-spread materialistic outlook of the early 19th century. It was accompanied by a newly awakened interest in the discredited tradition of magic. By the middle of the 19th century, Arthur Schopenhauer[2] went so far as to speak of an exoneration of ancient magic beliefs. He himself was ready to give credence to widely current reports of prophetic and clairvoyant capacities attributed to a growing number of "magnetized" subjects. One of them was the celebrated Seeress of Prevorst, described by the German physician and poet, Justinus Kerner. It was the fascination with reports of this order which, in 1882, led to the founding of the Society for Psychical Research in London, while on this side of the Atlantic mesmerist influences reached Mary Baker Eddy through Phineas Quimby, the watchmaker turned mental healer and magnetopath.

Despite the fanciful nature of some of Faria's and Puységur's claims, they deserve credit for their early emphasis on the psychological aspects of mesmeric phenomena. H. Bernheim hailed Faria as his forerunner in discovering the part played by suggestion in trance manifestations. Both Puységur's and Faria's work was, however, soon to be oveshadowed by the researches of James Braid, the Manchester surgeon, who brought out yet another aspect of the somnambulistic state.[3] Braid proved conclusively that what Mesmer had described as Animal Magnetism did not in reality exist. He insisted that virtually all mesmeric phenomena could be induced by such physiological means as fatigue of the eyelids and eye muscles, and stripped the trance state of its mysterious "magnetopathic" trappings. He described the phenomena by the terms neurohypnotism and neuro-hypnology, and finally settled for the term hypnosis, which has by now become a household word in many languages. Thus in Braid's hands Mesmer's myth was undergoing yet another transformation—or heteromorphosis —as Campbell would put it: all but deflated and demythologized, it was steered into more and more scientific channels.

How, then, did the Manchester surgeon try to prove his thesis of the physiological nature of mesmeric phenomena? "My first object was to prove," he reports in his *Neurohypnology*, "that the inability of the patient to open his eyes was caused by paralysing the levator muscle of the eyelids, through their continued action during the protracted fixed stare and thus rendering it physically impossible for him to open them." In one of his early experiments, he instructed his subject to sit down and maintain a fixed stare at the top of a wine bottle placed so much above him as to produce strain on the eyes and eyelids, to enable him to maintain a steady view of the object. "In three minutes his eyelids closed, a gush of tears ran down his cheeks, his head drooped, his face was slightly convulsed, he gave a groan and instantly fell into profound sleep, the respiration becoming slow, deep and sibilant, the right hand and arm being agitated by slight convulsive movements . . ." And Braid goes on to say: "This experiment not only *proved what I expected,* [author's italics] but also, by calling my attention to the spasmodic state of the muscle of the face and arm, the peculiar state of the respiration and the condition of the mind, as evinced on rousing the patient, tended to prove to my mind that I have got the key to the solution of mesmerism."

This seemed to be a thoroughly scientific and rational explanation of the hypnotic trance and the attenuated forms of the convulsive crises described by Mesmer. It was an explanation stripped of its magical implications and, above all, in good keeping with the prevailing physiological orientation of Braid's colleagues in the medical profession.

Yet despite his emphasis on thoroughly respectable neurophysiological facts, Braid's medical colleagues remained unimpressed. They distrusted and continued to reject a method tainted with the heritage of what the *Lancet* called the "gross humbug" of Mesmerism. Braid made his position still more precarious by his excursion into the field of phrenology. Phrenologists sought to discover—and to influence—a person's mental faculties by manipulating minor and major proturberances of his skull. Here, again, Braid's hypnotic influence upon his subjects may have set the trap for the spurious confirmation of his phrenological theories. His subjects happened to oblige by producing all the phrenological phenomena he had looked for.

His *Neurohypnology* contains the following description of what amounts to another example of doctrinal compliance in a woman patient: "Under *adhesiveness* and *friendship*" (that were supposed to be represented by certain protuberances of her skull) "she clasped me and on stimulating the organ of combativeness on the opposite side of the head, with the arm of that side, she struck two gentlemen (whom she imagined were about to attack me) in such a manner as nearly laying one on the floor, whilst with the other arm she held me in the most friendly manner. Under *benevolence* she seemed quite overwhelmed with compassion"—and so on and so forth.

Despite his embarrassing excursions into phrenology, Braid's attempt at a scientific interpretation of hypnotic phenomena has met with growing recognition after his death. It became an important stepping stone for the researches of Liébeault, Bernheim and Charcot, which in turn paved the way for the early experiments in hypnosis and hypnoanalysis carried out by Breuer and Freud.

Ultimately it was the painstaking clinical and experimental investigations of Liébeault and Bernheim of the Nancy School which developed a consistent psychological theory of hypnosis. Liébeault stressed the importance of suggestion in inducing sleep and pointed to the similarity of hypnosis to ordinary sleep. Both states, he insisted, result from a withdrawal of the subject's attention or "nervous energies" from reality, and both presuppose his willingness or consent to falling asleep.

Following in his footsteps, H. Bernheim raised the study of hypnosis to the status of academic respectability.[4] A professor at the University of Nancy, he hypnotized close to 10,000 subjects in the course of years. Not content with studying hypnotic suggestion and its close relationships to sleep, he made methodical use of positive and negative suggestions for the purpose of treatment. For example, he suggested a sense of well-being or the "disappearance of symptoms" to his patients. But he tried to go further than that. He sought to understand man and his motivations on the basis of psychological phenomena discovered in the hypnotic state, especially those described as automatisms and posthypnotic suggestions. A contemporary of Charcot, he refused to bow to the authority of his illustrious colleague and became the main spokesman of the Nancy School of hypnotism in its controversy with what is known as the Paris School, represented by Charcot and his followers.

*   *   *

Charcot's primary interest was in the field of neurology and neuropathology. It was from this vantage point that he turned to the study of both hysteria and hypnotic phenomena. He tried to show that hypnosis was basically an artificially induced hysteric condition and that the famous three stages of hypnotism had their counterparts in corresponding hysteric manifestations. Charcot, too, was at pains to make both hysteria and hypnotism clinically respectable. He sought to correlate hysteric disturbances with a predisposition to neuropathological disorders and stressed the part played by hereditary and constitutional factors in the susceptibility to both hysteria and hypnosis.[5]

Unfortunately the "Wizard of the Salpétrière," too, was not entirely safe from some of the mistakes made by his predecessors. Bernheim, in his controversy with the Paris School, pointed out that he had never been able to induce Charcot's three phases in his hypnotized subjects. "Once only did I see a subject who exhibited perfectly the three periods of lethargy, catalepsy and somnambulism. It was a young girl who had been at the Salpétrière for three years, and why should I not state the impression which I retained of the case? Subjected to special training by manipulations, imitating the phenomena which she saw produced in other somnambulists of the same school, taught by imitation to exhibit reflex phenomena in a certain typical order, the case was no longer one of natural hypnotism, but a product of false training, a true suggestive hypnotic neurosis."[4]

Thus, in Bernheim's view, responsibility for the error was to be laid squarely before the doorstep of the hypnotist. It was the hypnotist and his suggestions which accounted for the wide variety of manifestations, ranging from the trances and crises described by Mesmer, and the somnambulistics and "lucid" states studied by de Puységur and Abbé Faria, to the spectacular demonstrations of Charcot's "three phases" in his Tuesday lectures in the Salpétrière.

Put in our terms, Charcot, like his less scientific forerunners, was subject to the pitfalls of doctrinal compliance. His patients, too, tended to oblige. But their productions, like those initially studied by Braid, were clinically more respectable and, by all appearances, purged of the remaining vestiges of Mesmerism. Unfortunately, however, the elimination of the magic element from the theory and practice of hypnosis did not solve the enigma of hypnotic phenomena. Hypnotism managed to survive the deflation of the myths surrounding it, but no modern theory of hypnotism, Freudian, Pavlovian, or otherwise, has succeeded in replacing them with a wholly satisfactory scientific explanation. We shall see on a later page that, to solve the age-old riddle, the familiar notions of suggestion and reenactment of the early child-parent relationship has to be supplemented by the introduction of two more theoretical constructions: doctrinal compliance and the concept of the *existential shift*. They will be discussed in Chapters XII and XIII.

o   o   o

Meanwhile on the other side of the Atlantic a second major offshoot of the mesmeric myth made its appearance: Christian Science—a "science" which, in effect, constitutes the religiously refurbished branch of the myth. Paradoxically, the late 19th century was an era when extreme scientific materialism existed side by side with such radically antimaterialistic movements as Mary Baker Eddy's Christian Science, spiritualism, theosophy or anthroposophy.

Mary Baker Eddy's *Science and Health with a Key to the Scriptures* was first published in Boston in 1875. To millions of Americans it is not an ordinary book. It is the sacred text of a religion. It was hailed by her followers as a new revelation and it was denounced by her adversaries as the fabrication of a disturbed mind, compiled with the help of secretaries and ghost writers who gave it its final literary shape. It has been accused of plagiarism and described as a hodge-podge of early Christian mysticism, Hegelian philosophy and Mesmerian astrological speculations, presented in the flowery language of the period. But despite the logical inconsistencies of its reasoning and the absurdities of some of its statements, *Science and Health* must be classed among the most influential books of the late 19th century.[6]

Part of this influence is undoubtedly due to certain flashes of intuitive insight which it contains. There is, first and foremost, Mary Baker Eddy's emphasis on the part played by what she called the mortal mind, both conscious and unconscious, in the origin of disease, functional as well as organic. There is, secondly, her assertion that every disease, regardless of its nature, can be cured by spiritual, that is to say, psychological methods of treatment. There is, thirdly, her profound distrust of purely mechanical, impersonal methods of treatment, which were widely current in her time. Unfortunately, these flashes of insight were vitiated by exaggerated claims of cures and some intemperate attacks against the rules of hygiene, preventive inoculation, surgery and the medical profession in general.

The message handed down by her *Science and Health* is simple enough. It is that "matter possesses neither sensation nor life"; that human experiences show the "falsity of all material things" and that the only sufferer is "mortal mind, for the Divine Mind cannot suffer." This discovery, we are told, set Mrs. Eddy's thoughts to work and led her to the conviction that "mind is all and matter is nought" as the leading factor in "mind science."

From this it follows that the protagonists of the struggle for the recovery of the sick are not material vehicles of healing with "mortal mind" *versus* "Immortal Mind," writ large. The only true method of healing consists of rectifying a basic error: the error that "Immortal Mind" can be prey to disease or other afflictions "which the flesh is heir to."

It is one of Christian Science's basic propositions that this is not the case. And Mrs. Eddy assures the faithful: "If there is any mystery in Christian

Healing, it is the mystery which godliness always presents to the ungodly—the mystery arising from the laws of the eternal and unerring Mind."

"Faith in matter" has therefore to be abandoned as one of the first aberrations from the true faith. Faith in drugs, that is in medicine, is another aberration. What heals is the Divine Mind, "Life and Truth and Love." Their opposite is error, sin, sickness, disease and death. But all these latter are merely due to the false testimony of the senses. This false testimony evolves a subjective state of "mortal mind which this same so-called mind calls matter" and thereby obscures the "true sense of the spirit."

The story of the Christian Science movement has often been told and need not here be told again. But in order to understand its historical ties with the legacy left by Mesmer and his followers, we have to recall some of the salient features of Mrs. Eddy's life history. There are two flagrantly contradictory versions of this history. There are the pious chronicles of the life of a modern saint—if not of a second advent of Christ[7]—and there are the accounts of an eccentric personality, half fraud, half fanatic, suffering first from hysteric paralysis of the legs and later from ideas of grandeur and delusions of persecution.[8,9]

In her autobiography, Mrs. Eddy relates how in February, 1866 she fell on a slippery street in Lynn, Massachusetts. As a result of this fall she was left helpless, with both legs paralyzed. She connects her recovery from that illness with her discovery, in 1866, of Christian Science, adding that God had graciously prepared her, during many years, for the reception of this "final revelation of the absolute principle of the scientific mental healing."

But according to her nonsectarian and presumably less partisan biographers this story is incomplete. Stefan Zweig[8] describes in graphic detail the history of her cure from a preceding hysterical paralysis of her legs by Dr. Quimby, watchmaker, mesmerist, magnetopath and self-styled medical practitioner whom she had consulted in a hotel room in Portland, Maine, some time in 1862.

A week later, we are told, "Mary Baker Eddy, given up by all her doctors as an incurable invalid, had been restored to health. Once more she had the full use of her limbs, and able to climb the 182 steps to City Hall. She talked, she questioned, she rejoiced, she glowed with ardor; she was rejuvenated, and almost beautiful; she was bubbling over with activity and inspired with renewed energy—an energy unexcelled even in America."

This spectacular cure by purely mental means of a chronic affliction which the patient as well as her doctors considered organic and virtually incurable may have been the great turning point in Mary Baker Eddy's life. It hit her with the impact of a sudden religious experience, and carried with it the illuminating insight that her illness—nay, illness in general—was due to psychological causes and to nothing else. The surest way of conquering it therefore must call for essentially psychological means. More than that: if her illness (and illness in general) was solely in the mind, it was not a real illness—or rather, it was not real at all. Consequently, she reasoned that one only need convince the sufferer from any disease of the unreality, the fictitious nature, of his affliction and he would be cured.

Certainly this was an unwarranted oversimplification of a highly complicated state of affairs—a wholly illicit exploitation of a grain of truth contained in her reasoning. She did not say to herself, "I have been the victim of an incapacitating disease, largely imaginary in nature." She did not argue, "My legs only seemed to me to be paralyzed. There was really nothing the matter with my locomotor system or with my spinal cord, and once I made a supreme effort to snap out of my inertia I was cured—or allowed myself to be cured by good old Dr. Quimby, the watchmaker turned magnetopath." Instead, Mrs. Eddy, barely able to stand on her feet, wasted from lack of exercise, literally jumped to a conclusion of staggering import. In the blissful moment of her newly restored health, it became a self-evident truth to her that not only her illness, but *all* illnesses, regardless of their nature, were but matters of the mind and errors of man's misguided imagination. They were, in effect, unreal, nonexistent, and could therefore be conquered by a mere act of will in her great moment of illumination.

This may have been the way in which Mary Baker Eddy arrived at what to her, and her followers, appeared as a new and revolutionary insight, bound to save the world from the illusion of ill health and suffering and from the avoidable error of death. Thus her discovery of a cure-all for every woe was the result of a generalization which gradually grew to cosmic proportions of an originally wholly private experience. It was another manifestation of an effective myth, of a myth which, less than a century before, had passed through the doubtful medium of Mesmer's magnetopathic speculations, but which actually goes back to scriptural times and, beyond that, to the dawn of history.

REFERENCES

1. PODMORE, F.: cf. Chapter V (1).
2. SCHOPENHAUER, A.: Parerga und Paralipomena, Vol. I. Munich: R. Piper Verlag, 1913.
3. BRAID, JAMES: Neurohypnology, quoted from G. Murphy: An Historical Introduction to Modern Psychology, New York: Harcourt, Brace and World, 1949.
4. BERNHEIM, H.: Suggestive Therapeutics, New York: Putnam, 1880.
5. CHARCOT, J. M.: Leçons sur les Maladies du Systeme Nerveux, Progrés Medical, Paris, 1887-1888.
6. EDDY, MARY BAKER: Science and Health, with Key to the Scriptures, publ. by Trustees under Will of Mary Baker Eddy, Boston, 1934 (1875).
   ————————— Retrospection and Introspection, Boston, 1891.
7. WILBUR, S.: The Life of Mary Baker Eddy, New York: Concord Publ. Co., 1908.
8. ZWEIG, STEFAN, cf. Chapter V (2).
9. Encyclopedia Britannica, cf. Chapter V (3).

—VII—

Parapsychology or Testing the Limits of Myth

For, he argues pointedly,
That which cannot, must not be.
CHRISTIAN MORGENSTERN

We noted on an earlier page that despite the overriding rationalistic trend of our culture, the ancient tradition of magic never vanished completely from the Western world. It was lost sight of at times like an underground stream, but only to emerge again at unexpected times in the most unlikely places. We have seen how all orthodox religions condemned magic as heresy; how 17th century science denounced it as bigotry and superstition. We saw it masquerade as science in Sir Kenelm Digby's *Powder of Sympathy,* and operate behind the scene, in Mesmer's *Animal Magnetism.* It was purged from Mary Baker Eddy's Mother Church but only to stage an unofficial comeback through the back door, as it were. In the late 19th century it eked out a precarious existence in various cultist and sectarian movements but was strictly excluded from respectable society and academic circles of the time.

In 1882, with the founding in London of the English Society for Psychical Research, the underground stream broke to the surface again. It is true that describing the event in terms of a recurrence of magic is apt to raise eyebrows as well as objections. It was the time when Sir James Frazer relegated the magic creed to the opposite pole of science, and E. B. Tyler had branded it a "monstrous farrago." In Victorian England, magic had become a pariah word, and associating it with such respected names as F. W. H. Myers, the Cambridge classicist, Sir Oliver Lodge, the physicist, Henry Sidgwick, the philosopher, or other pioneers of the Society for Psychical Research could indeed easily be construed as a slight against their reputation.

In fact, the Society was founded precisely to remove the stigma of magic from the occult and to raise its investigation to the level of academic respectability. One of the first steps towards this goal was the introduction of a new nomenclature. Thought and action at a distance were no longer attributed to some ill-defined supernatural agency but described as "psychic phenomena" and neatly classified as telepathy, clairvoyance, precognition or telekinesis. Otherwise the noncommittal symbol *psi* was used for their designation. Survival after death or reincarnation were dissociated from religious dogma. They were viewed as hypotheses calling for possible verification in the mediumistic trance, by so-called cross correspondences between various mediums or other quasi-experimental procedures.

Thus with new vessels made available for the old wine, an eager band of amateur investigators proceeded to collect as many samples of the latest vintage as they could lay their hands on. They arranged for a "census of hallucinations" in England—a term meant to include such spontaneous occurrences as veridical dreams, premonitions, apparitions, and alleged telepathic messages from the living or from the dead.

A composite picture of many anecdotal reports of this type recorded in the literature of psychical research would read as follows: A sleeper, still dreaming, or just awakening from sleep, hears a voice crying out for help. The voice may be calling his name or merely sighing or murmuring in a barely audible manner. The dreamer is immediately aware that the person concerned is in a state of crisis, in mortal danger, or has met with an accident. In some cases the receiver of such an ostensible telepathic message interprets it as an apparition. He may then describe the scene in great detail, including some information which he could not apparently have obtained through ordinary sensory channels. In other cases, it is merely a spasm of sudden baseless anxiety connected with some indefinite danger threatening the absent friend or relation. Subsequent inquiry may then show that the apprehension was indeed justified.

Reports like these are reminiscent of the many accounts of prophetic visions, apparitions and divination which have come down to us from antiquity or the Middle Ages. They are still recurrent features of folklore and fairy tale in our day. The connection with magic is still more obvious in the purported occult phenomena occurring in the spirtualistic séance room, with all its traditional trappings. There are the claims of such physical phenomena as levitations, apports and materializations; there are reports of so-called spirit controls making cryptic utterances about past or future happenings, ostensibly beyond the range of the medium's normal cognition. They hark back to ancient and scriptural traditions of magicians and sorcerers, of seers and soothsayers, of Sybils and Pythias, dressed in the costume of the Victorian era, with some of their accessories borrowed from the wardrobe of Greek or Roman antiquity, from the Middle Ages or a romanticized Orient. Others amount to little more than popular misinterpretations of mental dissociation in an hysteric subject produced by persistent suggestions and indoctrination by a circle of "sitters," or spiritualistic investigators.

A complete break with the magical tradition was brought about with the advent of the experimental parapsychologist. By the use of such quantifiable materials as dice, ESP cards or ordinary playing cards, the experimenter seeks to arrive at statistically significant data confirming the operation of a "psi factor" under strictly controlled laboratory conditions.

It will be noted that in experiments of this order magic has been subjected to a process of plastic surgery, as it were, trying to make it change its appearance beyond recognition. Gone are the claims of sympathetic magic, divination or prophecy. Gone also are the high-sounding names, the heroic poses and the flowing costumes of the Victorian age. Magic—if magic it still be—is now made to fall in line with probabilistic methods of science and modern communication theory. Testimonial tablets and highly colored eye-witness reports of the past are replaced by reference to chi squares or criteria of statistical significance, and the spiritualistic séance room refurbished to serve as a parapsychological laboratory.

Another source of data has been the observations of apparent telepathic incidents in the psychoanalytic situation. Such observations go back to Freud himself[1a,1b] and have subsequently been reported by a number of psychoanalysts. In a typical case the patient produces a dream containing a combination of distinctive features in its manifest content which the dreamer cannot account for in his free associations. He just does not know "where they come from." However, to his surprise, the analyst may discover striking correspondences between these dynamically irreducible features and certain emotionally charged thoughts, expectations or other preoccupations of his own at the time the dream occurred.

The interpersonal situations in which such incidents emerge have been studied in some detail by several authors, including the present writer.[2,3,4] They have proposed, furthermore, several well-defined criteria by which the presumed telepathic nature of the incident can be judged. One such criterion is the *uniqueness* or specificity of a given element in the manifest content of the dream; another is the meaningful nature or *psychological significance* of its attempted telepathic interpretation, as opposed to the criterion of *statistical significance* relied upon by scientists and experimental parapsychologists.

The controversy touched off by the claims of these pioneers: by the early workers in psychical research; by the reports of laboratory experiments, and by the observations of a small group of psychiatrists and psychoanalysts is in many ways reminiscent of the treatment every rationalistic era has been wont to accord to lingering vestiges of magic and myth. H. von Helmholtz, the celebrated 19th century German physiologist, put it most succinctly: "Neither the testimony of all the fellows of the Royal Society, nor even the testimony of my own senses could lead me to believe in the transmission of thought from one person to another independently of the recognized channels of sensation." He was seconded by Lord Kelvin who held that the phenomena were due to "bad observation chiefly, mixed with the effects of wilful imposture," and by Henry Maudsley who rejected the evidence as nothing but *"Supernatural Seeming."*[5] A great many scientists of lesser standing have since assumed essentially the same position. So have, as we shall see, leading psychiatrists and psychoanalysts in the past decades.

It is true, modern mediums, psychics or sensitives are no longer burned at the stake as were the witches and sorcerers of a past age. But their depositions are ridiculed, brushed aside as delusion, hysteric phantasies or outright lies. The facts and figures presented by the experimental workers are attributed to clerical errors, statistical artifacts, "mathematical resonance" or fakery. George Price, the American biochemist, in 1955 seriously advanced the hypothesis of an international conspiracy of fraud and collusion to account for the results of J. B. Rhine, S. G. Soal and their associates.[6,7]

✿   ✿   ✿

Freud's early interest in the occult is a matter of historic record. He was greatly impressed with telepathic experiments carried out by Gilbert Murray with members of his family. Indeed we learn from Ernest Jones[8] that Freud himself, together with his daughter Anna, and Sandor Ferenczi, tried his hand at a few informal experiments of this kind. It was at that time that he wrote to Heeward Carrington, a well-known worker in psychical research, "If I had my life to live over again I should devote my life to psychical research rather than to psychoanalysis."

Freud's first published comments on the matter refer to incidents reported to him by patients who had consulted professional soothsayers or clairvoyants. Freud's interest was further enhanced by a correspondent who described to him an apparently telepathic dream involving the birth of twins to his second wife, while it was in actual fact his daughter who had given birth to twins during the same night. Freud was struck by the disguised incestuous inmplications of this dream once its telepathic origin was taken for granted. In any case, it was this episode which seems to have alerted him to the possibility that telepathic incidents are subject to much the same laws of repression, distortion, and secondary elaboration, as are dreams or neurotic symptoms. A number of apparently telepathic observations in his own practice followed suit. They were subsequently published in several articles and additions to his *Psychopathology of Everyday Life*, and to his magnum opus, *The Interpretation of Dreams*.

Freud's fascination by the occult was shared by some of his early associates. In 1920, Wilhelm Stekel published a book on telepathic dreams.[9] Freud's favorite disciple, Sandor Ferenczi, sought to engage Jung in a "crusade in the field of mysticism" and jestingly referred to himself as the "court astrologist" of his psychoanalytic confreres in Vienna. Yet even within Freud's inner circle there was dismay over the master's continued flirtation with the occult. The leading spokesman of the group was Freud's biographer, Ernest Jones. In a circular letter to his colleagues, he took an uncompromisingly hostile stand against what he felt were Freud's aberrations from the straight and narrow path. There still is "great opposition to psychoanalysis in England," he declared. A great part of this is based on "the imaginary idea that psychoanalysis operates with agents (the psyche), which are supposed to be independent of the body." The prejudice against such a hypothesis is equally strong; so strong indeed that "any mixture of the two subjects could have only one effect, that of delaying the assimilation of psychoanalysis." Jones therefore demands that "anyone wishing to write on telepathy will make it clear that he does so independently of psychoanalysis . . . This would be a simple act of justice to those analysts who, like myself, are far from convinced of the truth of telepathy and who cannot therefore welcome the possibility of their conviction about psychoanalysis becoming involved with something with which they do not agree. I should take up the same standpoint against any entanglement with any variety of philosophy, politics, etc."[8]

This is an astonishing statement for an author of the scientific standing of Ernest Jones to make. It seems to set considerations of political expediency above the demands of scientific research. It comes precariously close to the attitude of medieval ecclesiastical authorities seeking to defend the interest of the church from the dangers of free inquiry. Psychoanalytically speaking, it is suggestive of a reaction formation against the repressed—in this case, against the repudiated tradition of magic—of a reaction formation that has ranged, as we have seen, from the extremes of medieval witchburning to the rejection of Mesmer's observations by the French Academy of Sciences, or to the emotional bias shown by academic psychology against the younger science of psychoanalysis itself.

In a more recent discussion of the subject, Michal Balint, the noted English psychoanalyst granted the possible occurrence of telepathy in the psychoanalytic situation. Yet, as if to discourage timid souls from publishing such observations, he noted that if and when it occurred it was likely to be due to errors in psychoanalytic technique and therefore certainly nothing to boast about.[10]

Thus the reactions of the educated public, of academic science, psychology and even psychoanalysis against the threatened return of some latter-day derivative of magic has lost its violence, but certainly not its sting as far as its remaining or newly recruited advocates were concerned. The return of magic, like the return of the repressed in the Freudian sense, still meets with the familiar tendency to repression, denial or reaction formation. Indeed, the whole emotional and intellectual climate of Western civilization has remained dead set against it. It runs counter to the laws of Aristotelian logic, Euclidian geometry and Newtonian mechanics and the attending concept of a closed and self-contained personality structure. Modern man, as Robert Oppenheimer has pointed out, has developed a watertight, self-sealing system of knowledge. It is a system which permits virtually no exception from old established laws of nature and which measures the truth value of new scientific discoveries by the degree to which they are found to conform with these laws.

○   ○   ○

This is not the place to discuss the validity of the data presented by the workers in experimental parapsychology nor the merits of more recent reports of telepathy presented by psychoanalysts. More relevant to our issue is the unchanging posture of opposition current in our culture to admitting the very possibility of its occurrence.

Even some professional parapsychologists seem only prepared to deal with the dehydrated, deboned and filleted version of the real thing, and shrink from coming to grips with the *mysterium tremendum* of the total experience, real or imaginary, designated by the poker-faced symbol *psi*. It is as though a Western explorer, used to relegating accounts of the Abominable Snowman to the realm of fairy tale, had suddenly come face to face with him in the icy wastes of the Himalayan mountains and still refused to admit that such an animal really exists. He confines his attention to the footprints, the droppings or the nailparings of the beast, but refrains from setting his sights on the animal as a whole in its native habitat. Even the psychiatrist seems to be anxious to cast his occasional observations into the mold of strictly defined and circumscribed "combinations of distinctive features," psychological "tracer effects," or the like, in order to make them conform with currently acceptable scientific standards. (This, incidentally has been one of the professional failings which, among others, the present writer must plead to be guilty of.) Yet regardless whether or not the phenomena have been, or shall ultimately be, validated to everybody's satisfaction, we are again faced with the question of what, in the last analysis, is the reason for the latest bout of our culture with the long-repudiated tradition of magic. Attempts at a quasi-psychoanalytic explanation in terms of cultural repression of vestiges of primitive, prelogical or paleological tendencies surviving in modern man's mental organization merely amount to circular reasoning. They raise the question once more as to why such repression is really necessary. So does reference to the incompatibility of magical or primary process thinking with Freud's secondary processes. Jule Eisenbud's ingenious suggestion connecting the fear of magic with the fear of releasing omnipotent aggressive drives residing in the unconscious[3] touches only upon one side of the problem and makes no allowance for the possibility of balancing such drives with the parapsychological dimension of equally "omnipotent" constructive or libidinal impulses.

An at least preliminary answer may be found on turning our attention to the myth underlying the parapsychologist's quest. His myth has already been adumbrated in our discussion of healing action at a distance attributed to Paracelsus' Weapon Salve, to Sir Kenelm Digby's Powder of Sympathy or to Mesmer's animal magnetism. It is the myth proclaiming the omnipotent powers of human volition; the capacity of thought and action to reach out beyond the physiological confines of the individual; the individual's ability to follow the flights of his fancy to the stars above and to the netherworld below; it is a myth transcending the limitations of time, space and causality and holding the promise of mastery over life and death and the ultimate attainment of immortality.

Thus, while myths serving as the rationale for spiritual healing are limited to a comparatively small segment of man's quest for omnipotence and omniscience, the goal of psychical research is to encompass the whole spectrum. Its field of inquiry extends, as was noted above, from thought transference and clairvoyance to precognition, psychokinesis and survival after death. It is, one could say, an attempt at reenacting once more the archaic mystery play of magic, shorn of its mystery; a secularized, latter-day version of the original prototype stripped of its avowed magical intent and mythical rationale. Yet the barely disguised global aspirations of psychical research can still be gleaned from J. B. Rhine's candid, if somewhat naive, claim of the status of "experimental religion" for his researches.[6] The same aspirations can be discerned in the emotionally charged preoccupation of some workers in the field with proofs of survival after death; with reincarnation; or with "out of the body" experiences, quaintly labelled as "travelling clairvoyance," and reminiscent of the mythical flight of the shaman into heavens or into the netherworld. Last, but not least, it is the interest taken by some parapsychologists in the field of spiritual healing aimed at restoring the well-being of men, animals and even plants.

Viewed in the light of ancient mythical tradition all these aspirations are as many manifestations of *hybris* which, in ancient Greek tragedy, was bound to lead to the hero's undoing. We hinted on an earlier page that its classical representative is Aeschylus' Prometheus, who tried to cheat Zeus, the Father of the Gods, and subsequently stole the fire from him in order to give it to man. In Judeo-Christian tradition, the hero is none other than Adam, the first man, who likewise defied the Lord and ate from the Tree of Knowledge, thereby trying to usurp His role for himself and was expelled from the Garden of Eden. Yet another version is Beelzebub, the fallen angel, who openly rebelled against Jehovah and was cast into Hell as a punishment for his rebellion, or Marlowe's (and Goethe's) Dr. Faustus, who sold his soul to the Devil as the price for magic omnipotence and sensual bliss in this life.

This is not the place to follow the long line of culture heroes, rebels and defiers of divine law and harmony who were punished by the gods—or by society—for their heresy. Their crime was, as the classicists Jaeger[11] and Kerenyi[12] or, more recently, the psychiatrist Iago Galdstone,[13] have pointed out,[4,5] that they violated the "accord made with Zeus"; that they subverted the order of the cosmos, the laws of nature, as conceived by both Greek and Judeo-Christian concepts of order and law.

Western culture, for reasons which apparently are inherent in its basic design, has set itself up as the guardian of just this cosmic harmony or *status quo*. It rewards those who fall in line with it, and punishes those who dare to pit their wills against it. Yet this precisely is the crime of hybris which our culture attributes to magic and this also is the taint which is still attached to the magic tradition in its latest, expurgated, version of parapsychology or psychical research. Hence Western man's persistent distrust of its claims and aspirations. Put in terms of modern existentialist philosophy, the "world-design" of magic—and of its latter-day version, psychical research—is alien to contemporary Western man's mode of existence. Its espousal is predicated on what in Chapters XIII and XIV will be described as an *existential shift*—a shift which runs counter to the scientific temper of our age.

❖   ❖   ❖

The actual experimental findings claimed by the parapsychologists are, of course, another matter. Once their consideration is removed from the heat of emotionally charged controversy, from the distorting forces of rationalistic bias and cultural repression that militate against the existential shift, there seems to be little doubt that man, even Western man, does not merely cling to the illusion of being able to break through the barriers set by his innate mental equipment, but that, on rare occasions, he is actually capable of taking the improbable leap into a sphere presumptively exempt from the "laws of nature." The findings suggest that there are little cracks left in our closed, self-sealing psychological universe permitting such seeming irregularities. This, in effect, is the result suggested by painstaking statistical research carried out by the new science over the past decades.[6,7] Its point of departure may have been a disguised or tacitly implied myth. Some of its basic propositions may still be rooted in the ancient tradition of magic. But on testing the limits of its underlying myth, parapsychology seems to have hit upon moments and interpersonal configurations in which the myth happens to be at least marginally effective.

We shall see in a later chapter that both the powerful defenses operating to prevent the breakthrough of psi, as well as their occasional failure to hold the line, are facts of fundamental importance for our understanding of man. Their significance may be confined to the lunatic fringe of our culture, or to marginal situations in a person's struggle to hold his own and to maintain his identity. Still, any purportedly scientific psychotherapist or behavioral scientist who insists on keeping his eyes closed to marginal situations of this order may find himself in the same predicament as the mystic with his proverbial habit of closing his eyes to the realities of waking life.

REFERENCES

1. FREUD, S.: Psychoanalysis and Telepathy, transl. by G. Devereux, in: Psychoanalysis and the Occult, Intern. Univ. Press, New York 1953.
—————— Dreams and the Occult, in: New Introductory Lectures on Psychoanalysis, Hogarth Press, London 1939.
2. EHRENWALD, J.: Telepathy and Medical Psychology, W. W. Norton, New York 1948.
—————— New Dimensions of Deep Analysis, A Study of Telepathy in Interpersonal Relationships, Grune & Stratton, New York 1954.
—————— Psychiatric Aspects of Extrasensory Perception, Experimental Medicine and Surgery, Vol. 20, No. 1-2, 1962.
3. EISENBUD, J.: On the Use of Psi Hypothesis in Psychoanalysis, Int. Journ. Psychoanal., 36, 370-374, 1955.
—————— Telepathy and Problems of Psychoanalysis, in: Psychoanalysis and the Occult, ed. G. Devereux, Intern. Univ. Press, New York 1953.
4. SERVADIO, E.: Psychoanalysis and Telepathy, (ibid.)
—————— Transference and Thought Transference, Intern. Journ. Psychoanal. XXXVII, 1956.
—————— A Presumptively Telepathic-Precognitive Dream during Analysis, Ibid. XXXVI, 1955.
5. MAUDSLEY, H.: Body and Mind, Macmillan and Co. London 1873.
6. RHINE, J. B.: Extrasensory Perception, Bruce Humphries, Boston, 1964.
—————— New World of the Mind, W. Sloan, New York 1953.
—————— and PRATT, S. G.: Parapsychology, Frontier Science of the Mind, C. Thomas, Springfield 1957.
7. SOAL, S. G. and BATEMAN, F.: Modern Experiments in Telepathy, Yale Univ. Press, New Haven 1954.
8. JONES, E.: The Life and Work of Sigmund Freud, Basic Books, New York 1953.
9. STEKEL, W.: Der Telepathische Traum, J. Baum, Berlin 1920.
10. BALINT, M.: Notes on Parapsychology and Parapsychological Healing, Intern. Journ. Psychoanal. 36, 1955.
11. JAEGER, W.: Paideia, Oxford Univ. Press, New York 1945.
12. KERENYI, L.: Prometheus, Pantheon Books, New York 1959.
13. GLADSTONE, IAGO: Prometheus and the Gods, an Essay on Ecology, Bull. New York Academy of Medicine 40, 7, 1964.

Part Two

Scientific Psychotherapy: Rationale
without Myth?

— VIII —

Psychoanalysis: The Ascendancy of Reason

If there is one major cleavage which sets apart modern schools of psycho-therapy—psychoanalytic or otherwise—from earlier attempts at mental heal-ing, it is their uncompromising rejection of magic beliefs and practices. Magic aims at man's mastery and control over himself and over his en-vironment by his unrelenting quest for omnipotence. The religious devotee is ready to surrender this quest by renunciation of his selfish desires and in-terests in return for salvation. He seeks, and finds, a substitute for magic omnipotence by submission to a higher power and by mystic union or identification with it.

Modern man has never relinquished the quest for mastery and control. He has thrown overboard the techniques of magic, but only to replace them with the magic of technology. In contrast to the magician, he bases his actions on premises which can be tested and verified in the light of practical experience. On coming to grips with an object in the outside world, he asks himself: What is it? What is it for? How can I make it subservient to my purpose? The scientifically oriented psychotherapist ap-proaches the mental states of his patients in much the same way. He too wants to know how they tick and, above all, he seeks to devise a technique for their deliberate manipulation and control so as to effect the cure of his patients. Freud's system of psychoanalysis is the most ambitious and scientifically most consistent attempt in this direction.

It is true that Pierre Janet's discovery of mental processes operating inde-pendently of conscious volition and conscious sensory perception—the dis-covery of so-called psychic automatisms—anticipated some of the proposi-tions of psychoanalysis. Yet Janet's essentially rationalistic approach, his emphasis on the ego and its cognitive functions, made him stop short of formulating a consistent system of unconscious dynamics. E. von Hart-mann's *Philosophy of the Unconscious* focused on the area covered by Freud in name only; and C. G. Carus's concept of the psyche was at best a romantic anticipation of some aspects of Freudian thought.

Seen in historical perspective, psychoanalysis is a system of thought based on all the evidence, scientific and psychological, available at the turn of the century and brought into focus by the mind of a genius. But few of Freud's admirers and followers would go so far as to repeat Mesmer's naive claim that their particular brand of psychotherapy has in actual fact reached the "final stage of perfection." Psychoanalysis today could be compared with the state of theoretical physics before the Michelson-Morley experiments; before the advent of Einstein's theory of relativity; before Bohr's discovery of quantum mechanics and the subsequent development of nuclear physics. In a similar vein, the picture of man emerging from the psychoanalytic approach is comparable to the Euclidian or Newtonian picture of the universe to which such pioneers of the natural sciences as Darwin, Helmholtz, Robert Mayer and Mendeleev added the finishing touches. Evidently it is neither the complete nor the final picture. Yet within these historically determined limitations, psychoanalysis represents the boldest step in arriving at a naturalistic and scientifically verifiable concept of man viewed as *homo natura*. In so doing, it has sought to raise the study of human behavior to the level of the exact natural sciences.

Freud himself was brought up in the 19th century tradition of physiology and neuropathology. His major discoveries were inspired by the search for the same causal laws as were found to apply to the world of physical objects. When difficulties arose, he resorted to analogous reasoning; stressing the similarities that exist between man's instinctual drives and the behavior of liquids or of electrical currents as they were described by students of hydromechanics and electricity. His imagery abounds with such terms as repression, resistance, displacement, conversion and sublimation, borrowed from the vocabulary of 17th and 18th century mechanics, and his description of mental processes is based on the concept of mutually interchangeable forms of energy postulated by 19th century physics and physiology. He tried, quoting a phrase coined by E. Brunswick, to do for "mind" what physics had done for "matter."[1]

Freud's formulation of the libido theory is the crowning achievement of this approach.[2] Armed with this theory and with an ingenious array of subordinate hypotheses, psychoanalysis has indeed succeeded in giving a reasonable account of virtually all aspects of man's mental functioning. The emergence of the ego from the dark undifferentiated matrix of the id, the gradual delineation of the superego as a reflection of the demands met with by the ego in its social environment, and the dynamic interplay between the diverse parts of personality form the backdrop against which the struggle of intrapsychic forces is viewed. These forces themselves are thought to be derived from the vast pool of raw instinctual drives brought into focus within the boundaries of the organism, and their vicissitudes are traced in stupendous biographical detail from the first pangs of hunger and thirst and the compelling need for warmth and security, to the early stirrings of an amorphous sexual urge and its channelling into full-fledged genitally oriented object love.

Freud's concept of the death instinct represents something like the villain in this play. It is the psychological corollary of destruction and decay, the expression of man's ultimate submission to his personal destiny of extinction. Significantly enough, the death instinct is itself subject to the same laws of repression, displacement and conversion as its jaunty brother-in-arms, Eros, the instinct of love and life preservation. While Eros is the source of all the creative forces in the individual, in the family, and in society at large, the death instinct accounts for hate, dissension and strife in interpersonal relationships. It may boomerang back at the individual and become the source of self-hatred, of occasional masochistic tendencies culminating in self-destruction.

But irrespective of the controversial death instinct psychoanalytic theory affords a well-nigh flawless system of explanatory hypotheses for the wealth of man's mental manifestations, from slips of the tongue to wish dreams and nightmares; from stage fright to schizophrenia and other mental disorders. More than that, it gives a reasonable account for the psychodynamics of artistic creation, for the formation of myths, legends and fairy tales, and for a wealth of observations in the field of sociology, cultural anthropology and comparative study of religions. The beliefs, rites and social observances of many preliterate peoples seem to lend themselves to essentially the same interpretations that apply to the mentality of the child, the neurotic and the schizophrenic. In his celebrated *Totem and Taboo*, Freud has shown that magic and animism fit perfectly into such a picture. Animism is the projection of primitive man's fears and expectations into the outside world. His faith in magic is derived from his need to control the uncontrollable, to impose his will upon the outside world in much the same way that he is capable of exercising control over his own neuromuscular and skeletal system. This is what Freud has described as primitive man's implicit belief in the omnipotence of thought.

Psychoanalysis is thus the first system of psychology which has provided a modicum of understanding of primitive mentality and of the quest for omnipotence characteristic of prescientific methods of mental healing and technology. This is certainly a major scientific achievement and should afford a safeguard against allowing vestiges of magic thought and practices to go undetected in the psychoanalytic approach itself.

        ✿   ✿   ✿

However, on applying the psychoanalytic method to the history of psychoanalysis, we are struck by the discovery of a few flaws remaining in the picture. Clearly, such an approach cannot be satisfied with tracing the origins of psychoanalysis in the written records of human endeavor, thought and action. Nor can it confine its interest to explicit verbal statements and formulations which are laid down in psychoanalytic literature. The analytically oriented historian must probe beneath its manifest content, as it were. He must examine what will be described as its *metadynamics*. He must look for the hidden motivations, for the forgotten sources, for anonymous influences which have gone into its making. He must be alert to the presence of unconscious determinants and daily residues derived from preceding centuries—if not millennia. He must be prepared to find these determinants subject to the familiar laws of distortion, displacement and secondary elaboration which are known to operate on much deeper levels of human expression. Nor should the discovery of occasional evidence of reaction formation be altogether surprising to such an approach.

The fact is that psychoanalysis, like any major scientific doctrine, is historically derived from: (1) conscious assimilation and integration of its preceding cultural heritage; (2) from unconscious borrowing from, and inspiration by, that heritage; (3) from hidden determinants represented by mythicoreligious prototypes of theory making; and (4) from reaction formations to such primitive mythicoreligious vestiges.

We have already pointed to the similarity of Mesmer's concept of Animal Magnetism, of Sydenham's animal spirits, or of Liébeault's "nervous force" with the Freudian or Jungian concept of libido—to say nothing of the resemblance of Freud's dualistic theory of drives with Empedocles' myth of love and strife, or of the Polynesian mana-taboo formula, with its benevolent and nefarious aspects. Freud himself has given credit to another source of his conceptual framework: to Plato's celebrated fable of the Charioteer, representing the ego, and the Two Horses, representing instinctual drives. David Bakan,[3] the Jewish theologian, has called attention to another source of which Freud himself seems to have been largely unaware. This is the ancient Kabalistic tradition, especially the medieval book Zohar. This also proposes a tripartite structure of the soul and holds that the three parts are in constant conflict with each other. He suggests that Freud has assimilated such ideas through his Hassidic family background and goes as far as to say that the psychoanalytic system itself is "a scientific secularization of the religious Kabalah." Such a statement is certainly more provocative than convincing. But there can be no doubt that the Freudian picture of the mind carries all the hallmarks of medieval and early Renaissance imagery. The superego can readily be equated with heaven; the ego with earth; and the id with the Freudian—or Francesco-Josephinian —version of hell. The three respective realms of the Christian universe are features just as common in Renaissance painting and iconography as they are in contemporary psychoanalytic literature.

Among influences harking back to pre-Christian times is Freud's tendency to identify with the hero of Greek antiquity daring to descend to the netherworld in order to commune with the souls of the damned. His challenge to the gods: *Flectere si nequeo superos, Acheronta movebo** which

---

* "If I cannot bend the Superior Powers to my will, I am going to move the Acherontic Forces."

ne put as the Motto of an early edition of his *The Interpretation of Dreams,*
clearly expresses this identification. Like his declared purpose to "make the
unconscious conscious," it has the ring of Promethean rebellion against the
order of the universe laid down by Zeus and seems to give the lie to Freud's
seemingly stoic acquiescence to his own thesis of psychic determinism. His
identification with the Semite Hannibal, the would-be conqueror of the maternal city of Rome, or with Moses, the giver and preserver of law, are
variations on the same theme.

Freud's secret affinity to medieval Christian thought and the parallelism
between his theory of projection and ancient demonology had not escaped
his watchful eye. In a letter to Fliess, dated January 17, 1897, he writes:
"By the way, what have you to say to the suggestion that the whole of my
brand new theory of the primary origins of hysteria is already familiar and
has even been published a hundred times over, though several centuries
ago? Do you remember my always saying that the medieval theory of
possession held by the ecclesiastical courts was identical with our theory
of a foreign body in the splitting of consciousness?"[2c]

✿   ✿   ✿

We noted, however, that in spite of these points of resemblance, there
can be no greater contrast than that between the magico-mythical mentality
and the psychoanalytic approach. Magic, as described by Bronislaw
Malinowski,[4] is made up of three main ingredients: (1) the ritual, (2) the
spell, and (3) the personality of the magician, with his craving for omnipotence. This is certainly wholly incompatible with the basic rules of
psychoanalysis laid down by Freud. Yet Freudian analysis not only reacted
strongly against the magic position; it also shows evidence of reaction
formation against it. Not satisfied with repudiating the magic heritage,
Freud disowned religion as an illusion without a future and closed his
mind to the "oceanic feeling" characteristic of religious experience. Together with religion, he rejected all ritual, unless we regard the couch as
the last remnant of the temple sleep used by the ancients in their shrines of
healing. Likewise, psychoanalysis repudiated magical spells and incantations and made the analyst's silence mandatory. However, here again we
can discover vestiges of magic in those analysts who are still inclined to
overrate the power of words used in analytic interpretation. Lastly, psychoanalysis has done away once and for all with the therapist's claim to omnipotence, relegating it to the realm of neurosis or mental disorder.

Yet, the early writings of Freud still convey to the reader the dismay
over his own unexpected impact on some of his patients. His well-known
reluctance to use hypnosis as a therapeutic tool may well be interpreted as a
reaction formation against his own phantasies of omnipotence. Another
factor may have been Freud's realization of his uncanny capacity to cause

his patients—especially hysterics—to produce symptoms that would tend to support his own theoretical expectations. This is what, on a previous page, was described as doctrinal compliance. We shall see in Chapter XI that doctrinal compliance by the patient with the therapist's preconscious wishes and expectations has indeed played an important role in the making of the psychoanalytic system of thought, though certainly less so than in such prescientific systems of psychotherapy as Mesmerism, phrenology or even in some of the theories held by Charcot and the Paris school of psychiatry. Nevertheless, the last decades have seen a revival of pre-Freudian hypnotherapy brought up to date by the techniques of hypnoanalysis. In this instance one may speak of something like the "return of the repressed," though under clinically well-controlled conditions.

There is another aspect of primitive mentality which can be traced in the psychoanalytic approach. This is the tendency, inherent in the very structure of our language, to use symbols, metaphors and allegories in its formulations. The Freudian Ego, like Plato's Charioteer, is embattled by the untrammeled forces of instinct—the Two Horses in Plato's fable. It is plagued by a demanding parental Superego. It has to come to terms with a cold and impersonal reality, or it must, like an imprudent child, bear the consequences. It is the plaything of the forces of Eros and Thanatos, but it can nevertheless play the part of the censor, whose job it is to exclude unacceptable ideas from consciousness. More recently it has been bestowed a wide variety of higher synthetic and integrating powers, undreamed of by the ego of the early days of psychoanalysis.[5,6]

But we hinted that the mythical element is more deeply embedded in the psychoanalytic system than on the level of linguistics or psycholinguistics. The ultimate "metapsychological" foundation and common referent of its theoretical constructs and subordinate hypotheses is the libido theory. Inevitably Freud's concept of libido was influenced by the spirit of his time, as was Mesmer's notion of Animal Magnetism. This time the determining influence was the notion of energy as formulated by Robert Mayer, Boltzmann, Ostwald and other physicists of the late 19th century. This spiritual kinship of the concept of libido implied such scientific postulates as its preservation, quantifiability and transmutability into "other" forms of energy. It can be channelled into erogenous zones or various inner organs. It can cathect, like an electrical charge, both internal and external objects. It can be withdrawn from the outside world and invested on the ego or its boundaries with the outside world, or it can serve as a great reservoir from which libidinal charges or cathexes are being sent out to other parts of the mental structure.

We have noted that despite the wealth of empirical observations from which it was derived and of the ingenuity and precision of some of its formulations, the similarity of Freud's, or, for that matter, Jung's, libido theory of Liébeault's theory of "nervous forces," with Mesmer's "effluvia," or with Sydenham's "animal spirits" is unmistakable. Indeed, we hinted that its spiritual ancestry could be traced as far back as the Polynesian concept of mana and its forbidding counterpart of taboo. At a later stage of his career, when Freud revised his thory so as to include in his system the polarity of love and hate, of Eros and Thanatos, he expressly acknowledged the affinity of his dualistic formulation with Empedocles' myth of love and strife, of Eros and Tyche. "Our theory of instincts," he pointed out, "is, as it were, our mythology; the instincts are wonderfully vague, mythical beings. In our work we cannot take our eyes off them for a moment, yet at the same time we never see them clearly."

✿   ✿   ✿

It is on focussing on these levels of the Freudian system of thought that the remaining vestiges of its magico-mythical prehistory come out into the open. Needless to say, they were soon seized upon by his critics. To begin with, they tried to make the most of whatever historical links could be found between psychoanalysis, Mesmerism, phrenology and other cultist movements. Pierre Janet, Freud's noted contemporary, wrote in 1923: "Psychoanalysis is the last incarnation of practices, at once magical and psychological, which were characteristic of magnetism. It preserves as its characteristic features its boundless ambition and its obstinate struggle against academic science."[7] Freud did not fare better in the U. S. In 1920, a New York neurologist asked the American Neurological Association to take a stand against "transcendentalism and supernaturalism" and to "crush out Christian Science, Freudism and all that hash, rot and nonsense," while a contemporary German critic referred to it as a "simply gruesome old wives' psychiatry." Such recent authorities as H. Eysenck,[8] A. Salter,[9] or Percival Bailey[10] are no less intemperate in their attacks. Late reverberations of older, internal controversies can still be found in the polemic writings of today's dissenting schools of psychoanalysis from Alfred Adler to Karen Horney and Erich Fromm, to say nothing of the existentialists of our day.

Paradoxically, one of the most scathing attacks upon the hidden mystical assumptions of psychoanalytic doctrine come from quarters close to the modern psychoanalytic movement itself. Jules Masserman, erstwhile President of the American Academy of Psychoanalysis, has pointed out that Freudian theory abounds with a "most intriguing array of primitive mysticisms."[11] He compares the instinctual drives residing in the id with "surreptitious Seth or Siva; angry Ahriman; debauched Dionysios or lascivious Laki, influencing man from the Nether-region." Likewise, he sees the superego as a new version of Ra, Zeus, Zoroaster or Yahve; "Id,

Ego and Superego being actually engaged in strange deceptions, subversive alliances, desperate defenses and Pyrrhic victories—struggles as vivid and fanciful as any Indic mythology, Homeric legend or Norse Saga."

The derisive tone of these remarks is deceptive. Their intent is not ridicule or satire. They are the voice of the scientist engaged in the serious business of analytic self-searching and self-criticism, probing remorselessly into the roots of his basic assumptions. It should be recalled that Freud himself was plagued by doubts of the same order. They are expressed in many of his writings, as exemplied by his letter to Einstein a passage from which is chosen as the motto of this book.

However, Freud's, or for that matter, Masserman's, exposure of the mythological aspects of psychoanalytic doctrine has deeper implications than analytic self-searching and self-criticism. It is symptomatic of the tendency inherent in our culture to ferret out surviving vestiges of magic and to unmask myth, regardless of consequences. Indeed, it is only fitting for an age whose theologians are busy demythologizing religion to see to it that its scientists perform the same delicate operation on science. Freud's letter to Einstein is a reminder to physicists and psychoanalysts to do just that. Einstein, himself, was the foremost pioneer in this venture. It was his relativistic theory of physics that demolished the concepts of absolute time and space. Likewise, Bohr's quantum mechanics and Heisenberg's principle of indeterminacy have gone far to demote the time-honored fiction of causal law from its pride of place. In a similar vein, Goedel's theorem has shaken the belief in the infallibility of mathematical axioms. The result of this revision and reappraisal of the foundations of theoretical physics and mathematics has been a prodigious array of new technological inventions and the unprecedented expansion of man's mastery over nature at large.

Psychoanalysis has not, as yet, come within sight of this goal. But its critical self-searching, its quest for validation and ever greater precision of its formulations obviously moves towards it. The goal is to demote myth and to purge magic from its system of thought. It is the same goal that is pursued in analysis of the individual patient.

The ultimate value of such a venture is a matter of personal judgment. But even when measured by the self-validating standards of science, orthodox analysis tends to be more scientific than science itself. In the preceding chapter we pointed to the dangers of attempted integration at the price of elimination, denial or reaction formation. This is more likely to hamstring than to help scientific progress. There is growing consensus that continued reliance on a metapsychology rooted in 19th century concepts is becoming a stumbling block in the way of psychoanalysis aligning itself with the natural sciences, with probabilistic physics and quantum mechanics of the 20th century.

The more adventurous among a new generation of psychoanalysts are confident they can bring about the integration of their approach with the latest offshoots of the scientific method. With the help of cyberneticists, animal experimenters and psychopharmacologists, they are putting their theoretical assumptions to the test of quantifiable and repeatable experiments. Various projective techniques, sensory deprivation and isolation experiments, the visual distortion test,[12] and experimental dream research, have all supplied considerable supportive evidence as to the validity of their assumptions. At the same time, symposia and interdisciplinary discussions seek to translate the language of the newly revised psychoanalytic system of thought into terms of modern ego psychology, communication theory, symbolic logic and logical positivism. Thus, it is hoped, the gap between the behavioral and the natural sciences will ultimately be closed.

Has psychoanalysis as a therapeutic procedure been able to keep pace with the advances made by psychoanalysis as a science? Psychoanalysis, by now, has perhaps become the most thoroughly demythologized among modern schools of psychotherapy. But are its results in alleviating human suffering or in curing mental illness palpably superior to those of the other schools? No generally accepted criteria of cure or scales of improvement have as yet been developed. There is no consensus as to what may legitimately be called psychoanalysis, nor as to the clinical-diagnostic categories to which scales of improvement should be applied. We know, furthermore, that the samples of patient populations treated in various institutions or by individual therapists are virtually incommensurable. Worse still, the question of control groups rarely received serious consideration. Various roundtable conferences and "fact gathering" committees, e.g., one sponsored by the American Psychoanalytic Association, have not been able to resolve these difficulties. H. J. Eysenck, in several publications, and in a recent critical review of the literature, comes to the conclusion that the curative effects of psychotherapy in general are as yet unproven. Nor is there any evidence, he holds, that psychoanalysis as a therapeutic procedure is superior to other methods.[8a] Eysenck, an old crusader against the psychoanalytic position, certainly has an axe to grind. Yet J. Wilder,[13] S. Lesse,[14] and J. Marmor,[15] a noted analyst himself, have expressed similar ideas.

Lawrence Kubie, replying to such criticism, has rightly pointed out that psychoanalysts have been foremost among those seeking to validate their results by systematic inquiry and statistical evaluation.[16] Summarizing his own extensive experience, Kubie notes, however, that "at this point in human culture it is literally impossible to carry out such studies with precision."

It is true that psychoanalysis, more than any other school of thought, has been able to offer a consistent rationale for the therapeutic effects of insight, catharsis, dynamic interpretation, corrective emotional experiences and reeducation in the course of analytic therapy. Nevertheless many authorities, outside as well as inside the psychoanalytic camp, maintain that success or failure of psychotherapy does not necessarily depend on these factors. Judd Marmor[15] has pointed out that insight may in effect be largely due to what I described as doctrinal compliance.[12b] It may be a tell-tale sign of the patient's response to his therapist rather than an active therapeutic factor in its own right. No less important are patient expectations and the therapeutic motivations of the therapist, his personal integrity, competence, and previous experience, regardless of what school of psychotherapy he owes his allegiance. We shall see in Chapters XII and XIII that to this we have to add the part played by what will be described as the myth-induced existential shift: a shift transporting both therapist and patient to a new level of shared experience. More often than not, it is a shift countervailing their rationalistic outlook and reinforcing or restoring their susceptibility to myth.

*　　*　　*

We have seen how Freud's essentially mythophobic temper set him on a course bent on an increasing demythologization of psychoanalysis. Yet we have also indicated that there seems to be no clear correlation between its therapeutic value and the degree to which its demythologization has been successful. It may well be that there is no such thing as a wholly demythologized psychotherapy. If there is, it is likely to reduce its therapeutic potency. Like distilled water, it may lose its flavor and no longer quench the thirst of the thirsty.

This, in effect, is the paradox of classical analysis. As a consistent system of scientific thought, it has gone far to purge itself of the vestiges of magic and myth. As a treatment procedure, it can maintain its purity only at the price of impairing its therapeutic efficacy. It cannot apparently do without an "effective" myth. Freud himself has repeatedly gone on record confessing his lack of therapeutic motivations. He disowned, or dissociated himself from, his personal myth. But willy-nilly, the myth caught up with him. He became a *Medicin malgré lui*, as he himself put it. In a similar vein, psychoanalysis, despite its self-imposed demythologization and uncompromising scientific posture, has remained an effective myth at what, at the time of this writing, may well be the height of its life cycle.

REFERENCES

1. BRUNSWICK, E.: The Conceptual Framework of Psychology, Chicago Univ. Press, 1952.
2. FREUD, S.: The Standard Edition of the Complete Psychological Works of Sigmund Freud, ed.: J. Strachey, Hogarth Press, London 1955.

———— An Outline of Psychoanalysis, W. W. Norton, New York 1949.

———— Totem and Taboo, in: Basic Writings of Sigmund Freud, Modern Library, New York 1938.

———— Origins of Psychoanalysis, ed. M. Bonaparte, Basic Books, New York 1954.

3. BAKAN, D.: Sigmund Freud and the Jewish Mystical Tradition, Van Nostrand, Princeton 1958.

4. MALINOWSKI, B.: cf. Chapter V. (5).

5. HARTMANN, H.: Ego Psychology and Problems of Adaptation, Intern. Univ. Press, New York 1958.

6. NUNBERG, H.: Principles of Psychoanalysis, Intern. Univ. Press, New York 1955.

7. JANET, P.: Psychological Healing, Macmillan, New York 1929.

8. EYSENCK, H. J.: The Uses and Abuses of Psychology, Penguin, London 1953.
———— The Effects of Psychotherapy, Intern. Journ. of Psychiatry, 1.1. 1965.

9. SALTER, A.: The Case Against Psychoanalysis, Holt, Rinehart and Winston, Citadel, New York 1963.

10. BAILEY, P.: The Great Psychiatric Revolution, Amer. Journ. Psychiat. 113, 387-405, 1956.

11. MASSERMAN, J.: Science, Psychotherapy and Religion, in: Progress of Psychotherapy, ed. J. Masserman and J. L. Moreno, Vol. IV, Grune & Stratton, New York 1952.

12. EHRENWALD, J.: Visual Distortion Test, A Measure of Ego Strength, Arch. Gen. Psychiatry, Vol. 7, 30-38, July 1962.
———— The Visual Distortion Test, A Study in Experimental Psychiatry, Psych. Quart. (in press).
———— Doctrinal Compliance in Psychotherapy and Problems of Scientific Methodology, in: Progress in Psychotherapy, Vol. III, Grune & Stratton, New York 1958.

13. WILDER, J.: Facts and Figures in Psychotherapy, Journ. of Clin. Psychopathol. 7, 311-322, 1945.

14. LESSE, S.: Criteria for Evaluation of Results in Psychotherapy, Am. Journ. Psychother. XVIII, Suppl. 1, 1964.

15. MARMOR, J.: Psychoanalytic Therapy as an Educational Process, in: Science and Psychoanalysis, ed. J. Masserman, Vol. V, Grune & Stratton, New York 1962.
———— Psychoanalytic Therapy and Theories of Learning, ibid. Vol. VII, 1964.

16. KUBIE, L.: Psychoanalysis and Scientific Method, in: Psychoanalysis, Scientific Method and Philosophy, ed. Sidney Hook, Evergreen Books, Grove Press, New York 1960.

Freud and Jung: The Mythophobic vs. the Mythophilic Temper

It is of course ironical that I, a psychiatrist, should at almost every step of my experience have run into the same psychic material which is the stuff of the psychoses and is found in the insane. This is the fund of unconscious images which fatally confuse the mental patient. But it is also the matrix of a mythopoetic imagination which has vanished from our rational age.

JUNG

If Freud, spurred by his more orthodox Freudian followers, disavowed myth and protested, perhaps too much, his innocence of any oceanic feeling, Jung was totally committed to myth—primarily to myth of his own making— and at times became virtually engulfed in it.

Originally, the contrast in temper and temperament held a deep fascination for the two men. The fascination soon yielded to irritation, disappointment and, ultimately, to hostility. Freud became a deposed idol to Jung. To Freud, Jung became a prodigal son who deserted his father to espouse an alien creed. While in 1909, Freud still referred to him as his crown prince and heir apparent, by 1913 Jung was excommunicated from Freud's psychoanalytic congregation. The breach was deepened in the years to come by Jung's condoning—if not glorifying—of the Nazi movement and the Nazi myth, and by his accepting leadership in 1934 of the Nazi sponsored Supra-National Medical Society, with Dr. U. H. Goering, the Reichsmarschall's brother, as his German counterpart.

On the face of it, Freud's and Jung's disagreement derived from purely ideological motives. Jung,[1,1a,1b] like Adler, rejected Freud's thesis of sexuality as the principal factor in neurotic disorders. It is true, he agreed, that neurosis is often due to a disturbance in the dynamics of the patient's libido organization. But to Jung, libido is no longer identical with sex. It embraces the sum total of the vital energies of man. It is the life force itself. In a similar bold generalization, he extended the scope of the unconscious beyond that which has been repressed by the individual. The individual unconscious, he holds, merges into the collective unconscious, common to men of all races and all historical periods. The collective unconscious itself is the repository of what he described as the primordial images or archetypes. It forms the universal power house from which man's creative energies, myths and religious experiences are derived. Their occasional breakthrough into individual consciousness may give rise to mental illness, especially schizophrenia. Otherwise there exists a well-balanced complementary relationship between the conscious and unconscious parts of the personality. This balance, in conjunction with the particular way in which the individual is wont to relate to the outside world, is responsible for the two major types of personality described by Jung, the extrovert and the introvert type, and for the various subgroups which can be discerned within these two classes.

These are, however, only some of the features of Jung's system of thought, those which can readily be compared—or contrasted—with Freud's theories. But the major cleavage between Freud and Jung goes deeper than that. Freud's system has evolved from strictly scientific propositions. It is committed to an essentially mechanistic outlook on the world, governed by the laws of cause and effect. It is deterministic. Not so the universe of C. J. Jung. Jung's archetypes transgress the barriers of time and space. More than that, they are capable of breaking the ironclad laws of causality. They are endowed with frankly mystical "prospective" faculties. The soul itself, according to Jung, is the reaction of the personality to the unconscious and includes in every person both male and female elements, the animus and the anima, as well as the persona, or the person's reaction to the outside world. Jung has reached what his critics describe as an essentially mystical attitude late in his career. But he has steadily moved toward it from the outset. In one of his latest works, he contrasts the laws governing nature at large with an acausal or noncausal principle which, he feels, applies to the psychic realm and accounts for such unorthodox happenings as telepathy, clairvoyance and prophetic dreams.

In the view of his adversaries, Jung has thus broken faith with the scientific method and has reverted to the ancient belief in magic, alchemy and astrological correspondences between man and the universe, as it was held by ancient mystery cults, by Plato and the Neoplatonists, and by his great predecessor, Paracelsus von Hohenheim. There is reason to believe that Jung himself would have little quarrel with such a verdict.

In view of these basic differences it is not surprising that both Jung's and Freud's partisan followers sought the reasons for their ultimate spilt on ideological grounds. They made the most of their disagreement as to the part played by sex in neurosis, mental disorders and in human affairs in general. They pitted Freud's narrower concept of libido against Jung's notion of libido as the "life force" or "psychic energy" in the broadest sense. Edward Glover,[2] the noted English analyst, branded Jung's system as "the negation of every important part of Freudian theory." Jung, in his view, had abdicated the Freudian unconscious and replaced it with that shallow preconscious system described by Jung as the Personal Unconscious. "Jung," he stated, looks for the "mainspring of mind in a partly constitutional factor —the Collective Unconscious." In so doing he sacrifices the concept of individual unconscious conflict and loses sight of the dynamic aspects of depth psychology. This makes their two respective systems of thought mutually irreconcilable. Like the Copernician vs. the Ptolemaic views of the universe, they are literally worlds apart.

By contrast, Jolanda Jacobi,[3] one of the leading spokesmen of the Jungian school, accuses Freud of focusing exclusively on the pleasure principle and of ignoring the religious and spiritual aspects of man. Jung's theory, she asserts, opens up "the nonspecific synthetic function of the psyche for which there is no room in Freud's system." According to Jung, spiritual forces are just as important aspects of the psyche as Freud's instinctual drives. The spiritual is not a derivative of another factor but a principle *sui generis*. It represents, in Jacobi's phrase, "a counterpole to the world of natural drives." Again, Freud's system focuses in the main on the principle of cause and effect; Adler's on the *causa finalis*, on goals and purposes. But Jung's main concern is the formative forces that build a bridge between the unconscious and consciousness, or between the powers of "psychic opposites." Freud's method is reductive; Jung's prospective.

Jacobi traces the split between Jung and Freud to the criticism by Jung of Freud's theories in Jung's book *The Psychology of the Unconscious* (1912). "It showed that his (Jung's) conceptions were already diverging from Freud's and finally led in 1913 to his definitive break with the latter and with the psychoanalytic school."

It is an ironic commentary on the limitations of analytic depth perception that both Glover's and Jacobi's accounts tend to gloss over the part played in this state of affairs by the highly charged emotional relationship of the two men. The story of this relationship emerges in bits and pieces from Ernest Jones' classical biography of Freud[4] and it is put in sharp perspective in Jung's posthumous *Memories, Dreams, Reflections.*[1c] These two sources make it abundantly clear that Freud's and Jung's early association had all the hallmarks of a unique spiritual encounter, deeply stirring and rewarding for both the older and younger man. More recently it has been retraced in a sensitive study by Gustav Bychowski[5]; in critical reviews by H. Edelheit,[6] S. A. Leavy,[7] L. Mumford,[8] and others.

Jung was the son of a small town Protestant clergyman. Eight of his uncles were likewise Protestant parsons. He was brought up in a parochial environment which may well have looked with suspicion at people of different religious backgrounds or nationalities. This can be gleaned from an early childhood memory mentioned by Jung. The memory is of a

Jesuit priest whose sinister appearance had frightened the child and made him his boogyman for years to come.

By his own account, Jung was in his 30's when he first set foot in a Roman Catholic church. The church happened to be St. Stephen's Cathedral in Vienna and the time presumably his first meeting with Freud, the Jewish psychiatrist who dared speak openly of sex. Such a man may well have struck Jung as an even more eccentric figure than the apparition of the Catholic priest. In effect, Freud may have been the first Jewish intellectual of distinction with whom Jung had come into close contact. Conversely, Jung, 19 years Freud's junior, was the first gentile psychiatrist whose thinking proved to be congenial to Freud's and whose brilliant mind Freud recognized as a match to his own. The mutual attraction, as documented by their correspondence, seems to have been immediate. Freud in particular carried some of the ingredients of his stormy friendship with Wilhelm Fliess into the new relationship.

Freud himself gave a hint to that effect following his famous fainting incident in the Hotel Park in Munich in November, 1912. It was on that occasion that the two men had their first public disagreement concerning psychoanalytic policy and matters of prestige. Suddenly the older man fell to the floor in a dead faint. Jung, husky and strong-armed, lifted him up like a child and carried him to a sofa in an adjoining room. On coming to, Freud mumbled: "How sweet must it be to die . . ." Freud's own interpretation of the incident, as reported by Jones, linked it with a childhood memory: with Freud's feeling of guilt over death wishes directed against a baby brother who had actually died in his infancy. It was a case of triumph over a brother rival which, according to Jones,[4] was duplicated by the outcome of Freud's clash with Jung—a triumph for which he had to atone by his fainting fit.

Freud did not spell out the hidden connections of the incident with Fliess—or with what he himself had described as the homosexual undercurrents in their friendship. Their friendship had ended with a painful scene "four to six years" prior to the clash with Jung. By a strange coincidence, it had taken place in the same city, in the same hotel and, apparently, in the same hotel room in which the scene with Jung had occurred.

Jung's *Memoirs* contain references to a second fainting incident that took place in his presence. It happened following a professional meeting in which the Pharaoh Akhnaton's rebellion against his father Amenhotep had been the main topic of discussion. The consensus of those present was that the youthful pharaoh had harbored secret death wishes against Amenhotep. Jung, it is needless to say, rejected such an interpretation. It was apparently at that moment that Freud fell down on the floor in a dead faint.

✿   ✿   ✿

It is interesting to note at this point that one of the dreams Jung related to Freud about that time revolved around the same problem. Yet here again, Jung emphatically denied its Oedipal aspects. In the dream, as described in his *Memoirs*, Jung sees himself in the upper stories of a house, representing his personality structure. He descends to ever deeper and ultimately prehistoric levels of the building. On the deepest level he discovers two human skulls "obviously very old and half disintegrated." Jung remarks: "What chiefly interested Freud in this dream were the two skulls. He returned to them repeatedly and urged me to find a wish in connection with them. What did I think about those skulls? And who were they? I knew, perfectly well, of course, what he was driving at: that secret death wishes were concealed in the dream 'But what does he really expect of me?' I thought to myself. Toward whom would I have death wishes? *I felt violent resistance to any such interpretation* (author's italics). But I did not then trust my own judgment and wanted to hear Freud's opinion. I wanted to learn from him. Therefore I submitted to his intention and said, 'My wife and my sister-in-law'—after all I had to name someone whose death was worth the wishing!"

In Jung's interpretation the dream represents a structural diagram of the human psyche merging into the Collective Unconscious. Thus it foreshadows one of his major discoveries, with all its far-reaching metaphysical implications. Unfortunately, this "Jungian" reading of the dream still leaves the theme of the two skulls unaccounted for. But in the light of Freudian theory their meaning is rather transparent. By his own account, Jung's relationship with his father had always been precarious; at times it was openly hostile. The same ambivalence had marred his relationship with Freud. Viewed against this background, the two skulls, "very old and half disintegrated," are those of Jung's father and of Freud himself. They are the *corpora delicti* of double patricide, not of the flippantly admitted and subsequently discounted murder committed against his wife and sister-in-law.

Freud did not go on record with his interpretation of Jung's dream. But its hidden meaning must have left him with no doubt as to his "beloved son's" secret death wishes against him. Whether or not the fainting fit described by Jung represented Freud's unconscious response, or even surrender, to these wishes must remain a matter of speculation.

But whatever be the dynamics of the two fainting fits presided over by Jung, they are a measure of the deadly conflict of the two men. They are ominous symptoms of their mutual incompatibility that had led to the ultimate breakdown of their relationship. For Jung, Freud's whole system of thought could not possibly carry conviction because it would have forced him to confront his unresolved love-hate relationship with Freud, and it would have reopened the same ambivalence conflict in relation to his father. For Freud, Jung's implacable resistance and hostility was an ominous reminder of the tragic end of his friendship with Fliess. The rest of the problem was apparently taken care of by his healthy defenses. By his own account, Freud succeeded in integrating his latent homosexual trends with the rest of his personality and he came out of his ordeal a better man than before.

❋   ❋   ❋

There is an account of a cluster of much earlier dreams and obsessive phantasies in Jung's *Memoirs* which is relevant in the present context. In the dreams Jung saw himself descending a stairway into an underground chamber. There he came face to face with a huge tree trunk, 15 feet high, made of skin and naked flesh. It had an eye on top, emitted a dim light and was seated on a magnificent throne. He heard mother's voice call to him. "Yes, just look at him. That is the man-eater." Jung conjectures that the phallic tree trunk, the sinister Jesuit and the Lord Jesus (the latter two of whom he had been afraid of as a child) were one and the same thing. In a subsequent phantasy it was God who sat on the throne. The throne was placed on top of a big shiny cathedral, representing the world. To his horror, Jung could not suppress the image (or thought) of God suddenly defecating on his cathedral in such an explosive manner that the feces shattered its roof and broke its walls asunder.

To the Freudian analyst, here again, the latent meaning of the phantasies is envy, fear and hatred of the powerful, godlike father, possessed of super-human sexual and anal prowess. Jung remarks that not until the age of 65 had he been able to tell anybody of these horrifying, scatological dreams and phantasies.

In this instance his attempt to master the guilt attached to them amounts to a spectacular intellectual *tour de force*. After much soul searching and obsessive rumination, Jung concluded that his very blasphemic thoughts must have come from God himself; that God, who had permitted Adam and Eve to fall into sin, had also made him, Jung, dream the blasphemic dreams. But in so doing God had absolved him of the reponsibility for the unspeak-able crimes committed by the dreamer. In the last analysis it lay outside his province and could be placed squarely on the doorsteps of what he later was to describe as the archetypes which were themselves instruments of both God's cruelty and God's grace. This insight came to Jung with the power of a sudden illumination. It may in effect have been one of the sources of his celebrated theory of the collective unconscious teeming with a wealth of numenous archetypal images. Once this insight had dawned on him, Jung's conviction of its validity became unshakable. It has become the cornerstone of Jung's system of thought, of his personal myth—and of his anti-Freudian ego-defenses, as it were.

Put in psychoanalytic terms, a major part of his doctrine was in effect an ingenious system of rationalization, reaction formations and secondary elaborations. It was a system intended to explain, or explain away, his hostility against his father, his unconscious incestuous drives, his anal-sadistic impulses and thus to allay the tormenting guilt feelings associated with them. That his defenses gradually reached proportions of cosmic magnitude and striking philosophic profundity was obviously due to Jung's unique personality, his vast ego resources and his creative genius.

Needless to say, no Jungian analyst is likely to agree with such a causal-reductive, "Freudian," interpretation of Jung's case. He may retort that the hidden Oedipal or pre-Oedipal implications of his dreams, or the frankly scatological content of some of his fantasies must not obscure the broader vistas opened up by his discovery of the collective unconscious filled with the weird or awe-inspiring imagery of the archetypes. Presumably, Glover would have rejected such a concession. He emphatically denied the feasibility of any compromise between the Freudian and Jungian approach. Yet I am inclined to believe that Jung's fantasies were in effect over-determined in both the Freudian *and* the Jungian sense. They were meaningful as elaborate rationalizations and reaction formations against raw impulse and unresolved guilt. At the same time they may well be considered as creations of prodigious mythopoetic imagination which, as Jung put it, has vanished from our rational age.

*   *   *

There is another series of incidents described in Jung's *Memoirs* which strikes a more ominous note. Throughout his life Jung had a marked interest in the occult. His doctor's thesis dealt with the psychological interpretation of a spiritualistic medium who was incidentally a distant relative. He himself relates a number of seemingly telepathic incidents that had taken place in his childhood and later years. We noted that his book on synchronicity[1c] was an attempt to bring observations of this kind within a scientifically consistent frame of reference. One of his most spectacular accounts of this order is the splitting, with a loud report, and for no apparent reasons, of a solid walnut table top in his and his mother's presence. Both he and his mother were convinced that such a mysterious event must have had a "deeper meaning." Shortly thereafter a big bread knife snapped and, with an equally loud report, broke into several pieces. Jung adds to this story that he had carefully kept the pieces "to this day."

A later incident of this kind gains added significance by the fact that it was witnessed by Freud. During one of his visits to Vienna, Jung had asked Freud for his views concerning "occult" phenomena. "Because of his materialistic prejudice," writes Jung in his *Memoirs*, "he rejected this entire complex of questions as nonsensical and did so in terms of so shallow a positivism that I had difficulty in checking the sharp retort on the tip of my tongue . . . " And he continues: "While Freud was going on this way I had a curious sensation. It was as if my diaphragm was made of iron and were becoming red-hot, a glowing vault. At that moment there was such a loud report in the bookcase which stood right next to us that we both started up in alarm, fearing that the thing was to topple over us. I said to Freud, 'There, that is an example of a so-called catalytic exteriorization phenomenon,' i.e., a case of what parapsychologists today would call telekinesis. 'Oh come,' he exclaimed." Jung goes on to say: "Oh come, that is sheer bosh," was Freud's reaction to Jung's claim.

A few weeks later, in a letter to Jung dated April 6, 1909, Freud came back to the incident.[1c] After assuring him that he had given the phenomenon serious thought Freud writes: "My credulity. . . . vanished along with your personal presence. Once again for various inner reasons it seems to me wholly implausible that anything of the sort should occur. The furniture stands before me spiritless and dead, like nature, silent and godless before the poet after the passing of the gods of Greece." And he adds: "I therefore don once more my hornrimmed paternal spectacles and warn my dear son to keep a cool head and rather not understand something than make such great sacrifice for the sake of understanding."

At the end of his letter Freud seeks to soften this rebuke with the remark: "I . . . look forward to hearing more about your new investigations of the spook complex, my interest being the interest one has in a lovely delusion which one does not share oneself."

The tone of the letter is as cordial as ever, but from then on the ominous word *delusion* must have stood between the two men like an invisible wall. We know from Jung's own account that he himself was at times plagued by doubts as to his sanity—a fact obviously unsuspected on the conscious level by either Freud or Ernest Jones, however critical they may have been of Jung since the parting of their ways. But Jung confesses in his *Memoirs* that following his break with Freud he had lived under constant pressure, at times so strong that he thought "there was some psychic disturbance" in him. To his surprise, however, he found peace of mind in playing with building blocks—engaging in the game "as if it were a rite." In later years he was to replace this ritualistic version of occupational therapy by drawing and painting mandala symbols for hours on end.

In the autumn of 1913 and in spring 1914 he records a series of dreams featuring some world catastrophe which, in retrospect, Jung tries to interpret as presaging the First World War. Yet at the same time he asked himself whether he, the author of one of the first penetrating psychological studies of dementia praecox, was not "menaced by a psychosis." "An incessant stream of dreams and phantasies had been released," he notes, "and I did my best not to lose my head but to find some way to understand these strange things . . . Often I felt as if gigantic blocks of stone were tumbling down upon me.

One thunderstorm followed another . . . My enduring these storms was a question of brute strength. Others have been shattered by them—Nietzsche, Hoelderlin, and many others." But he felt there was a demonic strength in him that made him capable of enduring these assaults of the unconscious. At the same time he knew he had to let himself "plummet down" into his phantasies, even at the risk of losing command of himself. "And as a psychiatrist I realized only too well what that meant."

His dreams were filled with mythical imagery showing his identification with Siegfried or other legendary figures of the past. Or else they featured Salome, his *anima*; the Black Snake; the Horned Bull; or Philemon, his ghostly mentor, or Guru, with whom he had long conversations "walking in the garden."

Later still, when he was living in seclusion in the tower of his estate in Bollingen, Jung describes in graphic detail several incidents of haunting. One such incident happened in the winter of 1929. It began with an orchestra of auditory hallucinations, with the sounds of prowlers laughing, stamping their feet. "At the same time," he writes, "I had the visual image of several hundred dark clad figures, possibly peasant boys in their Sunday clothes who had come down from the mountains and were pouring in around the Tower on both sides, with a great deal of loud tramping and laughing, singing and playing accordion. Irritably, I thought, this is really the limit."

In this instance Jung's attempt at rationalizing his hallucinatory episode seems to be just as far fetched as in the telekinetic or poltergeist incidents. On discovering that a 17th century Swiss chronicler had described the neighborhood in which the haunting had occurred as a place "particularly notorious for spooks," indeed one in which the chronicler once had encountered a procession of men "just like" those seen by Jung 300 years later, Jung is satisfied that he, in his seclusion and solitude in the tower, had actually been so "sensitized" that he was able to perceive the procession of the same "departed folk" who happened to pass by *then* and *there*. In short, Jung turns the incident into a case of ESP, retrocognition, or synchronicity, trying to cast a delusional experience into the mold of traditional occult or "paranormal" occurrences. Few parapsychologists will concur with such an interpretation. But it may be mentioned by way of a footnote only that the late Dr. Nandor Fodor[9] did go on record with such a minority opinion and seriously suggested the reality of incidents of this order.

*   *   *

Viewed from the psychoanalytic point of view, some of the major propositions of Jung's system of thought have thus to be interpreted in terms of a tendency to denial, rationalization and reaction formation. They have the qualities of an elaborate system of defenses, even though this "Freudian" aspect by no means exhausts the broader implications of his theory of "complexes," of characterological types or of his concepts of the collective unconscious and the archetypes. Similar considerations apply to Jung's excursions into the occult. In order to account for his hallucinatory and delusional experiences, he resorted to the extraordinary device of formulating the theory of Synchronicity, coupled with more traditional occultistic, astrological and alchemistic notions. They amount to another ingenious attempt at rationalization and secondary elaboration: this time to explain—or to explain away—his otherwise well-concealed psychotic episodes.

Even his unfortunate thesis of a Jewish versus an Aryan unconscious, calling for a *Jewish* versus *Aryan* psychology, proposed in 1934[10] may be largely due to Jung's need to maintain his defenses in the face of the intolerable "Freudian" truths. Freud's excessive emphasis on sexuality, he stated, may have been valid for the Jewish psyche; but they were inapplicable to the Aryan soul. If this interpretation of Jung's embarrassing anti-Jewish pronouncements is correct, his indignation over being called anti-Semitic is understandable. They were not meant as insults against the Jews. Like G. B. Shaw's Warwick, sending Joan of Arc to her death at the stake, Jung too seemed to imply that they were merely a political—or in his case—a psychological necessity.

All but the supposedly most uncompromising "orthodox" psychoanalysts are likely to grant, however, that trying to sum up Jung's work and Jung's personality in terms of mere reaction formation, rationalization and secondary elaboration, would fail to do justice to his genius. It certainly runs counter to his "inner vision" of himself: to the way he saw himself *sub specie eternitatis.* This vision, he asserted, was one "which cannot be expressed in the language of science, but only by way of myth." Myth, to him, is in effect the ultimate arbiter of truth, and this is why he describes his *Memoirs* as an undertaking that tries to tell his "personal myth."

What, then, has been Jung's inner vision of himself and what order and coherence can be discerned in the vast mythopoetic outpouring which has gone into his life's work and into the making of his analytic psychology? Certainly, one major aspect is what he has called his personal myth, or rather, the cluster of myths which, like the gold-encrusted miniatures in an ancient illuminated manuscript, emblazoned his career. He confesses that "from the beginning I had a sense of destiny as though my life was assigned to me by fate and had to be fulfilled. . . . I did not have this certainty. It had me." He felt he belonged to the centuries, not to a limited space of time. At times his personality seemed to merge with Siegfried, the hero of German mythology. At times he felt an inner kinship with Job; with Plotinus the Gnostic; with Paracelsus von Hohenheim; or else with one of the great alchemists of the Middle Ages. These identifications were not just figures of speech. For Jung they had their roots in the collective unconscious. Symbols, myths and metaphors, as Gustav Bychowski has pointed out, were living, tangible realities to him. His vague hints of being an illegitimate descendent of Goethe point in the same direction. They are reminiscent of the motif of the mythical—or superhuman—birth of the hero to which Rank has called attention. Other aspects of Jung's personal myth are expressed in the rich imagery of the constituent parts of the Self: the *Animus*, the *Anima* and the *Shadow*—to say nothing of the *Soul* which is in turn a "splinter" of God or eternity itself. All these mythical *dramatis personae* seem to be derivatives of Jung's lifelong dialogue between what he called his number 1 and number 2 personalities—of the reflective and non-reflective aspects of his ego.

Another identity was that of the "psychic," the "medium"; of the prophet possessed of second sight, of powers of divination—in effect superman, omnipotent, omniscient, like God himself. It is this mystic participation with the divinity which, he felt, made it possible for him to pit his will against God, Fate, or the powers of the Archetypes themselves and to regain some of the freedom he had surrendered to them when he first conceived of the ego-alien powers residing in the collective unconscious. That in so doing he opened up anew the fateful cycle of free choice, with its attending burden of personal responsibility and guilt does not seem to him to be inconsistent with his youthful discovery that the same divine will that made him think blasphemic thoughts, had also bestowed on him the grace of divine forgiveness, since they, too, issued from God and were therefore beyond his volitional control.

Jung's concept of an all-pervading psychic principle or "energy" for which he adopted the Freudian term *libido* is one of the major myths which go beyond the range of personal mythmaking. Jung's libido, as defined—or obscured—by diverse verbose attempts to convey its meaning, is a hybrid product of science and mythology. In its "actualized form" it is described in terms of "such specific phenomena of the psyche as drive, wish, will, affect, performance, and the like."[3] Or else it is equated with "life-energy," capable of being displaced, transformed, and channelled by direct acts of will from one opposite to another. Above all, it is constant and imperishable, like the energy dealt with by the physical sciences. On another page, we are told that according to ancient notions of the soul, "the soul" itself is this force; its conservation is implied by the idea of its immortality, and in the Buddhistic and the primitive theory of transmigration is implied its unlimited capacity for undergoing transformation while being constantly conserved.

Among minor myths derived from this overall principle is Jung's reformulation of the ancient doctrine of opposites as represented by Yin and

Yang; by the Polynesian concepts of mana and taboo, or by the Persian myth of Ormuzd and Ahriman. Another archetypal image basic to Jung's system of thought[3] is the principle of "four-foldness." It comprises the four functions of thinking, feeling, intuition and sensation, with their complementary and compensatory relationships; the pictorial-geometric arrangements of the "tetrasomy"; the orientation according to the four points of the compass; etc. The same ordering principle is expressed in the mandala symbols characteristic of Tantric Buddhism, of Tibetan Thangkas or Navajo sand paintings.

Jung holds that with the appearance, in the course of therapy, of these symbols "equilibrium between the ego and the unconscious" can be established. If this is brought about and interpreted to the patient with the necessary tact and sensitiveness, the patient will be capable of integrating his archetypal contents with the rest of his personality. Thus what he had experienced before as the "Perils of the Soul," will become a source of new strength to him. Indeed, it may impart on the individual hitherto unknown powers of creativeness or mystic illumination.

Jung relates that during the darkest days of his withdrawal from the world in the Tower at Bollingen, he had been engaged in drawing, painting or contemplating mandala symbols for hours on end. He hints that mystic rituals of this order helped him regain his composure—if not his sanity. This moving account provides in effect one of the few glimpses into what may have been Jung's self-analysis, comparable to those that can be gleaned from Freud's correspondence with Fliess or from his *Interpretation of Dreams*. At the same time, it gives a sample of what may have been one of the therapeutic tehniques he had used with his patients.

❋   ❋   ❋

This dazzling tapestry of major and minor myths, personal and superpersonal, interwoven with a few faded threads of magic, alchemy and astrology, is in striking contrast with another picture: with the picture made up of Jung's monumental attempt at ordering and systematizing his visions in a scientifically consistent frame of reference. We have seen that these labors encompass his early association experiments; his studies on the psychology of dementia praecox; of characterological types; of alchemy and mythology of various primitive cultures; his intuitive anticipation of a "psychotoxic" theory of schizophrenia; to say nothing of his theory of synchronicity as a new principle of nature.

We noted that Freudian psychoanalysis would have little difficulty in reducing most of his propositions to a tendency to rationalizations and reaction-formations, if not to paranoid projections and ideas of grandeur, alternating with a prodigious capacity for sublimation. But attempts at such a dreary summation of the life's work of a genius would only prove that it cannot possibly be measured with a Freudian yardstick, much in the same way that any Jungian yardstick would fail to take the full measure of Freud's genius.

An example of such a misapprehension to which Jung had fallen victim himself is a dream recorded in his chapter on Sigmund Freud.[1c] In the dream he saw the ghost of a stooped, peevish looking elderly man in the uniform of an Austrian customs official, standing at the Swiss-Austrian border. The man had actually died years ago, but a voice said: "He was one of those who still couldn't die properly." In a second part of the dream Jung saw himself as a knight in full armor, with a white tunic into which was woven, front and back, a large red cross. Commenting on the dream Jung leaves no doubt that the knight was his own heroic archetype: Siegfried, Lohengrin or Parsifal—"full of life, completely real." This is certainly in stark contrast to the shadowy customs official representing Freud snooping for contraband smuggled over the border between the unconscious and the conscious—a fading apparition who "still could not properly die."

This, then, is Jung's account of a dream which contains in a capsule the "Jungian" appraisal of Freud's personality and a summary of Freud's imprint upon Jung's unconscious. It is a distressing *argumentum ad hominem*, tearing the one-time idol off its pedestal, reducing his work to that of a snooping customs official, and the man himself to what, in the eyes of the Swiss patrician and illegitimate descendant of Goethe, may have appeared as one of the lower forms of life.

On the other hand, Jung's self-portrait as a medieval knight, complete with shining armor and crusader's cross, throws the contrast between the two men into even sharper perspective. It makes it perfectly clear that Jung's crusade could not possibly be shared by Freud, that Jung could not possibly be expected to become a knight errant in the service of a Viennese Jew. It is as though the contrasting imagery of the dream conveyed Jung's answer to Freud's embarrassing, if not preposterous idea, that Jung be his "crown prince and heir apparent," and should ultimately assume leadership of a movement founded by the little man from the other side of the Alps—if not from the wrong side of the tracks.

But we indicated that the cleavage between Jung and Freud went deeper than doctrinal disagreements, ideological conflicts, or social or religious incompatibilities. Their cleavage, we noted, cut down to the innermost core of their personality makeups. Freud's attitude towards the unconscious, towards the raw, untrammeled forces of human nature was one of awe, suspicion and dread. Dreams, mental disorder, primitive mentality and even religion were manifestations of those Acherontic Powers which he had set out to expose for what they were, which he was determined to bend to his will; to neutralize by analysis and, if need be, to keep at bay by spectacular efforts of the Ego, the Charioteer of Plato's Two Horses.

This, it will be recalled, Freud hoped to achieve by the heroic feat of making the "unconscious conscious," or converting, by some act of psychic alchemy, raw instinctual drives into higher spiritual activities. But Freud soon departed from this elementary formula and psychoanalysts learned to use new techniques to achieve their goal. Ultimately Freud himself had doubts as to the scientific value of his metamorphical language. He disavowed myth to insure the integrity of knowledge. Myth became to him that which had to be overcome in order to establish the primacy of reason in human affairs. It is no wonder that in his view Jung's continued preoccupation with myth was a symptom of regression, presaging the Return of the Repressed. It is true that what Jung had to say about the power of primordial images, about the occult, about prophecies and poltergeists had struck sympathetic chords in Freud's mind. But for this very reason he was loath to listen to Jung's voice. It was a voice intoning a siren's song, full of danger and secret appeal. Freud tied himself to the mast of scientific knowledge in order to avoid being swept overboard.

The reverse was true for Jung. For him it was myth that had to maintain its supremacy and ultimate control over reason. He was ready to sacrifice knowledge to safeguard the integrity of myth. He disowned his mentor in order to keep faith with his myth. Like the radiologists at the turn of the century, dealing with the newly discovered radiations, both men were aware of the hazards of too close a contact with the powers of the unconscious. Some of the pioneers of radiology developed radiation burns and cancerous lesions of the skin. Freud made sure to steer clear of the danger zone in the nether regions of the mind. Jung did not, and nearly came to grief in the process.

REFERENCES

1. JUNG, C. G.: The Theory of Psychoanalysis, Nervous and Mental Diseases Monograph Series, No. 19, New York 1915.
   –––––– Collected Papers on Analytic Psychology, transl. by C. Long, Balliere, Tindal and Cox, London 1916.
   –––––– Modern Man in Search of a Soul, transl. C. F. Baynes and W. S. Dell, Kegan Paul, London 1934.
   –––––– Memories, Dreams, Reflections, ed. A. Jaffé, Pantheon Books, New York 1961.
   –––––– and PAULI, W.: Naturerklarung und Psyche, Rasche Verlag, Zurich 1952.
2. GLOVER, E.: Freud or Jung, W. W. Norton, New York 1950.
3. JACOBI, J.: The Psychology of C. G. Jung, Yale Univ. Press, New Haven, 1951.
4. JONES, E.: cf. Chapter VII (8).
5. BYCHOWSKI, G.: Freud and Jung: An Encounter, Israel. Annals of Psychiat. and Related Disciplines, 2.2. 1964.

6. EDELHEIT, H.: Jung's Memories, Dreams, Reflections, Psychoanal. Quart. 33, 561-566, 1964.
7. LEAVY, S. A.: A Footnote to Jung's Memories, Psychoanal. Quart. 33. 567-574, 1964.
8. MUMFORD, L.: The Revolt of the Demons, New Yorker, May 23, 1964.
9. FODOR, N.: Jung, Freud and a Newly Discovered Letter of 1909 on the Poltergeist Theme, The Psychoanal. Review 50, 2, 1963.
10. Cf. HARMS, E.: Carl Gustav Jung—Defender of Freud and the Jews, Psychiatr. Quart. April 1964.

Existential Psychotherapy: New Myths for Old?

My daughter was a freshman at college and had to prepare for an exam in contemporary philosophy. "Daddy, I am in an awful hurry," she said at the breakfast table. "They will ask me questions about existentialism. Can you tell me in five minutes what it is all about?" "No," I said, "I am afraid I can't. After all, it took Western civilization the better part of three thousand years trying to find out."

The fact is that whatever existentialism is supposed to be, it is easier to tell what it is not. It is not a philosophy satisfied with confining attention to either "matter" or "mind," or trying to explain one in terms of the other. Nor does it accept the old body-mind dichotomy of the two. It accepts science—the "natural sciences"—for what they are. It accepts psychology, sociology and psychoanalysis for what they are. Existentialism is prepared to grant extra-territorial privileges to the field proper of theology, art and the humanities. But existentialists claim that every one of these disciplines applies only to a limited segment of the totality of human experience, and leaves the most significant aspect of existence out of its frame of reference: The inner experience of being human, of being able to say not just "I think"— but also: "I feel; I suffer; I dread—and so do you, and so do we, and so do they." This inner certainty, they hold, is more certain than all the data supplied by the behavioral scientist or the pointer readings made by the physicist. It is a certainty accessible to man only, not to animals, nor to machines, nor to any one of man's electronic brain children or computer devices. Man only knows that he is "here." He alone is aware of his "being-in-the-world," of his *Dasein*, or of his *existential presence* as I prefer to call it. Therefore, to the existentialist, man's central experience, the fundamental ontological fact of being human, is his existential presence. All other experiences are encompassed in this overarching experiential fact and no descriptive, explanatory or philosophical statement about man is complete without making due allowance for this basic existential position.

Husserl's Phenomenology[1] is one of the major stepping stones—or rather a vast architectural complex of winding corridors and dark labyrinthine stairways—that has to be negotiated before gaining access to the inner sanctum of existential philosophy. Phenomenology aims at wiping off the slate all our preconceived ideas about body and mind; about time and space; about object and subject; about sensation and perception. It seeks to view whatever it looks at with the pristine purity of first man on the first day of creation. Yet the end product of the phenomenological structuring (or restructuring) of existence is about as complex as the structure of a living cell, of a living organism and indeed of the whole animal and vegetable kingdom, composed as it is of the various constituent particles of matter. In fact, following the steps by which Husserl, Heidegger,[2] Jaspers[3] or Erwin Strauss[4] arrived at their respective phenomenological positions is about as difficult for the novice in existential philosophy as is the step by step understanding of the complexities of modern biochemistry or molecular genetics to the specialist trained in other fields.

*   *   *

What, then, is the relevance of the newly opened existential perspective to the behavioral sciences and especially to the psychotherapist and psychiatrist?

To begin with, it has led to a complete reshuffling, reorganization and systematic reinterpretation of the data available at present. It is true that the reshuffling done by Ludwig Binswanger,[5] Medard Boss,[6] Eugen Minkowski[7] or Viktor Frankl[8] suggests nearly as many ordering principles as there are players shuffling the cards. Yet the rival ordering principles have several important points in common. They all hold that "existence precedes essence." They all stress the primacy of man's spiritual being, as opposed to his physical or naturalistic aspects. They all emphasize man's "finite" freedom of choice and action. His freedom, they hold, entails individual choice, responsibility and guilt. They all see man as the maker of meanings and values and therefore as the creator of his existential presence. They reject the old subject-object dichotomy, but contrast existence or being with Sartre's nonbeing or Heidegger's mere "Vorhandensein" of animals, tables, mountains, stars, and other physical objects. Man's existential presence is thus precariously balanced between being and nonbeing, between existence and nothingness, between freedom and determinism.

Viewing existence in these terms and approaching it in the footsteps of Heidegger or Sartre, Binswanger, Jaspers and Boss have arrived at what could be described as the existentialist version of a topographic picture of personality structure. However, for reasons indicated above, this version provides an inside and not an outside view of personality. In effect, it is a view which can no longer be termed "personality" or "structure" in the traditional Cartesian or Freudian sense. Its "center" is occupied by Heidegger's Dasein—by the existential presence. The existential presence stands outside or "transcends" the rest of the world, even though it remains an integral part of it. This central, luminous core has in turn three major aspects or realms: (1) the *Eigenwelt* or personal world, representing a person's relationship to himself, (2) the *Mitwelt*, or the world of social sharing, relationship and togetherness with other Daseins, and (3), the *Umwelt*, or the world of environmental objects which do not partake of the luminosity and freedom of the existential presence. The Umwelt corresponds with what the biologist Uexsküll described as the *Aussenwelt* of animals.[9] Binswanger submits that such a tripartite picture of man and his world eliminates the traditional dualism of body and soul, of object and subject and thereby overcomes the "fatal defect" of all psychology which is wont "to study mental processes as mere objects of knowledge and man himself as the thing outside the psychologist's inner experience." Karl Jaspers has developed a similar tripartite picture of the world, consisting of "being-there," "being oneself" and "being-in-itself." Jaspers, in contrast to Heidegger holds that these three "realms of being" are not reducible to one another. They are discontinuous even though, viewed together, they constitute a person's world design.

Man's world design or mode of existence varies, from person to person— as do Alfred Adler's "styles of life." It is different in Tom, Dick or Harry, even though the differences are blurred by contemporary mass culture and its attending "un-freedom." It may be "more different than in others" if we think of Heidegger, Binswanger, Sartre or Freud. What is particularly important in the present context, is that the world design shows specific, clinically distinctive features in the "alienated" personality of our time; in various neurotic or psychotic personalities and especially in schizophrenics.

A graphic illustration of a schizophrenic world design is the case of Ellen West described by Binswanger in stupendous biographical detail.[5] Ellen West was a highly gifted girl who felt that Fate had condemned her to be "fat and strong," Jewish and bourgeois, while she herself wanted to be thin, delicate and "ethereal." This insoluble conflict left her suspended between a higher, spiritual, "ethereal" world, and a gloomy, damp world "of the swamp and the grave." Unable to break through into the world of her own chosing, she consecrated her life to death and committed suicide in the end. Binswanger views her suicide as the ultimate assertion of her freedom, of freedom "that makes itself felt even in the insidious form of schizophrenia." Other modes of existence described by Binswanger, Gebsattel, Minkowski and others are the worlds of the manic, the depressive, the compulsive or the phobic, each with his idiosyncratic narrowing of world design, temporo-spatial structure, system of values, etc.

Another major proposition of modern dynamic psychiatry subjected to the process of reshuffling is the concept of the unconscious—Jungian or Freudian. In fact, many existentialists tend to deny the unconscious. "What is called the unconscious," they hold, "is still part of this given person" as Rollo May has pointed out.[10] "Being in any living sense is indivisible." They object to the splitting off of one aspect of "existence" from the other, and reject the "Witches Cauldron" or "cellar view" of the Freudian id. Binswanger has raised another objection. He takes issue with postulating "behind" the conscious personality an unconscious second person "which is certainly not permissible in existential analytic terms." Like Adler or Sullivan, he grants the phenomenological fact of forgetting or selective inattention, but he insists that the unconscious, as conceived by Freud, has no "world." As for the dream, Binswanger holds that it represents a particular world design or being in the world, "when the dreamer is entangled in the Eigenwelt in the sense of self-forgetfulness and, above all, in the sense of the optimistic flight of ideas."

Freud's dual instinct theory—the theory of sexual versus aggressive instincts—has likewise fallen victim to the existentialist reinterpretation of man and his world. Sex, to be sure, as well as aggression, has by no means been eliminated from the existentialist universe. But they derive their chief interest from the way in which they fit in with a person's "being in the world," and with his corresponding world design. Binswanger considers love as "the authentic mode of being human," a dual mode of existence which is, however, the "most hidden" and "the most severely repressed." In this respect, Binswanger closely follows the philosophy of Martin Buber.[11] Buber sees in love a transcendence of a person's relationship to the "other": a paradigm of what he calls "dialogical existence." A variation on this theme—or rather its pathological counterpart—is Ronald Kuhn's analysis of a sadistic murderer of a prostitute. Kuhn concludes in his study that "the murderer's world being what it was, his crime was not just possible, but unavoidable."[12] In other words, the sadistic expression of the sexual urge was his specific mode of existence, an integral part of his world design.

Heidegger's philosophy, as Sartre has pointed out, is essentially asexual. Mature sexuality, love in terms of Eros and Agape, seems to be included in his concept of care or "being-with." It is a notion which both Binswanger and Boss[6] have criticized leading, as it does, to a rather melancholy view of man. They both plead for the reinstatement of love—or at least of hope—into the existential presence.

Viktor Frankl, the Austrian existentialist or "logotherapist," views sexuality with more reserve. In a passage quoted in Professor Maurice Friedman's far-ranging anthology,[8] Frankl notes: "There is not the least thing to be objected to in the sexual drive as long as it is included in the personal realm; as soon and as long as the sexuality is personalized, personalized through love."

How much satisfaction this grudging concession to the sexual instinct would have given to Sigmund Freud is an open question. But it highlights the gulf that separates the existentialist from the psychoanalytic approach.

If Freud considered friendship and fellowship between men the product of sublimated sexuality, many existentialists tend to view sex as a demonic force: as a threat to man's capacity to "grasp another man in his being and to relate to him in an existentially authentic way."

All shades of existentialist opinion seem to agree, however, that man's living in a Mitwelt with his fellow men is a basic ontological fact. Hence man's need and man's capacity for a living *encounter*. The encounter, the dialogical meeting between person and person, as conceived by Buber, Binswanger, Boss or Hans Trueb, is perhaps the most important step made by existentialists in revising and reformulating basic psychodynamic terms. It is the encounter which provides the opportunity for the rekindling in the patient of what Binswanger has described as the "divine spark" in psychotherapy. This, he holds, can be achieved through "true communication from existence to existence which alone possesses with its light and warmth, also the fundamental power that makes any therapy work." According to Binswanger, Hans Trueb,[13] Buytendijk,[14] and other existentialists, this meeting of the therapist's and the patient's minds is a deeply meaningful human experience, which is bound to have a profound effect upon the patient's and the therapist's lives. It has therefore to be distinguished from the psychoanalytic concept of transference and countertransference. In the existential encounter two persons meet in a novel situation *here* and *now*, not as shadowy characters impersonating certain roles which they were ordained to play from early childhood. It is this fateful meeting of the two personalities involved in an encounter which, according to existentialist theory, provides the opportunity for the patient's personal growth, for the reconstruction of his personality and for his ultimate recovery. It opens up to the patient the living experience of another human being and thereby makes the experience of his own self— what Rollo May describes as the *I-am* experience—possible. It is this experience which the patient can pit against the existential anxiety of non-being, of nothingness or death. This should in turn pave the way for the solution of his particular problems of neurotic anxiety, neurotic guilt, alienation, or existential constriction. Hans Trueb sees in the encounter the "central issue" in all psychotherapy. It is "a confrontation of partners which the physician summons up in personal meeting and thanks to which the restoration of the patient's capacity for meeting begins."

❀   ❀   ❀

What are the therapeutic implications of this wholesale dismantling and reassembling of the picture of man and his world as proposed by existential analysts? Rollo May has rightly pointed out that, on the face of it, the activity of the existential analyst "does not usually differ from what the ordinary psychiatrist or psychoanalyst does." In fact, critics of the existentialist school of thought like to quote Molière's *Le Bourgeois Gentil-homme* in this context: Monsieur Jourdain is the man who had learned to his surprise that all his life he had been talking prose without knowing it. The critics note that despite the existentialist emphasis on a basically new philosophical approach, existential analysts continue to see their patients two or three times a week, listening to their troubles, exploring their life histories in a spirit of sympathetic understanding, looking for deeper meanings of their symptoms, dreams or phantasies and trying to convey to them a better understanding of their neurotic or otherwise warped, eccentric or extravagant ways of life. It is true, they do all this within the framework of the therapeutic situation seen as an encounter, on equal terms, of two human beings open to such an experience. But most psychoanalysts will protest that they too deal with their patients according to these principles wherever this is possible and clinically desirable. They will note that failing to do so would merely be indicative of the analyst's unresolved countertransference. They are also likely to agree that only authentic therapeutic motivations can provide the emotional climate needed for successful analysis.

On the other hand, it is also true that most psychiatrists associated with the existentialist movement had their early training along Freudian, Jungian or Adlerian lines. They include Binswanger and Boss in Switzerland, Rollo May, Harold Kelman, Antonia Wenkart, Thomas Hora and many others in this country. The present writer, though no card-carrying member of any particular school of thought, has followed an essentially psychoanalytic approach. Yet he feels that his horizon has likewise been expanded by the existentialist dimension.

The difference, then, indeed lies in the existential therapist's philosophical orientation; in his theoretical presuppositions, in his emotionally charged expectations and in his well-nigh mystical dedication to his work. It will be noted that it is precisely attitudes of this order which form the matrix of the "effective" myth. To be more specific, the difference between him and the psychoanalyst lies in their respective attitudes toward myth. While Freud acknowledged, with a sigh, as it were, the admixture of mythical elements to his system of thought, existential analysts seek to bring about a reconciliation of their philosophy with the resuscitated myths woven into its context. It is true that most of the time they use myth merely as figures of speech and do not seem to take them literally. But some of their doctrines, as they filter down to the small consumer, still bear the hallmarks of secular—or not quite secular—myths. Such crucial terms as *Dasein*, of being-in-the-world—of the existential presence—are esoteric concepts shrouded in mystery. Whatever their meaning, the metaphors used to bring them within the grasp of ordinary mortals hark back to the ancient myth of the struggle between Chaos and Cosmos, between darkness and light, between Ormudz and Ahriman. The existential presence itself is conceived of as an area of luminescence, a *Helligkeitsbereich*, in the surrounding darkness of nonexistence. "Mythically speaking, Being is the sea of light which glides off the self," as Karl Jaspers puts it.[3] According to the existentialist myth, it is not some extramundane agency, some *deus ex machina*, which throws the beam of light into the "dark backward and abyss of time." It is "Being"—the existential presence itself. This is how each Dasein carries within itself its particular world design and sets the stage for its idiosyncratic mode of existence. It is true that Heidegger, in proposing this view, has been at great pains to avoid the pitfalls of a long discarded solipsistic or transcendental-idealistic position. But here, again, it is more the metaphor than the abstruse metaphysical argument which sets the tone and is apt to persuade the philosophically unsophisticated.

Another recurrent metaphor is closely related to—or contrasted with—the concept of Dasein as luminiscence. It is the concept of *thrownness*. This is how Jacob Needleman,[5a] in his penetrating introduction to Binswanger's writings, tries to convey its meaning: "Man as a creature of nature is revealed in the thrownness of the Dasein, its 'that-it-is,' its *facticity*." "Has the Dasein as such ever freely decided and will it ever be able to decide as to whether it wants to come into 'existence' or not?" The Dasein, although it exists essentially for its own sake, . . . has nevertheless not itself laid the ground of its *being*. And also, as a creature "come into existence," it is and remains, thrown, determined, i.e., enclosed, possessed and compelled by beings in general. Consequently it is not 'completely free' in its world design either."

Thrownness is thus an existentialistic paraphrase of the concept of physical and psychic determinism, with an implied allusion to the randomicity versus rigid lawfulness that reigns in the inorganic world at large. But for the creative powers of the existential presence, men are thrown like dice into a cold and indifferent universe. In the last analysis thrownness evokes the picture of a newborn child cast into the world by the birth process. Viewed in this light it is a highly descriptive metaphorical term, devoid of any heuristic value or verifiable scientific connotation. But it conveys the basic existential mood of man aware of his limitations—and of his freedom to militate against them.

Most terms used in existential writings are of the same order. The concept of man's bodily existence, we are told, is the result of a natural-scientific reduction. This goes together with an alliance (or *koinoia*) of the soul "with that which is corporeal." At the same time the Dasein, to quote Needleman again, "distances itself from its bodily involvement, its thrownness, in order first to be fully 'free' as 'spirit'." On the other hand, "in psychoses the mind suffers from the disturbance in the organism, because the disturbance hinders its governance of the body and, in its receptive aspect, presents the mind with a distorted image of the world so that it, the mind, reacts abnormally."

Binswanger himself seems to subscribe to the ultimate mythological grounding of existentialism. "The man of antiquity," he states, "lived in a cosmos that determined even his most private secret choices, awake or in dreams"; and he quotes a famous passage from the classicist, W. F. Otto's, work on the *Gods of Greece*: "What in the moment of decision appear to us as motives, are for the initiated, acts of the gods. In them, and not in man's bottomless emotions, is to be found the depth and primary ground of everything of great significance which transpires in man."[15]

It is interesting to contrast this view with a passage from Spinoza's *Ethics*:

> "It will be sufficient if I here take as an axiom that which no one ought (to) dispute, namely that man is born ignorant of the causes of things, and that he has a desire, of which he is conscious, to seek that which is profitable to him. From this it follows . . . that he thinks himself free because he is conscious of his wishes and appetites, while at the same time he is ignorant of the causes by which he is led to wish and desire not dreaming what they are."

It may be no coincidence that Freud was profoundly influenced by Spinoza's thinking and used much the same argument as one of the cornerstones of his deterministic picture of man as *homo natura*. Both Freud and Spinoza made a clean break from the old mythological tradition as applied to human affairs and substituted passions or appetites, that is, unconscious instinctual drives, for myths or the gods of antiquity.

        ❋   ❋   ❋

It may be the very difficulty of conveying the meaning of the new existentialist myths in the discoursive language of science that is responsible for the turgid style, the copious verbiage, the endless repetitions characteristic of many existentialist writings. At times they evoke echoes of ancient Vedic or Homeric hymns, of solemn liturgical recitations, of oracular pronouncements or poetic diction. This impression is enhanced by the frequent use of neologisms which, just because they fall short of precise meaning, provide an extra stimulus to the reader's imagination. Their texts are inspirational rather than analytical. Like Latin, Greek or ancient Hebrew used in orthodox Roman Catholic or Jewish worship, they transport the believer into a realm removed from the routine of his workaday life. They bring about what will be described as an *existential shift*. Once this shift has been attained, it helps to put the therapist into the proper frame of mind for the therapeutic encounter with his patient in a sphere unfettered by social convention, self-seeking, competitive or mutually exploitative relationships. Thus the therapist's spiritual preparations for the encounter can be compared with the ritual of ablutions and purifications which were mandatory on the holy men or priestly healers of a past era.

The healing effects attributed to the encounter itself—to the "touching" of two souls on the spiritual plane—is in turn reminiscent of the healing powers ascribed to the *Royal Touch* or the laying on of hands described in the Scriptures. At this point the connection of the existentialist myth with ancient magic belief becomes unmistakable. It is the belief in omnipotence; in man's capacity to transcend the limitations of his personality; in his freedom to reach out beyond himself—and to make others capable of sharing the same experience.

It is true that these lofty aspirations are tempered by sobering second thoughts; by the realization of the finitude of freedom; of the limitations imposed on man by his Umwelt and by his own corporeal existence. Existentialism insists it is not a philosophy of "either-or" but of "both-one-thing-and-another." It seeks to bring about a reconciliation and reintegration of man's scientific and existential view of himself and the world. But it is precisely its renewed emphasis on freedom, choice and responsibility, whatever their rationale, which provides the existential therapist with a new set of therapeutic expectations—in effect with a new myth—upon which his approach to the patient is based. Existential therapy, as conceived by Hans Trueb, approaches the patient "as a fellow human being, a Thou, the original partner in a fully human meeting. It seeks out his stubborn self, this introvert captive of the psyche and will not release it." The therapist, Trueb declares, "*summons* the patient's self by name as the one called upon to answer, the one personally responsible, and by addressing it in this manner, challenges the self to disclose itself in itself in the new dialogue with the physician-partner. . . ."

For one who has accepted the existentialist position, a summons like this may be hard to resist. Indeed, this precisely may be the key factor in the existentialist appeal. Here again the procedure is reminiscent of ancient magic incantations, of exorcistic ritual, and its dynamic impact is more in the laps of the gods than in the hands of the therapist. He is unconcerned with the *metadynamics* of his approach.

Nor do we learn from the existential analysts how far their therapeutic optimism, if any, is borne out by the facts. They do not seem to be anxious to validate their claims of therapeutic results. Their writings are replete with anecdotal accounts of successful treatment—interspersed with candid reports of occasional suicides. The question of controlled studies or statistical evaluation of results is all but brushed aside. The quantitative approach seems to run counter to the spirit of the existential method itself. Yet if this is true, we have to realize that the existential therapist has virtually excluded himself from the mainstream of modern psychiatric research and treatment. Despite his protestations, the gap between his and the scientist's "modes of existence" remains open. They do not have a *koinos cosmos*—a common world—to share, and their dialogue is hampered by the different levels of discourse upon which they are poised.

❀   ❀   ❀

Freud and Binswanger had been friends for many years. Yet Freud's mythophobic, as opposed to Binswanger's mythophilic, temper was once more in the way of a true dialogical encounter. Binswanger's writings and his autobiographical account of their friendship[5b] testifies to his admiration for the greatness of Freud. But their correspondence shows that in the end they could only agree to disagree.

On the occasion of Freud's 80th birthday, Binswanger joined in the eulogies acclaiming the octogenarian as the pioneer explorer who gave the world the definitive picture of man viewed as *homo natura*—that is, man shorn of his spiritual aspects. This is part of Freud's reply to Binswanger's lecture:[17]

> Dear Friend:
> Your lecture was a pleasant surprise. Those who listened to it and reported to me were apparently unaffected: it must have been too difficult for them. Reading it I enjoyed your beautiful style, your erudition, the breadth of your horizon, your tact in contradicting me. When it comes to praise one can take unlimited quantities, as everyone knows.
> Of course, I don't believe you. I have always lived on the ground floor and in the basement (i.e. in the unconscious) of the building—you maintain that on changing one's viewpoint one can also see an upper floor housing such distinguished guests as religion, art and others . . . If I had another life to work ahead of me, I would dare to offer even those high-born people a home in my lowly hut. I already found one for religion when I stumbled on the category "neurosis of mankind." But we are probably talking at cross purposes and it will be centuries before our dispute is settled.

Still, their dispute always remained in a minor key. Theirs was a conflict of ideologies, not a clash between men. By contrast to the tragic break between Freud and Fliess, Freud and Adler, or Freud and Jung, their relationship was preserved by the saving grace of mutual respect.

We have pointed out that here again conclusive data as to the merits of existential analysis as a therapeutic procedure is still outstanding. But we also emphasized that the diverse schools always seemed to have mustered a large group of followers with commensurably larger numbers of patients who were satisfied that they were helped. Yet the paradoxical fact is that all this happened—and continues to happen—regardless of the mutually conflicting or even irreconcilable theories held by the various schools to which their therapists owed their allegiance. Each therapist, whatever school he belongs to, is able to point in perfectly good faith to a vast body of clinical findings that tend to confirm his particular theoretical position.

In the preceding chapters we have already called attention to the part played by doctrinal compliance in this state of affairs. In the chapters that follow we shall try to show that doctrinal compliance is more than an embarrassing source of error in the history of psychotherapy. Like the placebo in general medicine, doctrinal compliance may be a vehicle of powerful therapeutic influences brought to bear upon the patient. It may be the source of the therapist's self-fulfilling theoretical assumptions. It may be the carrier of his personal myth and the mediator of its therapeutic efficacy.

REFERENCES

1. HUSSERL, E.: Phenomenology, in: Encyclopedia Britannica, Vol. 17, 1954.
2. HEIDEGGER, M.: Being and Time, Harper and Row, New York 1963.
3. JASPERS, K.: Reason and Existence, Five Lectures, Noonday Press, New York 1955.
4. STRAUSS, E.: The Primary World of Senses, transl. J. Needleman Free Press of Glencoe, New York 1963.
5. BINSWANGER, L.: Being-in-the-World, Selected Papers, ed. J. Needleman, Basic Books, New York 1963.
   ———— The Case of Ellen West, in: Existence, ed. by Rollo May et al., Basic Books, New York 1958.
   ———— Erinnerungen an Sigmund Freud, Bern 1956.
6. BOSS, M.: Psychoanalse und Daseinsanalytic, Hans Huber, Bern 1957.
7. MINKOWSKI, E.: Findings in a Case of Schizophrenic Depression, in: Existence, ed. R. May et al. Basic Books, New York 1958.
8. FRANKL, V.: The Doctor and the Soul, transl. R. and C. Winston, Knopf, New York 1955.
   ———— in: The Worlds of Existentialism, ed. Maurice Friedman, Random House, New York 1964.
9. UEXSKÜLL, I.: Umwelt and Innenwelt der Tiere, Berlin 1921.
10. MAY, R.: The Origins and Significance of the Existential Movement in Psychotherapy, in: Existence, ed. R. May et al., Basic Books, New York 1958.
11. BUBER, M.: I and Thou, transl. R. G. Smith, Scribner Paperback, New York 1960.
12. KUHN, R.: The Attempted Murder of a Prostitute, in: (10).
13. TRUEB, H.: From the Self to the World, in: The Worlds of Existentialism (cf. 8a).
14. BUYTENDIJK, F. J. J.: Phenomenologie de la rencontre, Paris 1952.
15. OTTO, W. F.: Die Goetter Griechenlands, Verlag Cohen, Bonn.
16. SPINOZA, B.: Ethics, Part I.
17. FREUD, S.: Letters of Sigmund Freud, ed. E. L. Freud, McGraw-Hill, New York 1960.

Doctrinal Compliance—or Why the Therapist Is Always Right: A Digression into Scientific Methodology

Pre-Freudian psychotherapy, as well as Freudian analysis in its early days, conceived of its goals and motivations in comparatively simple terms. The therapist's motivation was to effect cures. The patient's purpose in consulting him was to be relieved of his symptoms. Today we know that the relationship of therapist and patient is determined by a multiplicity of factors, conscious and unconscious, usually described in terms of the transference-countertransference configuration. H. S. Sullivan shifted the focus altogether to existing interpersonal relationships and called attention to the therapist's role as a participant observer.[1] J. L. Moreno's emphasis on a symmetrical pattern of interaction between patient and therapist,[2] Carl Rogers' client-centered approach,[3] and the stress laid by Binswanger, Boss, Trueb and other existentialist therapists upon the encounter, upon fellowship and total self-investment, point in the same direction.

Our new picture of the therapeutic process goes further than that. It implies a reciprocal relationship in which the patient's behavioral attitudes, emotional reactions and even some of his symptoms are partly determined by the therapist's approach and in which his attitudes towards the patient are in turn influenced by the impact of the patient's personality upon him.

The therapist's contribution to this state of affairs can be described as the patient's doctrinal compliance: as compliance by the patient with the therapist's unconscious wishes and expectations regarding the validity of his theories and their apparent confirmation by the patient's productions. Doctrinal compliance is thus closely related to the familiar concept of suggestion but differs from it by its essentially unconscious nature. It is independent of the therapist's deliberate volition and explicit intentions. As a general rule both he and his patient remain unaware of its operation.

The possibility of such influences falsifying the outcome of psychotherapy has long been suspected. Freud's most vocal opponents stressed the part played by suggestion in the making of psychoanalytic theories. The same objection has remained a recurrent theme of Freud's critics up to our day. Yet Freud himself was by no means unaware of suggestion as a possible source of error in his theories, especially insofar as the role of early

Early versions of this Chapter appeared in the American Journal for Psychotherapy, 11.2.1957 and in Progress of Psychotherapy, Ed. J. Masserman and J. L. Moreno, Grune & Stratton, New York, 1958.

sexual traumata in the origin of hysteria was concerned. As early as 1897 he had found to his dismay that the accounts of his patients did not stand up to closer scrutiny; that he had been misled by their fictitious tales about rape, seduction and other molestation by unscrupulous parent figures. "I no longer believe in my female neurotics," he wrote in a letter to his friend, Wilhelm Fliess. He was forced to admit that there was "no indication of reality" in the unconscious, and that, consequently, it was nearly impossible to distinguish between reality and fiction in his patients' depositions.[4] In a revealing passage of his *Autobiographical Study*,[4a] he attributes some of his results to the "pressure of technical procedures which I used at the time." In another letter to Fliess, he remarks that certain aspects of this procedure may well be compared with the techniques used by the medieval exorcist on his victims.

Freud's concern about his initial impact upon his patients highlights the difference between himself and his prescientific forerunners. But his very willingness to compare their respective techniques calls for a closer look at what today would be described as "observer contamination" by the ecclesiastic brainwashers of medieval times.

The patients, in the medieval setting, were the unhappy women accused of witchcraft and sorcery. The "therapists" were the inquisitors, imbued with their fanatical belief in the evils of heresy, committed to saving the souls of their victims from damnation, if need be by the ultimate remedy of burning at the stake. The witches, subjected to the methods neatly catalogued by the Dominican monks, Kramer and Sprenger, in their *Malleus Maleficarum*,[5] produced all the evidence which was needed for their undoing, including such hysterical symptoms as the anesthetic spots or *tâches de diable* which were considered unfailing stigmata of witchcraft.

✻   ✿   ✿

In case of need the evidence was of an altogether different order. Aldous Huxley, in his study *The Devils of Loudun*,[6] describes in graphic detail how the unhappy nuns, subjected to months of systematic interrogation by the ecclesiastic courts, were ready to testify to having committed virtually every crime under the sun. It is interesting to note in this connection that the resident exorcist is quoted as stating that one of the accused, Soeur Jeanne, had repeatedly read his thoughts before he himself had uttered them. During the Loudun trials Cardinal Richelieu was the most powerful personage in France. It was with him in mind that the exorcist Laubardemond addressed the following questions to one of the "demoniacs":

"What do you say about the great Cardinal, the Protector of France?"

"He is the scourge of all my friends," answered the devil from the demoniac's mouth.

"Who are your friends?"

"The heretics."

"What are the other heroic aspects of this person?"

"His work for the relief of the people, the gift of government which he has received from God, his desire to preserve the peace . . . ."

All this was exactly what the exorcist wanted to hear and the hysterical nun, subjected to many weeks of brainwashing, obliged. It is impossible to decide whether or not a telepathic element was involved in such a performance. Nor is it permissible to describe the procedures of the inquisitors in terms of anything like modern psychotherapy. But there are three ingredients of the therapeutic situation which can be recognized in the ecclesiastic setting: the patient's profound emotional disturbance, reminiscent of hysteria in our sense; a "healer" seeking to effect her "cure" by psychological means; a "transference relationship" between the two, however warped and distorted this may have been. The result was unmistakable: the grafting of a new, iatrogenic neurosis upon the existing mental disorder. As it happened, the new syndrome seemed to be just what the doctor ordered. It amounted to a perfect corroboration of the exorcist's expectations, and met the needs of his own selfish or frankly sadistic countertransference.

Reverting to a more enlightened period, we have seen the operation of much the same principle in Mesmer's early exploits with the Misses Paradis and Oesterline. These exploits were followed by the mass hysteria elicited in the patients congregating around his magnetized *baquet* in Paris. The characteristic somnambulistic productions of patients treated by the Marquis de Puységur; the "lucid sleep" described by the Abbé Faria; some of the equally striking performances of patients consulting other magnetopaths or phrenologists, are variations on the same theme.

It will also be recalled that Charcot, the wizard of the Salpétrière, was likewise subject to the fallacies stemming from his own theoretical preconceptions regarding the nature of hypnotism and the *grande hysterie*.

More recent studies on "experimental bias" and "observer-contamination" have brought out new aspects of the problem. Skinner's techniques of "operant conditioning" have shown that the learning behavior of pigeons and other animals can be influenced to a striking degree by reinforcing responses desired by the experimenter with a few grains of corn or pellets of food. Comparable reactions were obtained with human subjects in the psychological laboratory. J. Greenspoon has found that the mere uttering by the experimenter of a grunting sound may influence a subject's speech in a characteristic manner, e.g., "affirmative" grunts induced him to use more plural nouns; "negative" grunts less plural nouns. Significantly, the effects of such operant conditioning were enhanced by the personal prestige enjoyed by the person in charge of the experiment.[7] Similar effects were described by Mandler and Kaplan,[8] and by L. Krasner. In true Skinnerian manner, Krasner went so far as to designate the therapist as a "social reinforcement machine."[9] On reviewing the literature, J. D. Frank concludes that "one person can influence the verbal reaction of another through very subtle cues, which may be so slight that they never come to the center of awareness."[10]

The relevance to our issue of such findings goes without saying. They may account for the well-known fact that patients undergoing therapy with Freudian analysts tend to produce Freudian dreams, Jungian patients to produce Jungian dreams, or Adlerian patients, Adlerian dreams. My own experiences during my apprenticeship in psychotherapy and psychoanalysis point in the same direction. During my Adlerian period my patients tended to produce characteristic Adlerian dreams. They gave way to more "Freudian" dreams during my subsequent prevailingly Freudian orientation. At yet another time I seemed to come across a cluster of seemingly telepathic dreams.

These are by no means isolated occurrences. Similar examples of doctrinal compliance have already been described by Stekel, by C. G. Jung and more recently by Judd Marmor.[11] Medard Boss gives a graphic illustration of the same principle in his *Psychoanalysis and Existential Analysis.*[12] He describes the case of a physician suffering from an obsessive compulsive neurosis. He had been treated over a period of eight years, first by a Freudian, secondly, by a Jungian, and thirdly by an existential analyst— presumably by Boss himself. One of the patient's recurrent dreams goes back to his Freudian period. The dreamer found himself on the ground floor of a church or church steeple when an old man—his venerated teacher of anatomy—brandished a huge scalpel and proceeded to cut through the foundations of the church, burying the patient under its ruins. The first analyst interpreted this dream in terms of the patient's Oedipus complex and castration fear. The second therapist saw in it an archetypal image, removed from the dreamer's personal responsibility, thus absolving him from any attending feeling of guilt. The existential analyst in turn helped the patient to realize that the Gothic church steeple actually stood for a powerful "object gesture" pointing upwards to the sky. "It was a beacon directing the gaze of man towards the house of God." Yet he, the patient, had been closing his mind to the beckoning and calling of the church spire. And in this attitude he had been encouraged by his revered, though cynical, professor of anatomy, thus cutting himself off from the deeper, religious roots of his existence. It was this unpaid debt to his unfulfilled potentialities which had left the patient with the sense of guilt, frustration and estrangement from the world.

Another dream of the patient while he was undergoing therapy with Dr. Boss strikes a novel note, presaging what can be described as an existential shift in the dreamer's mind. In the dream the patient found himself suspended by a rope above the baptismal basin of a church. Incapable of controlling a desperate urge to defecate, he relieved himself in the basin, while at the same time he felt virtually torn in two halves by the pull of the higher powers brought to bear on him from above: from the church bells to which the rope had been fastened.

Viewed from our angle, the first dream shows the patient's doctrinal compliance in his transition from one therapist towards another. Each interpretation gave the dream's latent meaning a new slant and each one seemed to be readily adopted by the patient. The second dream carries the imprint of the existentialist position in its manifest content. There are the earthbound, excremental aspects of human existence, and there is the need to realize one's higher, spiritual aspirations. Boss attributes the patient's illness to the disruptive conflict between these aspects, and his subsequent cure to the successful integration of the two.

As can be expected, Boss takes his own existential interpretation of the dream as the "last word." To him doctrinal compliance does not seem to be a source of "error." It is a prerequisite of the patient's therapeutic response, much in the same way as to the Catholic believer conversion to Catholicism is a prerequisite of salvation. Indeed, the patient's second dream seems to anticipate his impending conversion to the existential point of view and it may well be that this, more than his compliance with the theories of his previous therapists, accounts for his ultimate recovery.

*　　*　　*

Reverting to the field proper of psychoanalysis, in some instances a characteristic theme or motif seems to be making its appearance in the manifest content of dreams dreamed by seemingly widely separated clusters of patients. A striking example of this kind is a recent little epidemic of dreams representing what O. Isakower[13] and B. Lewin[14] described as the *dream screen*. It happened in the wake of their articles in the late 1940's, when several analysts, both in this country and in England, had come up with a number of similar observations. The dreams featured more or less prominently symbolic representations of mother's breast. Yet prior to Lewin's and Isakower's publications, dreams of this order had been rare, if not altogether absent, in psychoanalytic literature. Here, again, doctrinal compliance may be the responsible factor, even though the rival hypothesis of selective attention paid to the "new" feature cannot be ruled out.

The following observation of my own seems to be a minor contribution to the same "epidemic." In an article published in 1957, I had just discussed the merits of Lewin's paper in terms of doctrinal compliance. Yet I was wondering whether such an interpretation had given justice to his thesis. It was at that time that a patient of mine, a woman aged 46, with a marked homosexual attachment to her mother, reported an unmistakable "Lewinian" dream: "I stood with my husband at the shore of the ocean, looking at the surf in the evening light. Suddenly a huge wave came and engulfed me. The wave had the shape of a female breast." The patient had been breast-fed by her mother up to the age of three. She gave her associations of the female breast without any prompting from me. It was the first time since 1953, when I had became acquainted with Lewin's "dream screen," that I encountered such a graphic reference to it. Whether this apparent coincidence is merely due to the fact that I was especially alerted to the occurrence of dreams of this type, or to doctrinal compliance of an unusual —conceivably telepathic—kind must remain a matter of speculation. My own files, containing several thousand dreams recorded since 1953, seem to me to tip the balance in favor of the latter explanation.

Doctrinal compliance may also occur under conditions of conscious resistance to such compliance. This is illustrated by a critical review of my book, *New Dimensions of Deep Analysis,* by Peter H. Knapp, in the Psychoanalytic Quarterly (Vol. XXV, No. 1, 1956). Dr. Knapp, in his review, takes a rather skeptical view of the material—especially the dreams—presented in the book. But after expressing his doubts he goes on to say:

> "This review is not the product of mere destructive criticism. In proof, let me offer an incident. It occurred one morning after reading, on my way to work, in one of the case reports in this book (p. 174): ' . . . *it was at the public toilet in high school that he first noticed that other boys did not clean themselves following defecation in an upright position.*'" And Dr. Knapp goes on to say: "My first patient was late, having overslept. He had been awakened by a dream. Careful questioning established that the dream occurred within minutes of my having read that sentence. The central portion was as follows: the dreamer had moved his bowels, was standing up, his pants down, looking for the toilet paper to wipe himself. The dream was, of course, overdetermined. So, it happened, was an interest of mine at the moment in problems of soiling and cleansing. We were left with a remarkable double appearance of an unusual image, in my reading and a patient's dream. It could not conceivably have been transmitted through any sensory avenue."

Dr. Knapp's case is either one of mere coincidence—or psi-induced doctrinal compliance—*malgré lui,* as it were.

❖   ❖   ❖

The concerted evidence of doctrinal compliance, whatever its *modus operandi* brings us face to face with a crucial question. What are the criteria of valid observational data in the field of psychotherapy and in situations of the type of the clinical interview in general? On what grounds, if any, can we decide that a Freudian, Jungian, Adlerian or Rankian dream produced by a given patient is not merely the outcome of his doctrinal compliance? How can we be sure that it is not the effect of suggestion, empathic communication with his therapist, of operant reinforcement—or telepathic leakage? In short, how are we to rule out the basic methodological objection that the patient's productions are not of the nature of genuine clinical data, but merely reflect the preconceived ideas of his therapist and, by indirection, of the school of thought to which the therapist owes his allegiance? How can we be sure that his conclusions are not based on his own self-fulfilling expectations and their apparent confirmation by his patients' productions? The fact is that each one of the contemporary schools of psychotherapy has evolved a coherent and well-ordered system of thought. Each one can claim a considerable measure of success in its therapeutic approach. Each one has developed a set of logically consistent and well-integrated hypotheses whose validity is borne out over and over again by their findings. Yet the overall picture is one of a variety of conflicting, if not mutually exclusive, theoretical positions and basic principles.

Judd Marmor's[11] critical review of the field led him to much the same conclusions, independently from the present writer. Faced with these inconsistencies, Marmor suggests that they might be resolved by reference to the principle of parsimony; by the heuristic value of their respective propositions and by the predictive power of their assertions.

We have seen that Freud himself has by no means ignored the problem. According to Jones, Freud's solution—at least of the psychoanalyst's dilemma—was provided by his discovery of the Oedipus complex, derived in part from the insight gained through his self-analysis, in part from his study of the works of Sophocles and Shakespeare.[15] A month after the letter quoted on an earlier page, he writes to Fliess that, far from being discouraged, he was having the feeling "more of triumph than of defeat." He arrived at the conclusion "that love of the mother and jealousy of the father is a general phenomenon of early infancy and childhood." To bear out his thesis he points to the deeper psychological meaning of the Oedipus myth and to Hamlet's neurotic inhibitions.

I believe that these references to two great works of art are of decisive importance for an understanding of Freud's confidence in his own methodological approach. More generally, they point the way by which a reasonable validation of data derived in the psychotherapeutic situation can be sought. Though he never stated so explicitly, it is clear that Freud considered human documents of this order safe from the pitfalls of the "pressure of technical procedure" which he had used at that time. It may conceivably have been suggestion, operant reinforcement or telepathic leakage that was instrumental in his patients' production of fictitious memories of infantile seduction. But, in going back to the creative work of the playwright, Freud could once more feel to be on safe ground. In these instances, suggestion or other forms of doctrinal compliance with the therapist's preconceived ideas could safely be ruled out. From the outset they disposed of most objections which were to be raised by Freud's critics in the ensuing years. This is why the discovery of the Oedipus complex had become one of the cornerstones of the psychoanalytic system of thought.

More recently H. Eysenck, J. Wolpe and S. Rachman reexamined Freud's celebrated case of Little Hans in the light of what is here described as doctrinal compliance (H. Eysenck: *Fact and Fiction in Psychology*, Penguin Books, Baltimore 1965). There can be little doubt that here also observer bias may have colored the child's productions. As far back as 1948, I pointed to the same source of error in Melanie Klein's work with children (cf. Chapter VII).[2] Yet Eysenck and his associates ignore the all-important supportive evidence provided by contamination-proof documentary material. They empty both Oedipus and Little Hans out with the bath water. As a result, they weaken their own argument more than the Freudian position.

That the ultimate meaning of myths, like that of dreams, is by its very nature ambiguous is another matter. Indeed, its ambiguity may invite the use of mythical themes in support of a wide variety of more or less incompatible interpretations. Adler rejected any deeper symbolic meaning of the Oedipal myth. Fromm, Horney, Sullivan, all had their own reading.[16] Erich Neumann attacked Freud's interpretation as an attempt to "paint the early history of humanity in the likeness of a patriarchal bourgeois family of the 19th century" and proposed a new interpretation of his own.[17] Likewise, diverse existential philosophers have offered various reinterpretations of the ancient fable, emphasizing its desexualized, spiritual aspects.

Apparently nothing is more inviting to mythmaking than myths themselves. They grow in layers, form rings around a central theme like the rings of a tree, and it may be merely a matter of convention when the oldest, innermost layers are described as myths *par excellence*, while the outer, more recent ones are referred to as psychological interpretations, "ideologies," or are promoted to the status of scientific theories.

❊   ❊   ❊

Difficulties of validating basic findings and postulates of the diverse schools of psychotherapy—if not of the behavioral sciences in general—are not, however, confined to the behavioral field. The physicist, trying to reconcile his theories of gravitation with the electromagnetic theory of light, or the wave versus the particle concept in quantum theory, is faced, or has been faced, with similar problems.

Certain findings of quantum physics are particularly relevant at this point. Quantum theory has led to the conclusion that all methods of observing physical objects involve definite interference with the actual physical state of the object observed; conversely, the object invariably affects the physical state of the measuring instruments and ultimately the sense organs of the observer. We are assured that this is of no practical importance on the macrophysical level. But on the plane of microphysical events it plays havoc with many cherished concepts of classical physics. One of the consequences of this state of affairs has been formulated in Heisenberg's principle of indeterminacy. This much-quoted principle asserts that it is impossible to measure both the mass and the energy of an individual electron at the same time. The two events, we are told, are basically in a complementary relationship, as postulated by Nils Bohr. From this it has in turn been deduced that no verifiable predictions can be made about both the mass and the movements of particles on the subatomic scale.

A. S. Eddington, E. Schroedinger, P. Jordan, W. Pauli and other pioneers of quantum mechanics have described this state of affairs as a complete breakdown of the classical concept of causality. They suggest that on the microphysical scale observables can be predicted only in terms of statistical laws. Any attempt to go beyond an essentially probabilistic statement leads to anomalous assumptions such as action at a distance, and does not, in the words of Hans Reichenbach,[18] "fulfill the conditions which classical physics has set up for the description of nature." A. S. Eddington has gone so far as to say that "there is no strict causal behavior anywhere." In his view, the physicist may rightly be accused of opening his door once more to the "savages' demons," and to a basically mystical conception of the world.[19]

The relevance of Heisenberg's principle of indeterminacy or Reichenbach's causal anomalies to our issue has been specifically discussed by Pascual Jordan.[20] Taking his cue from Bohr's principle of complementarity, Jordan called attention to the apparent similarity between this principle and the mechanism of Freudian repression. On the physical plane, Jordan asserts, the position and the impulse of an electron are in a complementary relationship, the exact observation of the one excluding the exact observation of the other. Put in analytical terms, one *represses* the other, as it were. In a similar vein, he describes the relationship between the conscious and the unconscious, between that which represses and that which is repressed (e.g., in the case of secondary personalities), in terms of Bohr's complementarity. W. Pauli, in his study of Johannes Kepler, arrives at essentially similar conclusions.

As early as 1932, Nils Bohr called attention to another no less significant connection between his field of research and the behavioral sciences. "The necessity of considering the interaction between the measuring instruments and the object under investigation in atomic mechanics," he stated, "exhibits a close analogy to the peculiar difficulties in psychological analysis deriving from the fact that the mental content is invariably altered when the attention is concentrated on any special feature of it."[21] Yet we have seen that this interference is just as inescapable as the physicist's interference with the physical object observed on the microphysical plane. And it should once more be noted at this point that just as interference in physics is not necessarily confined to the microphysical scale, so doctrinal compliance is but one of the many possible ways in which interference by what H. S. Sullivan has called a "participant observer" may be brought to bear upon his subject.

❊   ❊   ❊

This leads to a further parallelism between the modern psychological and physical approaches. The "causal anomalies" suggested by the occurrence of doctrinal compliance in psychotherapy indicate that we cannot be sure whether our findings represent genuine productions of an individual patient or merely reflect our own preconceptions. We do not know whether our interpretation was made to fit the forthcoming evidence, or whether our evidence was called forth by the interpretations looming in the back of our minds. We cannot tell which came first—the therapist and his theories, or the patient and his neurotic symptoms. However, the fact is that, irrespective of the therapist's allegiance to one or the other of the rival schools, and regardless of the apparently inescapable epistemological difficulties in assessing their respective merits, psychotherapy—scientific and prescientific—has from time immemorial been a going concern: it has stood the test of application in practice. It has met the emotional needs of countless generations even though it has done so on the basis of inadequate theoretical presuppositions.

Exactly the same is true for Euclidian geometry and Newtonian mechanics in the physical sphere. We know that despite the revolutionary inroads of Einstein's theory of relativity into the concepts of absolute time and space, our measuring rods, our weighing machines and our grandfather's clocks are telling us the truth with a satisfactory degree of accuracy under terrestrial conditions. We likewise know that despite Heisenberg's principle of indeterminacy and notwithstanding the causal anomalies which it implies, the macroscopic behavior of physical objects is adequately predictable and subject to statistical laws in no way inferior to the classical laws of causality. They enable us to cope successfully with the world of material objects. In a similar vein, pre-Freudian, Freudian and non-Freudian psychotherapies have proved their value in everyday practice. They meet the emotional needs of large numbers of patients. They too serve their purpose on what might be called the *macropsychological* plane.

These correspondences between modern theoretical physics and clinical psychology will perhaps persuade the skeptic to be more tolerant with the shortcomings of the behavioral scientist. They are both faced with the same methodological difficulties and epistemological perplexities. A critic of parapsychology may even be ready to grant that the causal anomalies implied by the occurrence of so-called psi phenomena are by no means unprecedented in nature. They merely duplicate the causal anomalies that the physicist himself has learned to accept as intrinsic features of the world of quantum mechanics.

      *   *   *

How, then, does the occurrence of doctrinal compliance affect the making of our theories? To what extent is it likely to detract from the operational value of the working hypotheses used by the followers of the various schools of psychotherapy? I already called attention to Freud's first encounter with the problem and hinted by what streak of luck—or by what stroke of genius—he had found the way out of his dilemma.

He availed himself of the historical method to corroborate findings which, owing to difficulties inherent in the method of the clinical interview, would have otherwise remained equivocal. An historic account, an autobiographical statement or a work of art is basically free from the fallacies of suggestion, observer contamination, telepathic leakage or other influence emanating from a "participant observer." It is like the photographic tracings left by an electron in Wilson's cloud chamber. The scientist examining the photographic record cannot, after the event, alter the electron's path. Similarly, whatever the preconceived ideas of Freud, Rank or Jung regarding the motif of the Birth of the Hero or the archetypal image of the Great Mother, the trails blazed by the motifs themselves in myth, legend or poetic fiction are cultural realities subject, it is true, to various interpretations, but hardly debatable as factual evidence.

The testimony of historical data of this order gains added significance by their cumulative occurrence in many cultures. The Oedipus complex has been endemic in our society from classical antiquity up to our own time. It cannot be ascribed to the wide publicity accorded to current psychoanalytic concepts, to observer bias or doctrinal compliance. It has become one of the macropsychological facts of our cultural life. Similar considerations hold true for Freud's concept of castration anxiety; for his decoding of certain recurrent motifs of the dream; for Bleuler's concept of ambivalence in our mental life; for Adler's thesis of the feeling of inferiority and its compensation; for certain basic formulations regarding ego psychology; or for the vicissitudes of instinctual drives.

The significance of such cross validations in diverse schools of psychotherapy will be discussed in the concluding chapter. Findings of this order are further supported by direct observations in infants; by animal experiments or the analytic dream experiments going back to Otto Poetzl. There are the modern sensory deprivation and isolation experiments. There is the Rorschach; the TAT; there is the Visual Distortion Test, described by the present writer; and there is the methodical study by a "nonparticipant" observer, of tape recorded or televised therapeutic interviews introduced by F. Alexander.[22] All these data tend to support basic psychoanalytic postulates without evidence of more than the inevitable contamination with doctrinal compliance or experimenter bias.

Viewed in this light, even the apparent artifacts derived from doctrinal compliance appear in a new light. They are joint productions of the patient and the therapist, meaningful and psychologically significant in their own right. Once they have made their appearance in the psychoanalytic situation, they tend to establish a circular pattern of feedback: they may become legitimate idioms in an existing system of communication. Indeed with the widening ripples on the surface of such a system, they qualify as cultural, or subcultural, events in the making. Before long, they are likely to be adopted as new modes of psychological expression: as myths or archetypes *in statu nascendi*, as it were,—as *neo-types*, if you like. They become the "myths of our time" and derive their ultimate "existential validation" from the consensus of those who are ready to accept them as authentic statements of scientific truths.

At this point, however, the similarity between physical and psychological events—if it has not already been stretched too far—reaches its limits. The meeting of the physicist's measuring instruments and of the physical object measured by them obviously lacks the creative potentialities which are inherent in the meeting of the therapists and the patient's minds or, for that matter, of the minds of two persons in any setting. Their own interpretation of this meeting may be largely mythical, hamstrung by the limitations of language, vitiated by semantic confusion and by the difficulty of translating their statements into the exacting terms of symbolic logic or mathematics. Yet the impact of man upon man is certainly more profound and destined to be more fateful than that of the observer upon measuring instrument. There are perhaps few scientists who would deny that it is this encounter, this living interaction, verbal and nonverbal, between person and person which is most human in man and which distinguishes his behavior from that of the molecules or electrons engaged in the vagaries of their Brownian movements and quantum jumps.

Whether or not this difference is of an irreducible nature, or whether it merely exists in the eyes of the beholder, must remain a matter of speculation. Yet whatever will be the ultimate verdict on this score, one thing should have become sufficiently clear from our argument: on carrying their analyses to the present limits of their knowledge, both physicist and psychologist find themselves on common ground, if not in the same predicament. Despite the differences of their approach, they have evolved analogous methods of interpreting and controlling events encountered in their respective domains. Indeed, the two pictures of the world as they have emerged from the physicist's and the psychologist's labors could have been created by one and the same artist. They are companion pieces, conforming to the same style; they suggest the same basic idea, the identical overall design, even though they were executed by their respective authors in two entirely different media of creative expression.

REFERENCES

1. SULLIVAN, H. S.: Conceptions of Modern Psychiatry, William Alanson White Foundation, Washington 1947.
2. MORENO, J. L.: Who Shall Survive? Beacon House, New York 1953.
3. ROGERS, C.: Client-Centered Therapy: Its Current Practice, Implications and Theory, Houghton Mifflin, Boston 1951.
4. FREUD, S.: An Autobiographical Study, Standard Edition, London 1935.
————— Sigmund Freud's Letters, ed. M. Bonaparte et al., Basic Books, New York 1954.
5. Malleus Maleficarum, cf. Chapter II (4).
6. HUXLEY, A.: The Devils of Loudun, Harper and Bros., New York 1952.
7. GREENSPOON, J.: The Reinforcing Effect of Two Spoken Sounds on the Frequency of Two Responses, Amer. Psychologist 66, 409-416, 1955.
8. MANDLER, G. and KAPLAN, W. K.: Subjective Evaluation and Reinforcing Effect of a Verbal Stimulus, Science 129, 582-583, 1956.
9. KRASNER, L.: The Therapist as a Social Reinforcement Machine, Paper read at Second Conf. on Research in Psychotherapy, Univ. North Carolina, Chapel Hill, May 1961.
10. FRANK, J. D.: cf. Chapter IV (5).
11. MARMOR, J.: cf. Chapter VIII (15).
12. BOSS, M.: cf. Chapter X (6).
13. ISAKOWER, O.: A Contribution to the Pathopsychology of Phenomena Associated with Falling Asleep, Intern. Journ. Psychoanal. XIX, 1938.

14. LEWIN, B.: Sleep, the Mouth and the Dream Screen, Psychoanal. Quart. XV, 419, 1946.
15. JONES, E.: cf. Chapter VII (8).
16. MULLAHY, J.: Oedipus Myth and Complex, Heritage Press, New York 1948.
17. NEUMANN, E.: Ursprungsgeschichte des Bewusstseins, Rascher Verlag, Zurich 1949.
18. REICHENBACH, H.: The Rise of Scientific Philosophy, Univ. of California Press, Berkeley 1953.
19. JORDAN, P.: Verdrängung und Komplemetarität, Stramverlag, Hamburg 1947.
20. EDDINGTON, A. S.: The Nature of the Physical World, Macmillan, New York 1928.
21. BOHR, NILS: Atomic Physics and Human Knowledge, Wiley, New York 1958.
22. ALEXANDER, F.: Psychoanalytic Contributions to Short-Term Psychotherapy, in: Short-Term Psychotherapy, ed. R. L. Wolberg, Grune & Stratton, New York, 1965.

—XII—

Doctrinal Compliance, Transference and Therapeutic Response

The preceding discussion of doctrinal compliance as a major source of error in the making of theories in the behavioral sciences should not obscure other significant aspects of our issue. Doctrinal compliance in the therapeutic situation is more than just an impurity contaminating virtually all methods of mental healing. It is an important factor entering into three major phases of the therapeutic process itself.

We have seen that the first aspect of doctrinal compliance coincides with the self-fulfilling expectations built in, as it were, in the therapist's approach. While in the preceding chapter we went out of our way to caution against the traps and pitfalls that beset all theoretical formulations arrived at in this way, it may be well to realize at this point that the very presence—at the back of the therapist's mind—of a set of more or less systematized preconceived ideas and guiding principles is an important prerequisite of his success as a healer.

Obviously no therapist can approach his task without such a rationale. He needs the guidance of a reasonably coherent system of assumptions, strung together to form an overall theory of his patient's behavior. Magic itself was a prescientific theory of this order which derived a semblance of empirical justification through the circular feedback between the mind of the magician and that of his clients. Modern theories of psychological healing obtain much the same results on a higher plane of sophistication. But whatever label may be attached to the principles guiding the steps of the practitioner, he cannot do without such guiding principles. He cannot do without a compass to tell his position in his voyage on a dark, uncharted sea, even though his compass may not point in the exact direction of the North Pole. He has to use the sun, the moon or the stars to take his bearings, even though, like the seafarer of a past age, he may mistake them for mythological beings inhabiting the celestial sphere.

A psychotherapist without a rationale is like a magician without a myth, like a fish without water. Like a space traveler in a state of weightlessness, he is hampered when called upon to perform simple motor operations. It is a consistent scientific theory, however tentative it may be, which makes him earthbound, which puts his feet on the ground and provides him with the pull of intellectual gravitation to tell him where is up or down, and right or left in the psychological sphere.

This also explains the plight of the eclectic, exposed as he is to the influence of two or more conflicting psychological doctrines. He may be perfectly satisfied that his patient has formed an oedipal attachment to his mother in the classical Freudian tradition, but he may feel equally sure that all the patient wants from her is to keep his superiority in the maneuvering for power, characteristic of the family conflict viewed through Adlerian eyes.

It would not be surprising if a patient subjected to such an eclectic approach developed a new, iatrogenic neurosis, due to two conflicting series of stimuli. With all his propensity to doctrinal compliance, he would be at a loss as to how and in what direction he should comply.

This also is the reason why any criticism of the doctrine espoused by the partisans of a given school of thought is apt to provoke highly emotional reactions. He feels obligated to defend at all costs the validity of his assumptions and the integrity of his systematizations. They must form an impervious, self-sealing system, safe from being punctured by arguments based on premises other than his own. Its imperviousness to criticism is matched by his conviction that such criticism itself merely betrays the neurosis—or ignorance—of his would-be critic.

Undue sensitiveness to criticism has by no means been confined to lesser minds. Freud's impatience with slight deviations from his teachings is a matter of historic record. In some of his followers this impatience seems to have increased in inverse proportion with their stature as scientists. The same tendency can be discerned in the protagonists of virtually all other schools. The result, up to recent years, has been a dearth of interdisciplinary discussion—or even communication—between orthodox Freudians, Adlerians, and Jungians. With the same clinical restraint with which they refrain from attacking head-on the delusions of their paranoid patients, they avoid disputing each other's basic presuppositions. Occasional bricks dropped—or dissenting voices raised at closed scientific meetings—are apt to perplex speakers and to throw audiences into uproar. All-out debates with no holds barred might be more conducive to scientific truth, but not to the peace of mind of those engaged in the debate.

❖   ❖   ❖

A second major aspect of doctrinal compliance is tied up with the twin concepts of transference and countertransference in the psychoanalytic situation. Transference is usually described as the patient's tendency "to see in his analyst the return—the reincarnation—of some important figure out of his childhood past."[1] Consequently he transfers on him "feelings and reactions that undoubtedly applied to his model." This is how the analyst may become the target of the patient's love or resentment that had originally been directed to his father or mother.

Freud has shown that this course of events has far-reaching consequences for the progress of treatment. The transference relationship tends to become the arena in which the patient reenacts his unresolved conflicts, instead of remembering the original conflicts themselves. But if the patient can be helped to overcome his resistances and to fill in his memory gaps, he may become capable of resolving his old conflicts, of facing new social realities, unencumbered by past hurts, irrational fears and anxieties.

Transference, even in its positive manifestations, is not without dangers. In the early years of psychoanalysis, Freud was taken aback by the intensity of what he described as the "transference love" of his hysteric patients—all of them women. He was dismayed by the temptations with which they confronted the unwary and warned the novice from being misled by the adulation and blind infatuation encountered in his sexually frustrated admirers. While stressing the therapeutic importance of positive transference, he cautioned against seeking a shortcut to success by instructing the patient to "go ahead and fall in love with the analyst so that the treatment may make progress."[1a]

On the other hand, Freud emphasized the paramount therapeutic importance of a properly managed transference relationship. He was struck by its close similarity with suggestion on the one hand and with hypnotic states on the other. "We have only abandoned hypnosis in our methods," he noted, "to discover suggestion again in the shape of transference." But it was Sandor Ferenczi[2] who first called attention to the dynamic correlations between hypnotic phenomena and the hypnotized subject's transference on the experimenter as an authoritarian father surrogate or as a loving mother figure. In a similar vein B. Wolstein[3] has noted that at times therapeutic transference has the quality of posthypnotic suggestion. C. Fisher[4] suggested that the analyst behaves in some respects like a hypnotist, and the patient in some respects like a hypnotized subject—depending on the therapist's activity.

Ida Macalpin[5] has specifically come out with the observation that "analytic transference is a derivative of hypnosis, produced in a way comparable to hypnotic trance." A. Weitzenhofer,[6] who has no psychoanalytic axe to grind, likewise points to the similarity of hypnosis and transference: "Substantiation has been obtained for just every point of view," he noted. "Thus if the patient produces erotic material in which the therapist-hypnotist is the dominant figure, it is often concluded that Freud or Schilder are confirmed."

Freud soon discovered that there was another side to the coin: the therapist's countertransference on his patients. Although the analyst was called upon merely to reflect the patient's emotional attitudes without being personally involved in them, he too was occasionally prone to project his emotionally disturbed or distorted perception onto his patients. He too was apt to respond to his opposite number in terms of his fears, apprehensions, hostilities or other unresolved conflicts and instinctual drives. Needless to say that in this case the therapist fell short of his responsibilities as a detached clinical observer and was handicapped in the proper analytic management of his patients.

More than half a century has passed since the first formulation of these general principles and they have become common ground to most schools of psychotherapy up to our days. Yet it is true that since the early years of psychoanalysis "transference love" has lost much of its lustre. Nor does it hold the same threat as we are told it did to the venerable Dr. Joseph Breuer, Freud's mentor and early associate. But the reader going back to Freud's and Ferenzci's original writings on the matter will be left with the impression that the analysts of the early days, despite their protestations, had a hard time denying themselves the occasional fringe benefits of "narcissistic" gratifications accruing to them through the transference love, the adulation and admiration of their female patients.

We noted that Freud's first papers on transference love mention female patients only. He specifically refers to the woman "who shows by unmistakable allusions or openly avows she has fallen in love, like any other mortal woman, with the physician who is analyzing her." As a result "she may lose all understanding of, and interest in, the treatment and will not hear or speak of anything but her love, the return of which she demands. She has either given up her symptoms or else she ignores them; she even declares herself well." And Freud adds: "Any physician experiencing this for the first time will not find it easy to keep a grasp of the analytic situation and not to succumb to the illusion that the treatment is nearly at an end." Faced with this predicament Freud repeats time and again that the therapist must on no account derive any personal advantage from the patient's infatuation and demands, somewhat redundantly, that "the treatment must be carried through in a state of abstinence, in a state of renunciation, using the emotional energies sparked off in this way in the interest of the treatment."

The reader familiar with the story of Freud's long years of engagement as it is reflected in his correspondence with his fiancée will note a striking resemblance of his stern admonitions to the novice in psychoanalysis, and the general mood of self-imposed renunciation reflected in the letters to his "Little Princess." Viewed in this light, his article on transference love sounds like a belated echo of his own struggle for mastery over his instinctual drives in his formative years and during the period of his courtship with Martha.

But it is needless to say that the struggling young Viennese physician's sexual predicament was symptomatic of the cultural climate of his time.

It was a time when sexual repression was the order of the day—and more so of the night. It was a time when "illicit" sex was beset by a variety of dangers; when virtually all sexual activity—from masturbation to marital intercourse—was considered illicit, and its consequences ranged from social ostracism to venereal disease and suicide threatening all transgressors alike, from the Crown Prince down to his manservant; from the baroness down to her chambermaid. It was a time when the sight of an exposed ankle was enough to send shivers down the spine of a Peeping Tom, and when a girl caught with a young man unattended by a chaperone ran the risk of having her reputation ruined.

Little wonder that the psychoanalyst, being mortal, like the woman patient he was called upon to treat, brought all the emotional problems characteristic of the Francisco-Josephinian era into the treatment situation. Yet precisely because of his self-imposed renunciation and emotional discipline, his repressed libidinal strivings were bound to remain powerful motivational factors behind the scene. Thus the temptation to be receptive to their patients' pleas, and to reach out for their love and admiration may have been just as troubling to the analyst's peace of mind as were the corresponding desires for the analyst's affection to Freud's lovelorn female neurotics who sought "to destroy the physician's authority by bringing him *down* to the level of a lover," as Freud, in an unintentionally revealing sentence, put it.

If this is true, the highly charged "transference love" exhibited by some of his patients is the combined effect of two major factors. One is the patient's tendency to project on the therapist feelings that pertain to persons encountered in his past—as postulated by Freud. But another, no less important, factor derives from the therapist's own repressed wishes and expectations which are picked up and acted out by the patient in the transference situation. If so, her amorous behavior is in effect the patient's response to the therapist's own self-seeking or erotic needs for which the term countertransference would be somewhat a misnomer.

Put in other words, we are confronted with another version of doctrinal compliance: this time with *compliance by the patient with the therapist's doctrine of transference love.* In fact what we see in the cases described by Freud is more than mere doctrinal compliance: it is the dramatic acting out by the patient of the therapist's goal-inhibited erotic impulses, reinforced by the demands of her own unresolved infantile conflicts and dependency needs. Transference love is thus both artifact and fact of life revealed by the psychoanalytic method. Analytically speaking, it is "overdetermined."

❖ ❖ ❖

This interpretation is supported by the conspicuous absence in post-Freudian literature of reports concerning full-fledged erotic transference reactions. Evidently, their emergence is contingent on the same situation of circular feedback as the emergence of major or minor myths described in the introductory chapters. No less significant is the fact that with the passing of the Victorian age; with the loosening of sexual repressions, with the advent of Reich's Sexual Revolution and Orgone Box; or sex manuals for toddlers and teenagers, for homosexuals and lesbians—to say nothing of the relative security provided by antibiotics and anticonceptive pills—a new generation of patients (and more or less successfully analyzed analysts) has entered the stage to whom the sexual predicament of their forefathers is barely more than a historic curiosity. At the same time the stormy manifestations of transference love, as described by Freud, seem to be becoming more and more infrequent, if not altogether extinct. In its place, we witness the emergence of a new type of transference reaction—or transference neurosis—reflecting the change that has taken place in the cultural climate at large. We see the corrosive effects of alienation, detachment and isolation of the individual both from himself and from his society: the growing fragmentation of personality and interpersonal relationships. On the other hand, we can see both therapist and patient in the search for an escape from their predicament. Again the antidote seems to lie in the transference situation or in what existentialists describe as the encounter. This change is graphically illustrated by the case histories published by E. Fromm,[7] K. Horney,[8] H. Kelman,[9] Rollo May,[10] Thomas Hora[11] and other neo-Freudians and existential analysts. They show Western man's predicament in the middle of the 20th century: his quest for identity, for authentic human relationships, for communication and communing, as Harold Kelman put it. The main theme is no longer sexual fulfillment versus repression as it was advocated by Wilhelm Reich. It is encounter versus isolation and alienation from the self and society. Indeed it is largely the emphasis on these aspects of the human situation which distinguish the new approach from the orthodox analytic position.

A fragment from the case history of one of my patients illustrates the point. Florence, a woman of 29, said she married her husband for two wrong reasons: in order to get away from her father and from her previous psychoanalyst. She resumed therapy with me because she felt detached and frustrated in her marriage. Being a housewife and mother of two children was "not enough." Nor did her social life, card-playing or even painting mean anything to her any more. An affair with Bob, a married man seemed the only important thing in her life. Bob was in effect the substitute for her father, whom she loved and hated at the same time. However, her affair was largely confined to the fantasy level and proved equally unfulfilling as her married life. She felt she was drifting aimlessly in the world, guilt ridden over her failure as a wife and mother.

Florence's relationship to me was detached and seemingly unemotional. Yet after three months in analytic psychotherapy, with two or three sessions weekly, she confessed: "In the past my father and Bob had the power to make me feel important. Now I delegate this power to you. Now you make me feel I am worthwhile—that I am *I*. Not that I think you love me or that I think I am in love with you. But I think you approve of me and make me feel I am *me*. So I am not dependent on my father anymore. Will I feel overly dependent on you, too, when I keep on seeing you? But probably the very fact I have the feeling of self and not of inner emptiness when I am here is good. Perhaps in the end I will not need anybody to make me feel: I am me."

Three weeks later she had a dream in which she felt she and her family had met with some major unheaval—a flood or disaster. It resulted in a total change in the climate of North America. Yet she came out of it unscathed. Then her father, mother and grandfather all wanted to consult me. But she felt it was her turn now: she had the first claim on my services. The patient herself interpreted the upheaval or flood as symbolic of birth or rebirth. At the same time the "change in the climate" ushered in her new feeling of independence from her family. She added: "I feel some great thing has happened to me . . . I have a *self!* I am curious how it happened. Maybe it got touched off by feeling *myself* when I am here. First I had thought it must be an unpleasant, painful digging. But now it is not. Still—maybe it isn't worthless just because it came easily. I think I have accomplished what I came for. I have become much freer to go along, to see if I stay with my husband or leave him . . . "

The new element added to what would otherwise be described as a positive transference reaction in a patient who had not been able to resolve her attachment to her father—and to her previous analyst—had been the awareness that her inner emptiness has to be filled by *herself*—and not by falling in love with (or introjecting) the analyst. We see a human being engaged in the struggle of finding herself, and seeing victory—and an authentic existential shift—within her grasp.

That a similar event may take place even under conditions of negative transference is illustrated by the following observation. Sally R., a woman of 35, suffering from a character neurosis, has a history of severe emotional deprivations since early childhood. She said she got married in order to escape from an intolerable home situation. She resented her husband and her responsibilities as a mother of three children. On trying to obtain a legal abortion to end a fourth pregnancy she felt she was let down by her obstetrician and other doctors from whom she sought help. Ultimately she had to leave the country to have her pregnancy interrupted. Her relationship to me was guarded, though she was obviously in desperate need of sympathetic understanding and help to break out of her shell. In the third month of treatment she seemed to be loosening up, talked about trying to be herself and start life again "in a new key." The following dream expresses her struggle to reach her goal—even without the aid of others: "I was to have a baby, but I was not large and not really pregnant. I was in a hospital. My regular doctor was not there. There was another doctor. He was in conference with other doctors or gave a lecture on how to deliver a baby. But he just stood there, talking, and was not helping me. Here I was, the baby was to come any moment and no one gave a hand. I felt I was just case number so-and-so, standing in line to take my turn. He had no feelings."

The unfeeling doctor reminded the patient of her gynecologist or of her previous analyst. But she realized the baby to be born was she herself— if need be without outside help. She recalled: "Yes, at times I feel like busting inside so as to be reborn." She also admitted her doubts as to the genuineness of my interest in her. Her complaint of being just case number so-and-so testifies to her striking—though somewhat slanted—intuition regarding her therapist's attitude toward her. She related her dream at a time when I was writing up the case material contained in this chapter. Thus she seemed to provide another example of doctrinal compliance, coinciding with the first indication of a favorable therapeutic response.

Another case in point is a patient whose history was described elsewhere in more detail.[12] Mary I., now a woman of 32, had been brought up in a close symbiotic relationship with her domineering, obsessive-compulsive father. She herself was suffering from an obsessive-compulsive neurosis, superimposed on an underlying paranoid trend.

At 12 or 13 Mary developed a variety of obsessive-compulsive habits. She had to genuflect in the street, to count her steps, to touch certain objects with her hands. Other rituals were connected with toilet functions and food habits. When she was 17 her widowed father remarried, whereupon she moved out of her home and had a "nervous breakdown." Shortly thereafter, she married a fellow student. The marriage was annulled after a few months, to be followed by a series of thinly veiled homosexual attachments to older women. At the same time, Mary complained that her personality had undergone a change; she felt that she looked, talked and acted like a man. She dreamed that a "little man" was inside her chest, and she said it was he who flew into a temper when she was angry. She noticed that people in the street—mostly teenage boys—were making derisive remarks about her boyish looks and her masculine attire. At 22 she married again. Peter, two years her senior, was a passive, compliant young man, greatly devoted to the patient. Nevertheless, this marriage too was constantly on the verge of collapse and was interrupted by repeated periods of separation.

During nine years of intermittent analytic psychotherapy, Mary made several attempts at suicide, usually provoked by what she interpreted as major rejections by various paternal figures, including me. Her transference had all the hallmarks of her original symbiotic relationship with her father. "I will never break away from you," she said on one occasion. "I am now a part of you, as I was part of my father before I broke away from him. I have no identity of my own; without him or without you I am empty space inside. So long as mother was alive she and I lived together in an igloo, like Eskimos, miles away from other people. After that it was father. Now it is you." With the gradual resolution of her paranoid symptoms, the dissolution of her symbiotic transference neurosis became the overriding concern of the treatment. She was helped to realize that she had spent her life in a hopeless search for identity through symbiotic fusion with a male *alter ego*. "I want a leave of absence," she declared one day. "I know I lean too heavily on you. I efface myself so as to be in your good graces. But now I want to shift for myself. I said I wanted a child; but I said it as a self-betrayal to please you. I was your ventriloquist's dummy; I had given you the strings and I said what you wanted me to say." A month later, she reverted to the same point: "I want to try my wings; here it is a dead end. Peter (the patient's estranged husband) is coming back from G. Now it is a split allegiance; he or you. But I no longer feel compelled to stay with you. I know I have to leave you in the end. I want to leave without a handshake. I don't want your support any more. Yes, I no longer feel you push me out of the nest. I do feel I am getting mobilized to live again, to resume my marriage. I know I will work it out better away from you than with you." She did leave without a handshake and returned to her second husband.

Four years since the termination of her treatment, Mary is free from her previous symptoms. In the meantime she has given birth to a child and tends to channel her remaining compulsive trend toward his upbringing.

A combination of direct therapeutic response with doctrinal compliance is suggested by one of Harold Kelman's observations.[9] Following in the footsteps of Horney, and strongly influenced by Eastern thought, Kelman's therapeutic approach is based on a minimum of verbalized explanations. He emphasizes the patient's need for closeness, for communication, for "communing." Communing, he holds, is a form of nonverbal communication in which two persons establish contact or "continuity" on a level at which the dichotomy of object-subject relationship is resolved. It is an experience of "togetherness" and as such carries a profound therapeutic impact.

One of Kelman's cases was a demanding, blocked patient with difficulties in relating to his fellows. He started a particular session with an outburst of rage. With Dr. Kelman's help, he was led to experience its full emotional impact. Asked about his feelings afterwards, the patient replied that he had felt that working with his therapist was "like a team . . . What I mean is, it is hard to put in words, like I felt a kind of smoothness, the way we were working today." On another occasion he said "I don't put it in words any more . . . yet I felt it was a good session . . ." At another time: "Something I did not feel before. A feeling of directness from my spinal cord to you, through myself, as if I did not want to mark it. I just wanted it to be. Feels so good, exciting . . . I just like this sense of pure being . . ." Or: "I was feeling a new communication. Being right there and communicating right there . . . as I felt with Dad . . . flowing towards Dad . . . I feel all with you, I want to grasp you, completely unite."

Kelman does not seem to be concerned with the sexual symbolism hidden behind such utterances. Nor did it seem to have much relevance to the patient's progress in therapy. The important point was that he voiced the therapist's personal philosophy, to the point of supplying him with a graphic illustration of his ideas on communing. Yet, here again, the patient's response evidently involved more than mere doctrinal compliance. It was an authentic emotional experience marking a turning point on the patient's way to recovery.

A dream described by Thomas Hora[11] seems to mark a similar turning point in his patient. The patient was a man who prior to coming for treatment considered himself religiously indifferent: "I dreamt that I left home and found myself in a strange city in a foreign country. I discovered to my dismay that I didn't know the language of the people; I couldn't remember where I came from, I didn't know where I was heading. I experienced a sense of isolation, helplessness and anxiety. I was walking the street aimlessly, hoping to remember where I came from. But to no avail. At the height of my despair, I cried out: God help me. Then a single rain drop which impressed me as a tear drop fell from the sky and in the course of its falling, it reflected the sun in all the colors of the rainbow. I felt overwhelmed by this sight. The scene shifted and I found myself on my knees in a church. In the moment of awakening, the thought occurred to me that the meaning of life is to reflect in oneself the divine light, like the rain drop reflected the sun in the course of its falling from the sky."

Whatever are the merits of the patient's own interpretation of this dream, there can be little doubt that his poetic metaphor reflects not only the sun rays, symbolic of the "divine light," but also his therapist's personal philosophy shared in their existential encounter.

*   *   *

It will be noted that in these examples doctrinal compliance indeed assumes a new complexion. Far from being confined to an artifact confirming the therapist's pet scientific theories, or proving his power over the minds of his patients, it becomes a vehicle of therapeutic interventions in its own right. The therapist does not merely create his own evidence. He is instrumental in bringing about the patient's therapeutic response—he ignites the spark which leads to the desired change in the patient's life. He triggers off an "auspicious" cycle which may ultimately lead to his recovery. This, in effect, is the third aspect of doctrinal compliance.

Viewed in this light, Freud's transference-countertransference configuration is but a special case of doctrinal compliance in a broader sense. But while in the original psychoanalytic formulation countertransference is regarded as the villain in the play—or at least as an unwanted and illegitimate child issuing from the doctor-patient relationship—it now is cast in the role of a potentially active principle in the therapeutic process. Far from casting doubt on the analyst's character, personality or on the quality of his training analysis, we are led to realize that countertransference, derived as it is from the therapist's goal-inhibited, narcissistic or erotic strivings, may provide the emotional charge that goes into the making of his personal myth and may play an important part in his therapeutic impact upon the patient. Indeed, there is reason to believe that it is this emotional charge, tempered and controlled by the discipline of his analytic training which helps to make his interventions effective. In classical analysis they feed into the patient's transference neurosis, to be followed by its resolution through interpretation and methodical "working-through."

It is true that apparent cures, effected through transference, suggestion or doctrinal compliance alone are rarely of lasting value. They may help the patient to cope with an emotional emergency, to overcome an existing crisis or situational stress. They may be instrumental in substituting an incapacitating symptom or ego defense for one less incapacitating. But they seldom result in any permanent alteration of personality structure as demanded by psychoanalytic theory.

But some of the short-term therapeutic effects of doctrinal compliance have been impressive enough to provide the necessary feedback and reinforcement for the therapist's myth. Item by item, they may include the whole array of miraculous cures claimed by faith healers, cultists and prescientific therapists of the past. More than that, doctrinal compliance may be responsible for part of the results obtained with therapeutic agents, methods or procedures of proven value. If so, it converges with the protean manifestations of the placebo effect.

✿   ✿   ✿

There is a far cry from the existential approach to the diverse techniques of modern conditioned reflex therapy, reciprocal inhibition or desensitization. Yet they too lend added support to our argument. They are derived from Pavlov's animal experiments, from Skinner's operant conditioning based on thoroughly rational principles of learning theory. Armed with such credentials, H. Eysenck,[13] J. Wolpe,[14] A. Salter[15] and their associates claim they achieved therapeutic results far superior to those reported by psychoanalysts or followers of other "dynamic" schools of psychotherapy. At the same time they insist that the improvements, or even cures, obtained are exclusively due to genuine relearning or reconditioning and not to suggestion, positive transference or the like.

There can be no doubt as to the *bona fides* of such assertions. Yet careful review of the literature of behavioral therapy reveals that such familiar devices as systematic muscular relaxation "at times bordering on hypnosis" are frequent ingredients of the techniques used. Nor can such old standbys of the psychotherapeutic approach as exhortation, the show of optimism and of a willingness to help be avoided by the behavioral therapist.

In fact, Thigpen and Cleckley,[16] in an otherwise sympathetic review of Wolpe's work, suggest that at least part of his results may be due to causes other than Pavlovian conditioning. They specifically refer to "an intense and complex interpersonal configuration;" to Wolpe's "dynamic personality" inspiring his patients' faith in the procedure. In short, here too allowance has to be made for doctrinal compliance—and for the direct impact of the therapist's myth however camouflaged it may be. Whether or not the ambitious therapeutic claims made in behalf of the behavioral approach will stand the test of long-term followup observations will be for the future to decide.

Whatever the verdict, the behavioral therapists can at least claim reasonably sound scientific presuppositions to their credit. A variety of cultist and esoteric fads of our day, from Reich's Orgone Box to a weird assortment of magnetic or electronic contraptions cannot. Nevertheless, novel methods of treatment, like newly discovered drugs, have one advantage over old ones: they have not, as yet, had the time needed to disenchant their users. Most are likely to turn out to be little more than elaborate mechanical or psychological placebos. But they show that under favorable circumstances the shakiest theory, the bizarrest of myths, the absurdest claim may have its days of glory regardless of its short-lived therapeutic value.

The stubborn survival over the centuries of hypnosis as a therapeutic tool, even in the absence of a satisfactory scientific rationale, is an exception to this rule. We shall see in the chapters that follow that hypnotic phenomena bring the three aspects of doctrinal compliance, from confirmation of the therapist's pet scientific hypothesis and Freud's "transference love" to direct symptom removal, into sharper perspective. Unfortunately, however, the demonstrability of these points of resemblance still leaves the mystery of the *modus operandi* of both doctrinal compliance and hypnosis unresolved. On the contrary, it is a sobering reminder that our thinking about the therapist's personal impact upon his patient tends to move in a circle.

We hold that part of the patient's therapeutic response is due to doctrinal compliance or positive transference. We assume that transference is largely due to suggestion which in turn is usually considered an integral part of hypnotic phenomena. On the other hand, on trying to unravel the *modus operandi* of hypnotic suggestion, we are told that hypnosis is itself the product of the subject's transference upon the hypnotist. We are thus led to the embarrassing conclusion that at least part of the curative effects of psychotherapy in general results from a masked or diluted form of hypnosis, while hypnosis is in turn described as analytic transference in the raw, with both hypnotist and subject unaware of its operation.

What is the way out from this circular reasoning? We shall try to show that the answer can only be found on a level of discourse which does not presume to explain one set of observations by reference to another set of observations of the same order. We propose to discuss the diverse manifestations of hypnosis as a model case that should help us to formulate some explanatory principle of a higher order of conceptualization than the concepts of transference, doctrinal compliance, suggestion and hypnosis itself. One of the principles arrived at in this way will be designated as the *existential shift*.

REFERENCES

1. FREUD, S.: cf. Chapter VIII (2a).
   ——— Further Recommendations in the Technique of Psychoanalysis, Observa·
   tions on Transference Love (1915), Coll. Papers, Vol. 2, Basic Books, New
   York 1959.
   ——— Letters, ed. M. Bonaparte, cf. Chapter IX (4a).
2. FERENCZI, S.: The Psychoanalysis of Suggestion and Hypnosis, Transactions of the
   Psycho-Medical Soc. Vol. III, London 1952.
3. WOLSTEIN, B.: Transference, Its Meaning and Function in Psychoanalytic Therapy,
   Grune & Stratton, New York 1954.
4. FISHER, C.: Studies on the Nature of Suggestion, Part II, The Transference Meaning of Giving Suggestion, J. Am. Psychoanal. Assoc. 1, 333, 1953.
5. MACALPIN, I.: The Development of Transference, Psychoanal. Quart, 19, 1950.

6. WEITZENHOFER, A. General Technique of Hypnotism, Grune & Stratton, New York, 1957.
7. FROMM, E.: Man for Himself, Rinehart, New York 1947.
8. HORNEY, K.: The Neurotic Personality of Our Time, Norton, New York 1937.
9. KELMAN, H.: Communing and Relating, Am. J. Psychoanal. XVIII, 1, 1958.
10. MAY, R., ENGEL, E., ELLENBERGER, H. F.: Existence, Basic Books, New York 1958.
11. HORA, T.: Psychotherapy, Existence and Religion, in: Psychoanalysis and Existential Philosophy, ed. Ruitenbeek, Dutton Paperback, New York 1962.
12. EHRENWALD, J.: Neurosis in the Family and Patterns of Psychosocial Defense, Hoeber-Harper, New York 1964.
13. EYSENCK, H.: Behavior Therapy and the Neuroses, Pergamon Press, London 1960.
14. WOLPE, J.: The Conditioning Therapies, Holt, Rinehart and Winston, New York 1964.
15. SALTER, A.: Conditioned Reflex Therapy, Creative Age Press, New York 1949.
16. THIGPEN, C. H. and CLECKLEY, H. M.: Some Reflections on Psychoanalysis, Hypnosis and Faith Healing, in: (14).

— XIII —

Hypnotism and the Existential Shift:
Throwback to Magic?

An adult experimental subject is put into deep hypnotic trance. His eyes are closed, he is immobilized; his muscles are limp, cataleptic; he is indifferent to his surroundings but maintains close communication or rapport with the experimenter. The experimenter addresses him in a calm but firm tone of voice: "Now listen to me carefully. I am going to suggest to you that you go back in time, back into the past. You are getting smaller and smaller. Your arms and legs are getting smaller. They are shrinking. Your body is shrinking. You are going back to a time when you were very, very little. Can you see yourself? Your mother is holding you in her arms. You remember your nurse's name, do you? Now walk to the table over there, bring me the toy trumpet and blow it hard." The subject rises, walks to the table with the uncertain gait of a toddler, takes a cigarette holder, blows into it, pretending it is a trumpet.

This is a paraphrased transcript of an experiment in hypnotic-age regression or revivification of the type described by L. Wolberg,[1] M. Erickson[2] and many others. In some cases the "regressed" subject produces memories that had been lying dormant in his mind for many years. At times they amount to a spectacular recall of facts he had not been aware of before. It is the hynotized subject's apparent capacity to remember such material which made Breuer and Freud experiment with hypnosis as a means of recovering lost or repressed memories and of bringing about therapeutic catharsis. However Freud soon abandoned the procedure to replace it by the method of free association and the analysis of dreams as the "royal road" to the unconscious. Not till the 1940's did the impressive phenomena of age regression give rise to the renaissance of what is today described as hypnoanalysis.

Hypnoanalysis, it should be noted, is not satisfied with the hypnotist trying to talk existing symptoms out of existence. Hypnoanalysis is a shortcut to deep probing of the unconscious in order to bring repressed material into focus and to dispose of it in the transference relationship. As a therapeutic method it is guided by established psychoanalytic principles, using hypnotic rapport as a method for deepening analytic transference.

However, just because of the intensity of the transference relationship characteristic of the trance, hypnosis is apt to become a veritable breeding ground for doctrinal compliance in all its combinations and permutations.

Vaudeville hypnotists have turned phenomena of age regression into acts of showmanship, of the believe-it-or-not type. A science fiction writer developed the method of "dianetics" in which he claimed he carried the patient back "on the time track" to early infancy and, beyond that, to intrauterine life. Thus an auditor, i.e., a practitioner of dianetics, in all seriousness, related the following story to the present writer: Six subjects or "preclears" were carried back to their prenatal, preembryonal lives. They were made to recall the engrams or memory traces pertaining to their existence as spermatozoa, prior to fertilization of the maternal egg. None of the subjects, the auditor asserted, had any knowledge of the biological process of fertilization. Yet they described in great detail the course taken by the sperm, the histological structure of the spermatozoa themselves, the ciliary movements of their tails, and so on and so forth.

Even serious investigators allow themselves to be carried away by their spectacular influence upon their subjects. In one observation of this kind,[3] a homosexual patient, aged 38, produced a remarkable series of hypnotically induced dreams. They were "dramatic, eloquent in their revelation and precise in their dynamic implications" in a way which, in the author's words, was unparallelled in his 12 years of experience. Like many hypnotized subjects, the patient could be made to dream "of any topic, about any conflict or any person in his background—dreams that were far more dynamic, direct and clear than any noctural dreams." Another diagnostic and therapeutic tool used by the author was age regression. In the very first hypnotic session, he reports, the patient was made to regress to the age of six. To the author's surprise, he promptly recalled the following experience: "Mother likes daddy very much. She is always very nice to him and so glad when he comes home. . . . I know mummy needs daddy so I don't wish daddy to go away too badly. I felt bad in wishing daddy to go away." In one of the next sessions he can see a "large figure dominating everything. She is mother and looks like a madonna. She is tall and big and at her feet is a child tugging and pulling at her skirt"; and he goes on to say: She was all I needed for quite a long time, satisfying all my sexual needs . . . Girls interested me mainly because they were small replicas of mother and therefore substituting for her . . . Could not have sexual escapades with them because I could not have them with mother. . . . I must never have intercourse with any woman because that would in turn destroy mother. Homosexuality and masturbation were the only alternatives."

Certainly, this may well be taken as added confirmation of current psychoanalytic theories of homosexuality. But if so, the "fit" seems to be too good to be true. It is more likely that here again it is doctrinal compliance which made the patient's dreams and other productions "far more dynamic, direct and clear than any nocturnal dream"—that is, more revealing than dreams less directly subject to doctrinal compliance.

Some 50 years ago, before psychoanalytic principles had been accorded the wide recognition they have gained today, observations of this kind would have hardly been possible. Patients were not in the habit of producing deeply repressed Oedipal material in their first hypnotic trance. In any case, no one seems to have hit upon it up to 10 or 20 years ago. We have seen that instead, the literature had been replete with reports of spectacular feats of memory, of posthypnotic suggestions, demonstrating the subject's striking capacity for unconscious time appreciation, and the like. The present author's first paper published in his student years,[4] offers added experimental evidence of this kind. Going further back on the "time track," we find Charcot's notorious hypnotic artifacts elicited in his hysterical patients; we read of Pierre Janet's experiments with his celebrated subject, Léonie[5] who, he claimed, went into trance when hypnotized from a distance, in a telepathic way, as it were. It will be recalled that unusual feats of this order were in turn preceded by the "lucid sleep" of the Portuguese Abbé Faria; by the exploits of the Count de Puységur; by Mesmer's somnambulists; or by Justinus Kerner's *Seeress of Prevorst*. They are variations of the countless bizarre phenomena attributed to the spiritualistic trance, including levitations, materializations, communication with the dead, so-called cross correspondences, and so on and so forth.

Whether the trance manifestations found among Yogis of the Far East may legitimately be described in terms of hypnotic phenomena is debatable. The yoga sleep, like the hypnotic trance, can be induced by staring at an object, for instance at the subject's navel. But it is not predicated on the presence of a hypnotist. It is usually brought about by ritualized breathing exercises or by the assumption of diverse traditional postures by the Yogi himself. On the other hand, the Yogi, like the hypnotized subject, passes through several consecutive stages, the last phase being described as *Samahdi* or *enlightenment*. It is this stage which bears the closest resemblance to the hypnotic trance in the Western sense. Yet unlike the deeper stages of hypnosis, it is not accompanied by amnesia. It is a "real, remembered experience," described as a state of joy and ineffable blissfulness.[6] At the same time it is said to bestow miraculous powers of control over the Yogi's bodily functions and to be accompanied by mysterious healing powers.

The temple sleep practiced in ancient Egypt and Greece is yet another variation on the same theme. Presumably closely related to the hypnotic trance, it too may have been due to suggestion emanating from longstanding tradition; from the *genius loci* or from the person of the officiating priest. But here again, as in our previous examples, the hypnotized subjects' productions tended to reflect beliefs current in their culture or espoused by the priest. Their dreams had a veridical character; they came from the gods; they spoke the oracular language of Zeus of Dodona; of

Apollo of Delphi; they conveyed cryptic messages alluding to the ineffable secrets of Elusinian or Orphic mystery cults. In short, here again, it is doctrinal compliance which is responsible for the Protean forms of what in modern terms is described as hypnotic trance. Viewed in historic perspective, hypnotic trance acts like a mirror reflecting religious, cultist or scientific trends that prevail at a given time in a given culture, colored by the subject's and experimenter's personal myths.

*   *   *

But focusing attention on doctrinal compliance in a stricter sense gives justice only to one side of the picture. Equally important are the psychological aspects of hypnotic rapport: the emotional tie that exists between experimenter and hypnotized subject first noted by Bernheim.[7] More recently the pattern has been described in terms of dominance versus submission or, rather as a triad of compulsive compliance, amnesia and rationalization, equally characteristic of transference and suggestion.[8] Psychoanalytically speaking, the pattern is determined by unconscious libidinal fixation on the experimenter.[9] It results from reenactment of his childhood attitudes in relation to a supposedly omnipotent parent figure.[10] This view has since become widely accepted in psychoanalytic literature. It holds in effect that hypnosis is due to regression to an early infantile stage of libido organization, favoring the reactivation of "magic cravings"[11] or of such early infantile attitudes as dependence, obedience and masochistic submission to a parent substitute. We have seen that one of the strongest arguments in favor of this theory is the relative ease with which phenomena of age regression or revivification can be obtained. But we also noted that here again doctrinal compliance tends to exaggerate or falsify the "natural" tendency of the hypnotized subject to regress and generally to behave the way a hypnotized subject is supposed to behave.[12] In a similar vein, we have to realize that, as in the case of psychoanalytic transference, the phenomena of hypnotic rapport may be due to the hypnotist's own wishes and expectations, to his own unconscious needs for magic omnipotence, dominance and control. If so, they are in effect the subject's response to the experimenter's unabashed "countertransference."

Of even greater significance is the third aspect of doctrinal compliance characteristic of the hypnotic state: its power to remove a symptom, or at least to replace it with one less incapacitating or less disturbing to the patient and his family. Achieving short-lived cures of this order: making the lame walk and the blind see, has since the dawn of history been the main stock in trade of a long line of *bona fide* faith healers, Christian Scientists and hypnotists—as well as of a wide variety of quacks and charlatans.

The temporary nature of most of these effects should not, however, obscure the reality of the psychological and psychosomatic changes that can be obtained in the hypnotic trance. Disregarding the more extravagant claims that tend to becloud the issue, there is a vast body of contemporary experimental evidence testifying to the striking efficacy of hypnosis even on the neurophysiological plane. In particular, there are two sets of clinical observations which seem to be specific characteristics of the hypnotic state: (1) alterations of the muscular system and motor behavior of the hypnotized subject and (2) changes in his sensory functioning, especially in his responsiveness to pain. Immobilization, inhibition or retardation of the subject's reactions are generally considered as hallmarks of the trance. So are various degrees of analgesia. Analgesia may range from circumscribed anesthetic spots—the *tâches de diable* discovered by the medieval witch hunters—to similar artifacts obtained by Charcot, or from the fire walkers of various Far Eastern and East European sects to deep surgical anesthesia used by surgeons, dentists, obstetricians and other medical specialists. There are, furthermore, the numerous reports of weals, blisters or other tissue changes observed, or alterations of psychogalvanic reflexes, blood pressure, or the EEG obtained in hypnotized persons. There are the accounts of striking sensory hypersensitiveness, of unusual feats of memory and, last but not least, the controversial claims of a variety of occult or paranormal phenomena associated with the trance. It is chiefly manifestations of this order which are responsible for the aura of mystery that surrounds hypnotic phenomena up to our day. It is a mystery which, in spite of the concerted efforts of generations of scientific investigators, still is in the way of integrating all pertinent data with our overall system of scientific thought.

Yet we have seen that the difficulty is not confined to the "paranormal" or "lunatic fringe" of hypnotic manifestations. We emphasized that attempts to explain along analytic lines even the more elementary therapeutic effects attributed to hypnosis or to psychoanalytic transference are vitiated by circular reasoning. Positive transference, we learn, may conceivably be described in terms of a masked or attenuated hypnosis. But such a statement is of little help when we are told that hypnosis has in turn to be interpreted as a transference reaction *par excellence*. The problem is further complicated when we are prepared to include some of the more controversial "paranormal" trance phenomena into our purview. Indeed, it may well be that it is precisely their precarious proximity to magic and occultism, and their apparent incompatibility with the familiar laws of physics and psychodynamics which is responsible for their banishment into the lunatic fringe of our culture. As a result, some of our ancient prejudices gainst the heritage of magic has rubbed off on hypnosis itself.

❊   ❊   ❊

The fact is that none of the existing theories of hypnosis is able to do justice to the whole spectrum of hypnotic phenomena. Psychoanalytic theory has gone far toward this goal. Nevertheless it has difficulty in accounting for some of the analytically more indigestible facts of mental life, including those of the hypnotic trance. Observations of autosuggestion, self-hypnosis, the Yogi sleep, to say nothing of alleged paranormal phenomena, defy attempts at reducing them to the plane of projection, suggestion, analytic transference, parataxic distortion, or doctrinal compliance alone. The problem can be shelved or set aside by laying it before the doorstep of another person upon whom the patient is supposed to project or "transfer," or with whose wishes, or theoretical expectations he is supposed to comply. But such a sleight of hand does not tell who it is that "calls the shots" in the first place; who gives the hypnotist (or the self-hypnotic subject) the mandate and the power to effect such striking changes in his mental or bodily processes as are characteristic of the hypnotic trance. It does not tell where his new and seemingly unlimited degree of freedom to touch off the hypnotic chain of events comes from. The customary answer that the hypnotist's or, for that matter, the therapist's mandate is derived from the patient's corresponding wishes and expectations; from existing social and religious needs or cultural mores, is merely another way of evading the issue.

What the clinical observer or even a nonparticipant viewer of a recorded session can see is the therapist's change of role—his transformation into a latter-day magician, supposedly possessed of quasi-omnipotent powers. The therapist acting out this role is the same person as he has been before. But his script transports him to an archaic, prelogical level of functioning, closer to primitive mentality than to the mentality of modern man. His opposite number, the hypnotized subject, readily follows his lead in this transformation. Prompted by his own magic cravings, he conforms with the hypnotist's commands. He joins him in his episode of regression.

It is difficult to describe this state of affairs in terms of ordinary volitional acts, choices or motivations. The initiation of purportedly magic actions seems to be the primitive prototype of modern man's quest for freedom; a forerunner of his real (or imaginary) ability to make free choices and to initiate autonomous actions in his own right. In the eyes of primitive man this semblance of freedom may well have appeared as a feat of supernatural prowess. Conversely, it could be stated that primitive man's claim of magic omnipotence is the archaic prototype of the modern concept of free will.

Viewed in this light, the hypnotist's self-induced regression to magic seems to carry him back from the reality—or from the illusion—of freedom to a lower rung on the evolutionary ladder of self-determination. The fact is that his "freedom" to act as a hypnotist is limited by various factors beyond his control—interpersonal, situational and cultural. His claim of magic omnipotence may convince his subject; but like that of his primitive forerunner, it is in effect deceptive and self-deceptive. The only argument in his favor is the fact that his lost measure of freedom is made up by a corresponding increase in the leverage of his verbalized and nonverbalized volitional impulses.

* * *

Whether or not Western man's much vaunted (and at times deplored) freedom of volition is a reality after all, or just as fallacious as the magician's claim of omnipotence must be respectfully passed to the philosopher to decide. Fortunately, our argument can dispense with a definitive verdict on this score. The fact is that, like Spinoza's falling stone obeying the pull of gravity, most of us may at times be persuaded by the irrefutable inner certainty of freedom. Freedom is one of our social *a prioris*, as it were. At other times we may bow our heads to the equally cogent evidence of a strictly deterministic scheme of human affairs. To this we have to add the intriguing phenomenological fact that we may nevertheless feel free to lean toward either one or the other alternative: to opt for freedom or determinism, as the case may be—to choose between the two existential positions. "My first act of free will is to believe in free will," as William James put it.[13]

In the last analysis the two conflicting philosophies derive their rationale from two contrasting sets of myths: the myth of a foreordained, strictly deterministic universe, congenial to man of antiquity or to ancient Far Eastern tradition; and the myth of free will, close to the heart of Western man and his Promethean or Faustian quest for individuation and self-realization. Yet Western man, whatever his avowed philosophical outlook, his scientific credo or religious persuasion, is subject to recurrent existential shifts in either direction. He may be convinced that he is part of a strictly deterministic, causal chain of events. Still, his likes and dislikes, his goals and aspirations are geared to the reality—or to the myth—of freedom of choice and self-determination.

The same dichotomy runs through Western man's continued wavering between a magic versus a pragmatic view of causality. It involves the same shift of attitudes that occurs in the Polynesian native who performs his magic rituals when setting out for a fishing expedition on the open sea, but makes sure at the same time that his fishing gear, his paddles and canoes are fit for their practical purpose. This is what anthropologists have described as the principle of dual causality, characteristic of primitive man. But we have pointed out that the same principle can also be discerned in the superstitious practices of his contemporary Western counterpart, from the Governor's Lady smashing a bottle of champagne against the bow of a newly launched battleship to the atomic physicist hanging a horseshoe on his entrance door. The dichotomy between the sacred and the profane; between our age-old tradition to break the workaday routine of daily life with a spell of "prayer and meditation" in church, synagogue or Sunday School is based on the same principle. It too is a derivative of primitive man's propensity for dual causality. It, too, is predicated on our capacity to shift from one existential modality to another. So is the theological dichotomy between Caesar and Christ; between the earthly city and the City of God. So is the Kantian antinomy of *noumenal* versus *phenomenal* categories of being.

The contemporary psychiatrist and psychoanalyst is caught right in the middle of these dichotomies. His whole cultural conditioning, his scientific training and philosophical indoctrination has placed him in the center of a well-ordered universe, regulated by the laws of cause and effect, mental and physical. He is supposed to function in a world in which there is no place for such irregular events as "Oceanic feelings," ecstasies or "peak experiences" as described by A. Maslow.[14] If and when they occur, they have to be explained in terms of regressive phantasies, as states of depersonalization, as repetition compulsions, or what not. The same is true for the *modus operandi* of the therapist's personal impact upon his patient. It too has to be explained in the usual causal-reductive terms of psychotherapy. This precisely is the reason why some of the apparent irregularities of the hypnotic trance still tend to baffle sober clinical observers. This also is the reason why Freud had to abandon, early in his career, hypnosis as a therapeutic tool. Its scientifically unaccountable aspects, its remaining vestiges of magic ran counter to his mythophobic temper.

Yet hypnotic trance and its attenuated forms: suggestion, psychoanalytic transference and doctrinal compliance, remain facts of the psychotherapist's daily practice. It is true, while engaged in his usual routine, he does not stop to think that his activities are in effect predicated on the principle of dual causality: that all the time an elusive and scientifically uncontrollable factor is skirting his dynamically well-defined clinical approach. But whenever he decides to use hypnosis or hypnoanalytic techniques he is bound to abandon—if only for a brief moment—his scientific frame of reference, his cultural conditioning, his well-established analytic position, and to allow himself to be drawn (or to regress into) the illusion of freedom, of magic omnipotence, and to a resurgence of faith in the power of his personal myth. This total reorientation and reorganization of the therapist's inner experience, and the attending change of his approach to his patient and to the world at large is our prime example of the existential shift.

It is readily understood that as a general rule the existential shift includes a corresponding shift in the inner experience of the patient. Nor is it confined to the therapist-patient relationship. We hinted that it is part and parcel of a broad spectrum of religious experiences: it is an indispensable prerequisite of all creative activities; it is a *sine qua non* of ESP and other parapsychological phenomena: of functioning on the psi level. It is perhaps the last, but also the strongest, stronghold of modern man's belief in the possibility of personal freedom and self-transcendence. In effect, it is more than a belief, a metaphysical concept or a philosophical doctrine. It has all the hallmarks of an effective myth which feeds into the therapeutic motivations of even the most scientifically oriented scientific psychotherapist and it sustains the faith of even the most thoroughly demythologized Protestant clergyman.

*   *   *

In the rarified air of esthetic experience the existential shift occurs in more subtle ways but in virtually unlimited shades, gradations and existential modalities. The actor impersonating a stage character, and the audience responding to his performance, are transported into worlds of their own, heroic, farcical, surrealistic, absurd—as the case may be. The viewer of an early Renaissance painting may find himself enveloped in the luminosity of an Umbrian landscape, the dwelling place of ethereal beings, all stillness, translucent color and measured repose. Or else, he may find himself face to face with the tortured canvases of Picasso's *Guernica* series, substituting jarred, broken and distorted shapes for animate or inanimate objects. He may be exposed to the turbulent splashes of action painting or drawn into the dizzying vortex of contemporary "op" art. Marcel Proust put it succinctly when he stated: "Only through art can we get outside of ourselves and know another's view of the universe which is not the same as ours and see landscapes which would otherwise have remained unknown to us like the landscapes of the moon. Thanks to art, instead of seeing a single world, our own, we see it multiply until we have before us as many worlds as there are original artists."

Some of these deviations from our standard way of experience may be little more than pathological aberrations—sound and fury, signifying nothing. They may be due to psychological entropy, to the encroachment of randomicity upon the basic trend for order and lawfulness, patterning organic life and human affairs in general. But they too are indicative of man's craving for ever recurrent changes in his posture in the universe, of his perpetual search for existential shifts, striking new chords in the depth of his being—even though the notes sounded may be jarring and the new postures found may bring only temporary relief.

Be that as it may, the existential shift, as it is described here, marks that "finite" area of freedom, real or imaginary, without which religious experience, creative self-expression and effective psychotherapeutic intervention is hardly possible. It might be presumptuous to claim for it the status of a consistent, testable and verifiable scientific hypothesis. Indeed, the occurrence of the existential shift may largely be of the nature of a myth. But if so, it too has abundantly proven to be effective.

REFERENCES

1. WOLBERG, L.: Medical Hypnosis, Grune & Stratton, New York 1948.
2. ERICKSON, M. H.: Hypnosis, A General Review, Diseases of the Nervous System, 2, 1941.
3. REGARDIE, F. J.: Analysis of a Homosexual, Psychiatr. Quart. 23, 1949.
4. EHRENWALD, J.: Versuche zur Zeitauffassung des Unbewussten. Archiv fur Psychologie XLV, 1922.
5. JANET, P.: Note sur quelques Phenomenes de somnambulisme, Revue Philosophique de la France et de l'étrangers 21, 212-223, 1886.
6. BEHANAN, K.: cf. Chapter III (9).
7. BERNHEIM, H.: Suggestive Therapeutics, Putnam, New York 1880.
8. SPIEGEL, H.: Hypnosis and Transference: A Theoretical Formulation in: Psychoanalysis and Human Values, ed. J. Masserman, Grune & Stratton, New York 1960.
9. WOLSTEIN, B.: cf. Chapter XII (3).
10. FERENCZI, S.: cf. Chapter XII (2).
11. RADO, S.: Relationship of Short-Term Psychotherapy to Developmental Stages of Maturation and Stages of Treatment Behavior, in: Short-Term Psychotherapy, ed. L. Wolberg, Grune & Stratton, New York 1965.
12. BARBER, T. X.: The Concept of Hypnosis, J. Psychol. 45, 115, 1958.
13. JAMES, W.: Some Problems of Philosophy, Longmans, Green and Co., New York 1911.
14. MASLOW, A.: Cognition of Being in the Peak Experience Presid. Address, Divis. of Personality and Social Psychology, Amer. Psychol. Assoc., Chicago, Ill. 1956.

— XIV —

What Triggers the Existential Shift?

How does the existential shift come about? Does it eventuate like a theophany by the grace of God? Is it a "peak experience" accessible to a privileged few only? Can it be imparted to others by a charismatic personality? Can it be attained by some spiritual discipline, intellectual training or indoctrinaton? Is there a short cut towards it through the alchemy of one or the other of the modern psychomimetic drugs?

We are told by the theologians that to the true believer it comes unsolicited and unsought for, the way the Lord appeared to Moses in the burning brush. But a lesser breed of seekers after God has to undergo the rigorous discipline of spiritual exercises, aided by self-immolation, fasting, ablutions and purification rites. Pythias of ancient Greece resorted to inhaling intoxicating fumes; the priests and priestesses of ancient Mayan cults to Peyote in order to bridge the gulf between this and the other world. The shamans, the dervishes of Siberia or the Far East hit upon orgiastic dances, the beating of drums, the mumbling of nonsense syllables, the chanting of hymns to achieve the same purpose. The self-mortifications, the ritualistic postures and breathing exercises of the Indian yogis were mentioned on an earlier page. The Zen masters, with their avowed purpose of confounding the minds of their pupils, are another variation on the theme, aiming as they do at an existential shift from a rationalistic position to *satori*, the ineffable, immediate experience of the self and of its unity with the world.

The Western patient consulting his analyst is likewise subjected to an existential shift, though in a minor key. Made to recline on the couch, he finds himself in the presence of a silent, unseen, inactive and nondirective helpmate—the diametrical opposite of the priestly healer, the moral philosopher, the spiritual mentor, or the controlling father figure of pre-Freudian psychotherapy. The contrast is greater still if Freudian analysis is viewed against the authoritarian background of the young Freud and his time. Challenging the patient's tendency to denial and rationalization, breaking down his defenses and opening the door for the upsurge of free associations, dreams and phantasies from the unconscious is another expedient in the service of an existential shift.

What applies to the patient undergoing psychoanalytic treatment is equally true for the student of psychoanalysis. His training analysis takes him into a world ideally removed from the exigencies of his worldly pursuits. His conscious reasoning, his functioning on the cognitive level is demoted to the level of "secondary" processes and his focus shifted to mental events of an altogether different nature: to what is now upgraded to the status of "primary" processes. He is taught to recognize and to come to grips, both in himself and in others, with what is habitually ignored, repressed or denied in the routine of everyday life. The process is reinforced by the terms of his psychoanalytic apprenticeship. As a student of psychoanalysis, "seeing the light," producing the sought-for material, is rewarded by what Greenspoon described[1] as the "affirmative grunts" made by the operator in the laboratory experiment: in this case by the analysand's mentor in the psychoanalytic situation. Failing this, he may come up against the analyst's barely audible grunts of disapprobation or telltale silences. The rewarding pellets of anticipated favorable reports on his progress act as further reinforcements of the analysand's doctrinal compliance and of his efforts to maintain his functioning on the plane of the newly attained existential shift.

There can be no doubt as to the pragmatic value of this method as a means of gaining knowledge and self-knowledge, and of inculcating the spirit of detached scientific inquiry into an elite of dedicated students of the human mind. But unless both analyst and patient learn to use the momentum gained by the existential shift, their work is likely to remain little more than an intellectual exercise. Staying on the straight and narrow path of science—physical or behavioral—is one matter. Being capable of shifting gears in order to negotiate the climb to the sphere of psychological closeness and existential encounter with the patient is another. The detached scientific observer can at best register this shift in terms of a seeming irregularity in the familiar dynamics of transference, of parataxic distortion, of interpersonal relationships. But on trying to make allowance for its significance in the broader context of the treatment situation we have to realize that it is more than that. It is the existential shift which sets the stage for the analytic transference and provides the emotional charge that makes such therapeutic interventions as cathartic release, interpretation, ventilation or working-through truly effective. In short, it readmits the banished myth into the therapist's and the patient's universe.

Yet the concept of the existential shift is not a complete stranger to psychoanalytic theory. It was anticipated by E. Kris' description of the creative artist's attitude towards his work.[2] The artist, Kris holds, must be capable of oscillating between primary and secondary levels of functioning. He must be able to relax his ego function in a purposeful and controlled fashion, fluctuating between "functional regression and control." This is what Heinz Hartmann has described as regression in the service of the ego.[3]

The therapist's abrupt transformation into a hypnotist, as described in the preceding chapter, is a graphic illustration of the same principle. His dramatic shift from a pragmatic to a magic level of functioning is predicated on a self-imposed regression—in this case in the service of *treatment*. The same applies, though to a lesser degree, to any psychotherapist in an authentic treatment situation. He too tends to mobilize his personal myth, and he also tends to regress in his attempt to do so. More recently, Maxwell Gitelson[4] introduced the concept of regression in the service of treatment into psychoanalytic literature. However he, as well as Hartmann and Kris, uses the term regression exclusively in reference to a person's individual development and maturation. The term as it is used here comes closer to what can be described as *cultural* regression. It implies the emergence of archaic patterns of orientation to the world at large. In short, the therapist's postulated regression is merely another instance of an existential shift—of a shift from the discursive, causal-reductive level of functioning to one removed from the categories of "regression" or "progression" and their attending conventional value judgments.

* * *

We have seen that under modern conditions myth is the joint creation of the therapist, the patient and the culture in which they are immersed. It is reinforced by feedback from the particular school of thought to which the therapist owes his allegiance. But it is sparked by what we have described as the myth—or reality—of his personal freedom. This belief is pitted against the concerted evidence of all the external determining factors which he knows are responsible for his choices and decisions. Still, the therapist cannot help but approach his task confident that he is capable of taking a hand in changing the course of natural events, both in himself and in his patient. Indeed we noted that part of his therapeutic impact is predicated on the presence—and on the contagious quality—of this conviction.

Yet precisely because of the deterministic thinking prevailing on our culture, such an attitude requires a well-nigh audible shifting of gears on the part of both therapist and patient. This is illustrated by the example of the scientifically trained psychiatrist donning the mantle of the magician and playing the part of the omnipotent hypnotist. It may well be that he himself is satisfied that all that is involved in such a venture is to assume a new, or rather an old-fashioned and traditionally well-defined, professional role. Yet in my experience such role playing is not enough in order to be effective. The hypnotist must not just pretend to be playing the role of the hypnotist. He must project himself, heart and soul, into the act. The same is true for the subject. Unless he comes thoroughly prepared and groomed for the performance, he too may find it difficult to effect the shift from a more or less self-directing, autonomous mode of existence to that of a psychological marionette, leaving it temporarily to the hypnotist to pull his wires of action and to monitor his perceptions.

An existential shift along different lines, less profound but even more impressive because of its avowed dramatic purpose, is exemplified by J. L. Moreno's psychodrama.[5] It expressly aims at bringing about a shift by calling on the patient to act out roles other than those into which he was cast by his neurosis, by his place in the family or in the community at large. Whatever its merits as a method of treatment, psychodrama is a graphic illustration of how a latter-day medicine man readies himself and his audience for the moment of dramatic make believe and regression in the service of treatment.

An introductory speech conveying spontaneity, humor and warmth more than information, initiates a period of warm-up. As far as the therapist is concerned it is a period of method acting which seems to be needed in order to convince himself that he is in effect the psychodramatist, Dr. Moreno—a conviction which is soon shared, however, by an equally convinced audience. Yet once this *re*mythologization of the therapist's role has come to pass, the stage is set for the existential shift with its attending role reversals; the intervention of "auxiliary egos"; cathartic acting out and, hopefully, for the patient's therapeutic response.

❖   ❖   ❖

A closer look into the dynamics of the existential shift can be gained from an unexpected vantage point: from methodical parapsychological studies of factors favoring extrasensory perception. The vast literature on the subject cannot be reviewed in the present context. It contains a wealth of experimental observations showing how success in the field is predicated, among other things, on the conviction held by both experimenter and subject that ESP is in fact possible. This was particularly borne out by Gertrude Schmeidler's *"sheep* and *goat"* experiments,[6] in which college students affirming their faith in the possibility of ESP—the *sheep*—scored high in excess of chance expectation, while skeptics—the *goats*—failed to do so. In a similar vein, a number of psychoanalysts found strongly suggestive positive correlations between the occurrence in their patients of telepathic dreams and other ESP manifestations with the existing transference-countertransference relationship. Another set of predisposing and conditioning factors seems to be what I described as a physiological *minus function* and its compensation or overcompensation on an unusual level of functioning. It is the combination and concatenation of these circumstances which seems to trigger off the shift, however ephemeral, from one modality of functioning to another.[7]

Although few workers in the field seem to have realized the importance of the existential shift as the key factor in bringing about psi phenomena, there can be little doubt that a successful subject (or experimenter) in ESP must have the capacity to function, concurrently or alternatively, on both the psi level and on the ordinary, "reality-oriented" level of experience. The subject in particular must be wide awake to ordinary psychic reality, or else he cannot tell his tale and make his private experience public. At the same time, he must be attuned to psi, or else he has no private experience to relate. Yet as a general rule, the existential shift involved in parapsychological experiences is less spectacular than in the hypnotic trance. It does not require a noticeable switching of gears. Popular accounts of the occurrences are often overdrawn, with Victorian curlicues or touches of technicolor added to make them more impressive. It may well be that a barely perceptible background "noise" of psi is a constant feature of our mental organization even though its perception is not encouraged by the pragmatic needs of reality testing under standard conditions. Indeed we have seen in Chapter VII that the existential shift to parapsychological experiences is too close to a repressed, repudiated, magical level of functioning to be culturally or even biologically desirable. Its precarious proximity to mental disorder is illustrated by the striking similarity of certain paranoid delusions with current parapsychological theories. Paranoid patients may welcome this similarity as an exoneration of their delusional trend, but to some students of psychical research it still carries an ominous connotation.

Whether or not various classes of neuroses and mental disorders should likewise be described in terms of the existential shift is a matter of semantics. Phenomenological and existential psychiatrists from Erwin Strauss[8] and Eugene Minkowski[9] to Binswanger[10] and Gebsattel[11] have done just this. Again, viewing drug-induced changes of experience in such terms has certainly much in its favor. Intoxicating beverages, vapors and fumes, and extracts prepared from snakeroot, mushrooms or the Peyote have long been used as attempted shortcuts to Dionysian raptures, ecstasies or religious illuminations. The recent discovery of such "consciousness expanding" or psychedelic drugs as LSD 25 or mescaline is wholly in the same tradition. Their devotees insist that they are indeed capable of bringing about major changes in a person's mode of existence.[12] Yet it is doubtful if they can evoke in the individual something that has not been there from the outset or which has not been imparted on him by the experimenter and his associates by way of doctrinal compliance. Opium, hashish or mescaline may well be one man's "artificial paradise," or the drug that makes his "eyes enchanted." Yet it may also be another man's nausea, hangover or temporary mental disorder. As far as true enhancement of a person's creative abilities or, for that matter, of his capacity for extrasensory perception is concerned, experimental work with mescaline or LSD 25 has so far been disappointing.[13]

Nevertheless, since the days of Noah and Dionysius, intoxicating beverages—the ancestors of today's psychomimetic or psychedelic drugs—have been used as a means of transporting man to both the highest peaks and the lower depths of ecstatic or orgiastic experience. The bacchanalia of ancient Rome served as periodically scheduled occasions for the uninhibited acting out by both sexes of instinctual drives, sexual or otherwise. The existential shift in this case was tolerated or even sanctioned by religious custom. But it was helped by the chemical effects of alcoholic indulgence, less so by myth.

Much the same is true for the part played by social imbibing in our days. The superego has been defined as that part of personality which can be dissolved in alcohol. Whatever it does to the superego, it certainly removes inhibitions in those who drink in order to lose their inhibitions. This is one of the reasons for the frequent use of alcohol as an opening gambit for lovers who find it difficult to make the transition from the level of social to the level of sexual intercourse. Alcohol in itself is not an aphrodisiac, but it is used by many as a catalyst for love-making. The combination of "wine, women and song" has become a syndrome in many cultures, resorted to in order to lighten the burden of cultural demands, of philistine boredom and compulsive respectability.

❋   ❋   ❋

The following case history is an example of a recurrent existential shift of psychotic proportions, each time initiated by the patient's irresistible urge to go on a drinking bout. The patient, Alfred H., is a married man in his middle 30's. A gifted artist of Jewish background, he was ashamed of three things: of his Jewishness, of his short stature and of his first name Aron, which he had changed into Alfred or Alf. Yet analysis showed that his inferiority feelings covered up a deeper problem from which he sought escape in his drinking sprees: he was a latent homosexual, afraid to appear a "sissy" and to fall short of his goals of masculine prowess. Apart from sexual difficulties with his wife, he showed little evidence of overt neurotic conflict. He was successful in his career, popular with his cronies and was generally regarded as a model husband. But every two or three months he would suddenly drop out of sight, make the rounds of bars in disreputable neighborhoods. Once sufficiently intoxicated—plastered as he put it—he would shed his Alf identity: the mask of the law abiding citizen and well-established professional. He would change back to his despised Aron personality. Unwashed, unshaven, he would make obscene phone calls, pick up colored women for brief, and invariably unsuccessful, sexual encounters.

Hours of seemingly aimless cruising would ultimately bring him to the verge of overt homosexual activities with Negro "tough guys." Usually these encounters too remained abortive. After an absence of two or three nights, the patient returned to his wife, frustrated, remorseful and shaken by his experiences. Resuming his identity as the well-adjusted and professionally successful Alfred H., he would remorsefully bow to his wife's reproaches and promise never to get drunk and never to go into hiding again.

Patients of this type are usually diagnosed as suffering from dipsomania. But even this condensed sketch of Alf's psychodynamics indicates that the underlying problem was his urge to allow his passive homosexual inclinations to take the upper hand, to drop the mask of heterosexual adjustment and to descend to what he himself described as the lower depths, leading him, step by step, closer to "dirty" sexual acting out with prostitutes and to the final degradation of offering himself to men as an object to anal-sadistic abuse. These sudden shifts from a seemingly normal, heterosexual orientation into the role of an anally fixated would-be homosexual were undoubtedly occasioned by the pressures of his repressed instinctual drives. But in this case—unlike in its socially condoned Dionysian function—alcohol had become a link in a complex chain of events resulting in a shift to a psychotically distorted caricature of the Dionysian mode of existence.

It should be noted, however, that even here the responsibility for this state of affairs rests with the patient's unresolved conflicts and not with the chemical trigger which he chose to pull in order to be transported into his world of booze, prostitutes and masochistic self-degradation. It was a shift to what Alf himself described as the "lower depths"; it amounted to a temporary possession from *below*, instead of from *above*, as Paul Tillich put it.

It may be no coincidence, however, that here for once the triggering agent was not a man-made myth but a man-made intoxicating agent. Myth tends to exert its pull in the opposite direction. As a general rule, it serves the goal of man's self-enhancement; it is the instrument of his Faustian drive to transcend himself. Joseph Campbell's description of the "supernormal releaser effect" of myth is perhaps the most concise formulation of this role of myth in human affairs.[14]

It is readily understood that crude physicochemical interventions are not likely to duplicate such effects. Banging your fist against a pinball machine may make its mechanism unstuck. The malfunctioning of an electronic computer requires a much more sophisticated engineering approach. The human mind does not take kindly to either kind of treatment. It is geared to responding to the symbolic leverage of gestures, spoken words, metaphors and myths. At times it may indeed be capable of responding to "nothing but" myth. This is borne out by our "case history" of Sir Kenelm Digby's *Powder of Sympathy* in which an inert chemical nostrum administered to the patient from a distance was attended by striking remedial effects (see Chapter IV).

On the other hand newer clinical evidence indicates that an effective chemical compound may occasionally trigger off an existential shift duplicating the psychological impact of myth. This is documented by a vast number of observations published in recent psychiatric literature. Yet the *modus operandi* of the various tranquilizing or energizing drugs, and the rationale underlying their prescription, is worlds apart from our argument—so much so that the very discussion, in the present context, of the existential shift following their administration seems to require an existential shift of its own.

❊   ❊   ❊

The point is illustrated by the following case history. The patient, Rhoda M., is a woman of 42, the mother of two children. Since the age of 19, following a "nervous breakdown," she had been undergoing analytic psychotherapy with a female analyst. It lasted, with brief interruptions, till the analyst's death. During this period of 17 years, Rhoda became increasingly dependent on her, duplicating a symbiotic pattern that had existed between herself and a doting, emotionally disturbed mother. Rhoda's father had committed suicide when she was 26, by "cutting his throat." Her own clinical history was that of recurrent depressive episodes with anorexia, vomiting, and periods of alcoholic indulgence. Her transference on her previous analyst had a marked homosexual coloring. Her early sex play was with an older sister and with girls of her own age. Rhoda was an ineffectual mother and her two children showed signs of emotional disturbance. Her relationship to her husband was clinging and dependent, while at the same time she sought to dominate him and considered him intellectually her inferior.

On her analyst's death, Rhoda went into another depressive episode and was referred to me for treatment. Once more she tried to establish a clinging-dependent relationship with her doctor. This time it was vitiated, however, by her latent homosexual trend and by her resentment of the male. She drank, refused to take her medication and developed various phobic symptoms. She threw up, became anorectic and lost 15 pounds. Since she was virtually "unanalyzable," hospitalization and another attempt at persuading her to accept medication was decided. In the favorable therapeutic milieu of the hospital, aided by a sympathetic staff nurse who took the place of her female love object, Rhoda was ready to switch from alcohol to an energizing drug, given together with a mild tranquilizer.

The rest of her story would have to be written up in a bilingual, if not trilingual case report. Put in the language of organic, clinical psychiatry,

Rhoda soon responded well to the new medication. In 10 to 12 days her appetite and sleep showed marked improvement. Her depression lifted. She took renewed interest in her family, visited her home on weekends and was anxious to obtain her discharge from the hospital. In three weeks of hospitalization she put on 12 pounds and seemed to regain her emotional balance. In the fourth week she was discharged from the hospital. Thus a case of chronic depression in an emotionally unstable neurotic patient was cured by the combination of milieu therapy and a powerful psychomimetic agent, in this case the drug Elavil. While the exact nature of drug effects of this order is controversial they are usually attributed to changes in the enzyme system of the brain, affecting the metabolism of individual brain cells and of neurophysiological regulatory functions in general.

Put in a language closer to the level of our present discourse, the changes effected by the drug had all the hallmarks of an existential shift. It was a global change from a childish-dependent, if not infantile, position to a new level of functioning in virtually all walks of life. Rhoda had gone through life craving for love—and food—which she was unable to digest or to keep down. She reached out for relationships which were in effect poor substitutes for the real thing: for a mother who would continue to cater to her infantile needs. With all the analytic treatment she had received, Rhoda took no interest in life except for gratifications of this order. It was this stalemate from which she was jolted out by the drug, aided by a good mother figure and the favorable hospital environment.

Trying to combine the organic with the psychoanalytic point of view, it could be stated that in this case the energizing drug had been capable of replacing depleted energy levels of the psychic apparatus—of replenishing libidinal cathexes—and thus tipped the balance from a depressive to a more adequate level of psychological functioning.[15] It may be argued, furthermore, that her preceding analysis, followed by the switch to a new therapist—and his myth—was of added help in her making the break from her symbiotic mother and thus contributed to Rhoda's recovery.

Whatever the underlying psychodynamics or pharmacodynamics, from then on Rhoda seemed capable of marshalling previously untapped personality resources. She became more efficient as a mother, and the existing emotional difficulties with her children were relieved. Her husband who had been suffering from recurrent attacks of hives lost his food allergies. Rhoda took up dancing and swimming again and became socially more outgoing. She was no longer impeded by her fear of traveling nor of eating in restaurants. During the past two years she has maintained her improvement. Whereas in the preceding 18 years, she was never able to do without therapy, she is no longer clamoring for "her sessions." Since her discharge from the hospital she was seen on two or three occasions only and showed no desire for more analytic probing. Nor did I make any attempts to do so. Psychoanalytically speaking, Rhoda's improvement may well be described merely as a flight into health. But it is also indicative of her ability to maintain her newly acquired level of functioning as an independent human being.

*   *   *

That an existential shift may occasionally be initiated by purely psychological means, even in the face of the patient's apparent resistance, is illustrated by the following observation: Jim J. is a married man of 34, father of two children. He is a gifted electrical engineer who has never been able to put his talents to practical use. Some of his inventions were patented or ready in the mock-up stage, but he kept stalling and delayed the steps necessary for their marketing. He treated his wife like a mother figure, but was bossy and domineering at the same time. He was given to daydreaming and preoccupied with thinly veiled sado-masochistic phantasies. He was moody with his children, vacillating between indulgence and irritability. Six years of intensive psychoanalysis with a competent woman analyst provided him with ample insight into his problems. It helped him to understand his Oedipal and pre-Oedipal problems; the reasons for his flight into phantasy; for his inability to take constructive actions; for his alienation and sense of futility in general. But analysis did not succeed in breaking his stalemate. On being referred to me by his first analyst, Jim continued his pattern of self-searching and intellectual self-scrutiny, shot through with obsessive-compulsive ruminations. Again, "insight" seemed to be piling upon "insight," yet always devoid of emotional concommitants. Eight more months on the couch brought very little progress. It took me nearly as long to realize that what he really wanted was a therapist ready to bring his subdued rebellion against the parent figure out into the open; to provoke a showdown; to accept the ensuing expression of anger with good humor, thereby showing the patient that anger did not kill; that he had come of age at long last and was capable of fending for himself, of taking action without losing control of his emotional balance.

"Do you really think that all this talk will ever get you on your feet?" I told him after one of his obsessive recitations. "Face it; you have been on the cross roads, stalling, dragging your feet long enough. It's not up to me to break this pattern. It's up to you to choose between dependence or independence. If the choice were to be made by me, it would be worthless."
"There is no question what I want," Jim retorted. "But it is a damned business . . . Damn it." (He beat the couch with his fist.) "It won't come in a flash; not just in a moment. I am not a mystic. Are you? If you are,

don't try this stuff on me. It's not done by trying. Trying consciously . . .
I am not a weightlifter. Maybe I should say to myself I am my own
man . . . but don't tell me suddenly my ego will emerge triumphant;
Nonsense! What I need is some success now to lift my ego . . ."

The patient's angry outburst was the turning point in the course of treatment. He took active steps to launch one of his projects, entered negotia-
tions to sell his invention, and followed through by opening an office. At
the same time he became more spontaneous in his relationship with his
wife, less moody with his children, and permitted himself to show an occasional glimmer of warmth in relation to me.

To put this turn of events in the proper perspective we have to realize
that the change that took place in the wake of my intervention came by no
means out of the blue. It marked the end point of a series of judgments,
conscious or unconscious, as to the patient's readiness for change, including
what turned out to be the proper interpretation and its right timing on my
part. Nor did the effected existential shift herald the end of treatment.
Rather, it was the signal for continuing therapy in a new key. Thus contrary to the patient's charge of introducing a mystic element into the
therapeutic situation, my intervention was an essentially rational therapeutic step. Nevertheless, it was one predicated on the therapist's belief in
the potential efficacy of such interventions in general, on the therapist's
freedom to act at the "favorable moment" and, by indirection, of his belief
in his personal myth.

       *   *   *

Active interventions of this order are usually frowned upon by analysts.
Yet Freud himself did not hesitate to encourage his phobic patients to try
to break their pattern when "the time was ripe." The treatment of alco-
holics and drug addicts requires even more active interventions by the
therapist if and when he feels the patient is capable of making the decisive
step. This is illustrated by the following example:

Herma B. is an unmarried woman of 29, the younger sister of a woman
who had undergone analytic psychotherapy with me 12 years ago. The
older sister, "successfully analyzed," good looking, happily married and
mother of two children, put Herma under some pressure to seek my help.
Herma had been a career girl, but for no apparent reason, had quit her
job and spent a year and a half in total idleness in her parents' home. She
had an emotionaly unrewarding love affair with a jazz musician. Apart
from that she withdrew from social life, became increasingly moody,
irritable and difficult to live with.

She started therapy by breaking the first three or four appointments.
Without a word she would keep me waiting, or else she would phone at

the end of the hour allotted to her advising me that she would pay for the broken appointment. Ultimately she came close to the end of her hour to tell me that she had nothing to talk about. I felt that in the face of this formidable resistance interpretation alone would be of no avail. Instead I gave her a frank statement of my professional dilemma: It would be un-ethical for me to accept payments for services which I was unable to render. I would therefore have to stop trying to treat her or else I would have to leave it up to her to break her next appointment again—with the understanding that I would have to accept the resulting financial loss since I would accept no more fees for unkept hours.

Herma promptly put me to the test of my good faith and broke her next appointment. Only following these maneuverings was she ready to appear for her sessions with greater regularity, though she came late most of the time. It took her three months before she would tell me the story of her rivalry with her hated and beloved sister; of her struggles with a cold, rejecting and compulsive mother; of her masochistic relationship with the jazz musician, etc. Her life was filled with compulsive rituals and obses-sive ruminations. She was suffering from various phobias. She collected "junk" and always came with a handbag weighing 15 to 20 pounds, con-taining books or unnecessary articles of clothing. She had been constipated since childhood and claimed she had only one or two bowel movements a week. She felt alienated, detached and asked me one day: "Doctor, do I have a universe left? Has it got a center?" Tearfully she recounted a re-cent argument with her father in the course of which he had slapped her face. Following this session she confessed, at long last, that for the last three years she had been taking increasing doses of amphetamines: 15-30-45 mg per day. She had been introduced to the habit by her lover, the jazz musician. Yet she broke up their relationship before starting treatment with me. Nevertheless, Herma still remained inaccessible to analytic therapy. All she could remember were a few disjointed childhood recollec-tions. She had slept in the same bed with her sister. She "may have had" a crush on her and she always felt that it was impossible to compete with her. One day Herma surprised me with the question: "Do you think I should try to get a job now? Shall I move out of my parents' home?" I inquired about side effects of the drug. I hinted that her insomnia and irritability would be in her way. At a later session Herma reported that she had cut down the drug intake to 10-15 mg per day. She confessed that she was now using a nasal spray and wondered whether it too contained amphetamine. It did, and I told her so. At this moment I asked her about the "junk" (i.e., the fetish objects) she carried in her bag. She opened it willingly. It was stacked with vials, boxes and bottles containing dexedrine, benzedrine, dexamyl, and various nasal sprays. I said: "What about getting rid of all this stuff? What about throwing it into my wastepaper basket? What about a total break with the past? An auto-da-fé so that the past is burned in effigy? A ritualistic cremation of what you continue to hang on to in an infantile way?" Herma joined me in laughing at my suggestion. She threw her "junk," including a few letters from the jazz musician, into the wastepaper basket. A week later Herma applied for a job. She was back to work after another week. Her parents, her sister and Herma herself felt she had become a new person. She said she no longer lived in a haze; she could concentrate again. Her sleep improved; her constipation disappeared; she felt full of "zip and go"; her obsessive-compulsive trend receded and her phobias seemed to have gone underground. Once relieved of her more incapacitating neurotic symptoms she felt no more need for her pills or sprays.

A. Kielholz,[16] H. Ellenberger,[17] H. Kelman[18] and other existentialists and post-Freudian analysts have described similar dramatic changes in the course of psychotherapy in terms of the Hippocratic *kairos*, usually translated as the *favorable moment*. *Kairos*, in the words of H. Kelman is a "spiritual event in the life history of an illness, be it physical, psychological, moral or involve confronting a whole way of life." Ellenberger describes it as an inner experience in which "something new is revealed, new horizons opened, one's *weltanschauung* is revised and sometimes the whole personality is reconstructed." In short, it is an experience facilitated by transference, culminating in the encounter and triggered by an existential shift.

*　　*　　*

What then are the varieties of the existential shift? What is the baseline from which shifts are supposed to depart, and what is their relevance to our current concepts of psychodynamics? We have seen that the shift may be short-lived or enduring. It may be incomplete or all-encompassing covering the whole register of a person's experience. It may include an individual's biological adaptations and his ego defenses. It may amount to a major spiritual experience, from ecstasy to religious conversion; from the raptures of St. Theresa of Avila to Swedenborg's excursions into a succession of Heavenly Spheres. It may remove the devotee from contact with mundane reality and transport him into a state of *satori* taught by the Zen masters, or into the *samadhi* sought by the Yogis.

The shift may manifest itself merely as a *form fruste* of the total experience, involving a cleavage between a person's workaday life and his occasional forrays into the religious or spiritual sphere. It may be barely perceptible, involving fleeting and often unrecognized parapsychological occurrences. It may amount to a split personality of the Jekyll-and-Hyde or the Aron-and-Alf type described above. It may involve shifts of a person's sexual standards, from marital to extramarital activities; from public to private life. The demons of evil may coexist in the individual—or in a whole nation—with love of music, poetry and *gemütlichkeit*. Exemplary civic virtue may alternate with episodes of revelry and wild abandon; a masochistic posture may alternate with uninhibited sadistic behavior. Seemingly normal social adjustment may be a cover-up for crippling character defenses and detached, alienated personalities. Put in Jungian terms, the shift may involve an alternation between an extrovert and introvert orientation towards the world; between the *anima* and the *animus*; between supremacy of the self and the soul. Psychoanalytically speaking, the shift may involve a change from one level of organization to another level of organization or integration of personality; from secondary process functioning to primary process functioning; from the supremacy of the ego to the supremacy of the id, with the attending redistribution of the individual's libidinal cathexis.

Viewed in this light, mental health is nothing but a privileged existential position, a syndrome of adaptations, geared to the subjective needs or the objective requirements of a given individual in a given culture at a given time. His existential shifts, sparked by his own motivation, programmed by his genetic equipment and conditioned by environmental influences, including psychological treatment, are in effect fluctuations that may exert their pull upward or downward from an arbitrary baseline of adaptive solutions, chosen by himself or defined for him by his family or culture.

Such a relativistic formulation of mental health is in turn contingent on a relativistic formulation of the means and goals of psychotherapy. In a tribal culture dominated by magic, any treatment that aims at instituting the primacy of Freud's reality principle over and above the primitive quest for omnipotence may prove little short of courting of disaster. Ruth Benedict has pointed to the need for similar relativistic considerations in judging "what is good" for a Zuni *versus* a Quakiutl Indian of North America.[19] Again, in the spiritually oriented cultures of the Far East renunciation, loss of selfhood, and masochistic surrender is the goal. They are the price paid for salvation and for the alleviation of suffering. The sacred books of the East are in effect textbooks teaching the devotee how to bring about the existential shift from existence to nonexistence and the deliverance from the Wheel of Change.

Needless to say, Western man of the scientific era pursues entirely different goals. He enlists his therapist's aid so as to realize and to assert his selfhood; to be successful in his private and public affairs; to make a better adjustment to his culture and yet to be spared the "discontents" associated with his civilization. But at the same time he has a crying need to escape from the demands of adjustment and conformity. He expects his therapeutic experience to transport him to levels of existence barred to him by his loss—or repudiation—of both magic and religion. Still, he has not altogether gotten over his craving for either magic or religion. We noted that psychotherapy in our day is in effect called upon to provide a substitute for the lost religious and magic experience; concurrent with or even contrary to its avowed purpose, it finds itself in the paradoxical position of trying to serve two masters at the same time. It seeks to live up to its self-imposed rationalistic standards. Yet, by trial and error, by accident or by design, it continues to meet the patient's basic need for recurrent existential shifts. We have seen that modern existential therapy has no qualms to enlist myth as well as a thinly veiled (or academically draped) latter-day version of magic in its therapeutic armamentarium. It is ready to avail itself of the proven techniques of psychodynamics, or at least to pay lipservice to its accomplishments. But it still places its main emphasis on the existential encounter—that is, on a special aspect of what we described as the existential shift. We also noted that even psychoanalysis, in spite of its strictly scientific aspirations, still leaves the door open for the same contingency. Whether or not allowance is made in the analytic system of thought for its occurrence, the existential shift is an integral part of the analytic process—much in the same way that hypnotic rapport has been an important aspect of Mesmeric trance, or suggestion a key factor in the placebo effect.

✳ ✳ ✳

It may be objected at this point that our thesis of recurrent existential shifts—of the relentless pulls and pressures in the direction of change—is in contrast with one of the basic characteristics of the life process: with the tendency to maintain an existing level of the organism's vital balance or homeostasis. We know that the organism has powerful regulatory functions at its disposal to safeguard an optimal "internal milieu," its level of blood pressure, temperature, electrolyte balance, and blood sugar. This is what W. B. Cannon called the *Wisdom of the Body*.[20] Yet this wisdom is constantly challenged by the apparent folly of the mind to reach out for an infinite variety of new stimuli and ever recurrent novel situations with which it has to cope. Western man does not subscribe to the Nirvana principle. Freud himself contrasted the organism's need for relaxation and release of tension with the "stimulus hunger" of instincts. In a similar vein, Goethe's *Dauer im Wechsel*: the enduring element in change, has to be contrasted with the principle of recurrent fluctuations superimposed on the baseline of the body's physiological adaptations and on an existing level of defenses marshalled by the ego to safeguard the homeostatic balance of the mind.

The insatiable craving for a specific set of pleasurable stimuli is illustrated by a series of recent laboratory experiments with rats. Electrodes implanted in certain areas of their brains drive the animals to repeat self-administered electric stimuli to the point of total physical exhaustion. Some authorities hold that drug addiction in humans follows the same principle. But as a general rule man is not satisfied with pulling the same lever and administering the same modes of pleasurable stimuli to himself over and over again. He craves for what William James described as the spiritual "novelties of the world."[21] His biosocial and cultural development refuses to be forced into the Procrustean bed of Freud's repetition compulsion or, for that matter, into his two-dimensional scheme of the love versus the death instinct. Man is a versatile animal with a virtually unlimited capacity of adaptation to multiple levels of functioning, and he insists on making the most of this capacity. Like the child trying to open all doors, to pull out all drawers, to climb on all chairs and to push all buttons in his nursery, he is bent on exploring all frontiers, on exhausting all possibilities and on actualizing all his innate potentials. Schizophrenia is perhaps nothing but a miscarried attempt in this direction—a pathological level of adaptation affecting both mental and physical aspects. Viewed in this light, therapy—even electric shock therapy—is an attempt to jolt the patient out of his pathological level of adaptation so as to help him attain a more satisfactory level of adaptive solutions. In many neuroses and mental disorders rearranging existing pathological defenses in order to establish a new homeostatis balance in effect amounts to achieving a successful existential shift.

Alternatively, the shift may represent a minor or major phase in a person's developmental history or "individuation." It may be subtle and barely perceptible to the naked eye. Or else it may involve a dramatic change comparable to the molting of a snake or to the emergence of a butterfly from the chrysalis stage. The decisive feature is the attainment of a new, autonomous and viable psychological configuration in all its interrelated and interdependent existential dimensions.

Yet the capacity of rehearsing in phantasy a vast, indeed infinite, variety of modes of existence and thus duplicating, on the psychological plane, virtually the whole repertoire of the evolutionary process apparently is an essential characteristic of being human. Having made allowance for man's finite freedom to pursue this goal is perhaps one of the major contributions of modern existentialist thought. But at least equal credit has to go to William James for his formulation of the "pluralistic multiverse" and of "free will as a meliorative doctrine";[21] to Gardner Murphy's thesis of man's virtually unlimited potentialities;[22] and to Kurt Goldstein's postulated drive for self-actualization[23] as the drive presiding over all other human drives.

Summing up, there are three major methods of triggering the existential shift. One is the soaring thrust of myth: man's unique means of asserting his identity, of spelling out his destiny and of trying to transcend himself in the process. The second is psychotherapy with its overt or covert reliance on the therapist's personal myth, aided by modern psychodynamic techniques. The third is the chemical short-cut to change, a direct attack upon raw nerve endings, synapses and brain cells throwing physiological regulatory functions temporarily out of kilter, but hopeful of restoring them on a new baseline. Yet we noted that even in the face of major chemical interventions man and his myth still have the last word in determining the particular mode of existence—or the level of adaptation—at which his vital balance will ultimately come to rest.

REFERENCES

1. GREENSPOON, J.: cf. Chapter XI (7).
2. KRIS, E.: Psychoanalytic Exploration of Art, Allen & Unwin, London 1953.
3. HARTMANN, H.: cf. Chapter VIII (5).
4. GITELSON, M.: The Curative Factors in Psychoanalysis, The First Phase of Psychoanalysis, Int. J. Psychoan. 43, 194-211, 1962.
5. MORENO, J. L.: Fundamental Rules and Technique of Psychodrama, in: Progress in Psychotherapy, Vol. III, Grune & Stratton, New York 1958.
6. SCHMEIDLER, G. R. and McCONNELL, R. A.: ESP and Personality Patterns, Yale Univ. Press, New Haven 1958.
7. EHRENWALD, J.: Telepathy and Medical Psychology, W. W. Norton, New York 1948.
8. STRAUSS, E.: cf. Chapter X (4).
9. MINKOWSKI, E.: cf. Chapter X (7).
10. BINSWANGER, L.: Insanity as a Life-Historical Phenomenon and as Mental Disease: The Case of Ilse, in: Existence, ed. R. May, Basic Books, New York 1958.
11. GEBSATTEL, V. E.: The World of the Compulsive, ibid.
12. MAUPIN, E. W.: Zen Buddhism: A Psychological Review, Psychedelic Review 5, 1965.
13. CAVANNA, R. and SERVADIO, E.: ESP Experiments with LSD 25 and Psilocybin. Parapsychology Foundation, New York 1964.
14. CAMPBELL, J.: cf. Chapter I (13).
15. OSTROW, M.: Drugs in Psychoanalysis and Psychotherapy, Basic Books, New York 1962.
16. KIELHOLTZ, A.: Von Kairos zum Problem der Kurpfuscherei, Schweizer Med. Woschr. 86, 35. 1956.
17. ELLENBERGER, H.: A Clinical Introduction to Psychiatric Phenomenology and Existential Analysis, in: Existence, ed. R. May et al., Basic Books, New York 1958.
18. KELMAN, H.: cf. Chapter XII (9).
——————— "Kairos" and the Therapeutic Process, Journ. Existential Psychiatry I, 2, 1960.
19. BENEDICT, R.: Patterns of Culture, Houghton Mifflin, Boston 1934.
20. CANNON, B.: The Wisdom of the Body, W. W. Norton, New York 1932.
21. JAMES, W.: Pragmatism, Longmans, Green and Co., New York 1907.
22. MURPHY, G.: Human Potentialities, Basic Books, New York 1958.
23. GOLDSTEIN, K.: The Organism, Beacon Press, Boston 1963.

Part Three

Not by Myth Alone: Attempt at Integration

—XV—

Myth, Medication and the Leverage Hypothesis

With all the emphasis placed in our preceding discussion on myth, on myth-induced existential shifts and both the patient's and the therapist's regression in the service of treatment, it may be as well to try to strike a balance between these primitive ingredients of the therapeutic process and its more conventional scientific aspect. Clearly, it is never myth or regression to mythical dimensions alone that "cures." Nor does science or the scientific method divorced from the therapist's motivations and personal impact upon the patient. It is the proper blend of the two ingredients—even though the odds against stability of such a psychological compound may seem to be formidable.

On the most elementary level the power of myth is illustrated by the medicine man or priestly healer, with his sense of magic omnipotence brought to bear upon the sick who pin their faith on his powers of healing. Myth, at this stage, is a set of tacitly implied yet firmly held convictions serving as the rationale for the healer's magic rites and ceremonies and for the recital of his supernatural credentials. On a more sophisticated level myth may be invoked by way of a direct appeal to the priest's tutelary spirits, gods or patron saints. More or less dramatically staged healing rituals are predicated on much the same principles. Words, gestures or symbolic actions are used to force the hand of the divinity; to coax or coerce it to effect the desired course of events. The slower the god's response to such an appeal, the more frantic becomes the magician or medicine man's behavior and the greater the fervor of the priest's prayers or devotional exercises.

We noted how, in the course of the millennia, magic, ritualistic gesture, and the purported omnipotence of movement were gradually replaced by the more economical magic of words, symbols and metaphors. In the end myth served to articulate and to rationalize a wide variety of healing practices, mental or physical. Paracelsus' Weapon Salve or Digby's Powder of Sympathy were supposed to cure wounds at a distance. Mesmer's Animal Magnetism was claimed to be equally effective in diverse nonsurgical afflictions of body and mind. With the formulation of such physical concepts as ether, energy, electric charge, or electromagnetic field, and with the advent of their psychological counterparts in terms of Bernheim's "nervous energy"; of Janet's *niveau mental*; of the Freudian or Jungian concepts of libido, we enter into the scientific phase of pyschotherapy.

162

Myth, at this stage, has been wholly obliterated, or at least camou-flaged, by formulations bearing all the hallmarks of science. In effect some of Freud's early associates tried to equate the concepts of physical energy and libido.[1] Thus, it was hoped, psychoanalysis would ultimately merge with the rest of scientific disciplines. This development towards increasing demythologization of psychotherapy, with the associated expurgation of magic and myth, is illustrated in Figure 1.

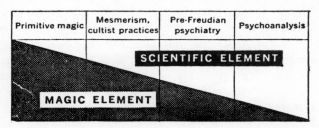

Fig. 1. (Reproduced from *New Dimensions of Deep Analysis, A Study of Telepathy in Interpersonal Relationships*, by Jan Ehrenwald, 1954.)

Yet we have seen that even at the present high water mark of scientific psychotherapy the analyst's inner certainty as to the validity of his doctrine has remained an important factor in securing the patient's doctrinal com-pliance, his positive transference, and, by indirection, his therapeutic re-sponse. Still, if the therapist had embarked on his career with a ling-ering faith in his omnipotence, this has certainly been brought into the open and dispelled by his training analysis. Whatever remnants of such attitudes survived the purge are either driven underground or else they are relegated into the dubious realm of countertransference.

✿   ✿   ✿

Whether or not it is permissible to correlate the emotional charge attached to the therapist's theories with the power of myth is debatable. Some of my psychoanalytic friends have taken umbrage at my doing so and scoffed at the suggestion that magic and myth have not altogether been expurgated from our approach but have merely gone underground. Such critics seem to regard the continuity of historic development of psychotherapy from the medicine man to Freud as a matter of embarrassment, and any reference to surviving mythical elements in the Freudian system of thought little short of blasphemic. Myth in our scientific age has become nearly as repre-hensible as sex in Victorian society. This is why, on the face of it, Freud's system of thought has in effect become distinctly "mythophobic." Still, we noted that some of its basic postulates have nevertheless attained the per-suasive power of modern myths. By contrast to Jung's archetypes, they have graduated to become "neotypes," as it were. (See Chapter XI). It may well be that it is the very mythical underpinning which makes some of Freud's neotypes therapeutically effective. At the same time, however, it may account for the vehemence of partisan reaction to any threat involving the integrity of a dogmatic Freudian position.

The contrast between the emotional and at times explosive quality of partisan debate in this and in other fields of science is unmistakable. Physicists may differ among themselves as to the merits of the Maxwell-Faraday equations, or of Heisenberg's principle of uncertainty. Astronomers may hold opposing views regarding the "big bang" or "steady state" theory of the origin of the universe. But they are no longer in the habit of excommunicating each other from their respective scientific associations for doing so. This precisely has been a frequent occurrence in the history of modern psychotherapy. It has marred interdisciplinary communication up to our day.

At a recent professional convention I witnessed the furious outburst of a respected colleague against a speaker showing films of experimental neuroses in monkeys, purporting to disprove the validity of classical Freudian libido theory. "This man is a fraud, a criminal!" were some of the more printable epithets used in the ensuing private discussion. Needless to say that Jungian, Adlerian or Horneyan analysts are by no means less sensitive to critical scrutiny of their doctrines—to say nothing of the frankly belligerent tone of some recent anti-Freudian polemics by advocates of modern behavioral or desensitization therapies. So-called eclectics tend to display a much greater degree of tolerance with the positions of the diverse schools. It may be no coincidence that at the same time, they do not hold firmly established and sharply defined positions of their own. Such flexibility is conducive to greater understanding of other people's views. But it may leave the eclectic adrift amidst the currents and crosscurrents of scientific opinion of their time, with the attending intellectual uncertainties and adverse effects upon their therapeutic results.

We noted in Chapter XII that the integrity of a given, self-sealing, system of therapeutic thought is an indispensable prerequisite of the therapist's logically consistent approach to his patients. Yet his striking sensitiveness to whatever might be construed as an attack against the validity of his doctrine, is obviously more than a matter of intellectual intolerance or self-righteousness. Attacks, or even hints of such attacks, become a threat to the myth held by the group to which he owes his allegiance and thereby to his treasured personal myth. As in the case of the appendix which betrays its presence only when it is inflamed, any tampering with the therapist's myth becomes a noxious irritant, threatening his efficacy as a healer, undermining his professional prowess, his earning capacity—if not his masculine identity. Such reactions and overreactions to what amounts to a narcissistic injury are in effect the undesirable byproducts of what we described as regression in the service of treatment. For obvious reasons, such regression is not always confined to the job on hand. It may spread over related—or even unrelated—aspects of the therapist's professional life and may well strike the uninvolved observer as a show of excessive partisanship. However, it may be well to realize that the very vehemence of the therapist's reaction may merely reflect the intensity of his involvement and dedication to his personal myth. At the same time it may amount to a measure of the persistent viability of myth and unconscious motivation in the minds of even the most sophisticatd psychotherapists of our day.

Paradoxically, the unmasking of such unconscious attitudes still tends to offend the sensibilities of the champions of scientific orthodoxy. Like occasional telepathic incidents in the therapeutic situation, myth must be swept under the carpet or disowned as a political liability. Yet it is needless to say that here, as in other fields of science, political expediency should not stand in the way of objective inquiry. All the more so since, in the writer's experience, removal of the blind spot concealing the part played by myth—or constructive countertransference—in the analyst's mind by no means impairs his therapeutic impact upon the patient. On the contrary, the shock of recognition may be conducive to the analyst's newly gained capacity to admit (or readmit) myth into his frame of reference and thereby into his therapeutic armamentarium. Provided it does not serve as a cloak for delusion, the integration of the mythical level with his total personality is indeed an important step in his growth as a therapist. It is in effect merely another confirmation of a proven principle of the psychoanalytic method and should not call for apologies in the present context.

*　　*　　*

How then does the power of symbol, metaphor and myth effect the therapeutic process? To understand its *modus operandi* we have to realize that our thinking, language and other symbolic behavior is not apart from, but an integral part of, human nature and nature at large. Indeed nature and language are "inwardly akin," as L. Whorf put it.[2] Using a term introduced by gestalt psychologists, they are *isomorphic*. This is why one is capable of affecting the other. On the most primitive level, rites and incantations seek to influence the behavior of objects in the outside world, from rain clouds to broken bones or the heart of a reluctant lover. On a higher level of sophistication, e.g., in ancient Indian culture, this technique becomes *Mantram* or Mantric art, leading up to the familar Yoga practices. "Therein," we are told by Whorf, "the *Mantram* becomes the manifold of conscious patterns, contrived to assist the consciousness into the noumenal pattern world—whereupon it is 'in the driver's seat.' It can then set the human organism to transmit and amplify the thousandfold forces which such organism normally transmits only at unobservable low intensities."

On the other end of the scale we are confronted with the specialized formula language of the mathematician, the physicist or engineer, enabling him to perform highly sophisticated technological operations in his laboratory or power plant. Except for the biochemical, neurophysiological or related interventions made possible by these remote control effects of language, they fall outside the scope of the present inquiry.

There is, however, one area in which physiological interventions call for our special attention. We have seen that such psychotropic drugs as the diverse tranquilizers and energizers seem to be capable of doing just what the magic of words, symbols, metaphors and myths is cut out to do. Indeed, some authorities claim that drugs can do one better than words. By direct action upon the organism, they are said to be capable of bringing about changes which man's communicative behavior can effect laboriously and in a circuitous way only. Such consciousness expanding or psychedelic agents as mescaline, LSD 25 or psilocybin are credited with opening up to their users hitherto unknown realms of mystical or religious experience and creative self-expression.

This, it should be noted, has up until recently been considered the sole prerogative of the spoken word, of the written message, of a poem, a sacred text or, in the psychotherapeutic situation, of hypnotic suggestion, ventilation, or analytic interpretation. The fact is that each one of these seemingly heterogenous interventions with human personality has a differential leverage of its own, ranging from small to large, from helpful to harmful, from physiologically wholesome and ego-syntonic to frankly pathological or destructive to the individual.

Shifting our attention to symbolic communication, verbal and nonverbal, in a stricter sense, a graded scale of psychophysiological leverage effects is readily discernible. Clearly the leverage of the equation $3 \times 3 = 9$ will be minimal. Except for some hidden numerological meaning it may hold for the cabalist, it conveys a point of rather redundant information, and nothing else. But Goethe's Dr. Faust was overawed by the sight of the pentagram on the threshold of his study. His latter-day descendant, C. G. Jung, attributed profound archetypal significance to the figure four and considered the mandala a symbol of deep spiritual revelation. Viewed in this context, the *experiential* significance of the numerals 3, 4, or 5 is far in excess of their *referential* connotation. This is why their affective leverage may reach deep into a person's unconscious. This is still more true when the symbol is primarily of an experiential nature: when the Star-Spangled Banner or the Union Jack flutters in the breeze; when the Nazi swastika offends my sensibilities; when I am brought face to face with T. S. Eliot's Wasteland; or when Camus' version of the Sysiphus myth presses home to me the tragic aspects of the human situation. Thus my response to the spoken or written word, the impact of symbol, metaphor or myth ranges all the way from information, insight and edification, to the inner stirrings of affect and its psychosomatic corollaries; from goose pimples to palpitations; from tears to twinges of intestinal discomfort. There is, behavioristically speaking, a gradient of leverage effects possessed by a broad spectrum of symbolic or communicative behavior. The smallest leverage attaches to verbal cues whose effect is confined to cortical neurons and synapses. Their leverage effect increases with the overspill of affective response into various autonomic and sympathetic centers, and from there into the viscera, smooth muscles, glands or endocrine organs.

Needless to say that this vast array of psychological cues and concommitant responses cannot be compressed into the old S-R, or stimulus-response, formula. Cues emanating from outside are part of a highly complex field situation to which the individual responds in terms of his structural or autochthonous makeup; of his genetic programming; of his cultural experience, educational conditioning and various situational factors. In the psychoanalytic situation his response may be further determined by varying degrees of doctrinal compliance, by his positive or negative transference on the therapist.

We noted that perhaps the most effective cue emanating from the therapist's person is his personal myth. It is closely wrapped up with his conviction and unspoken promise that he shall be able to help the patient; and it is sustained and reinforced by the patient's trust and expectancy that he will indeed be helped. Yet here again, the leverage effect of the therapist's myth, and the patient's trust and expectancy depends on a wide variety of factors, personal and interpersonal, mental and physical, psychosocial, religious and cultural. We have seen that the efficacy of both major and minor myths varies with the stages of their life cycle, with the spontaneity and authenticity of convictions held by their protagonists and with the therapist's capacity to inspire confidence in his patients. Their effect may be aided by his skill in exploiting his personal prestige or, if necessary, by his readiness to dispense with the paraphernalia of professional authority. It will be recalled that Mesmer's personal myth was shortlived both in Vienna and during his sojourn in Paris. Freud, aware of such pitfalls, strenously objected to being hailed as a healer in the tradition of pre-scientific psychotherapy, and ended up as a *medicin malgré lui*. On the other hand, we have seen Jung going all out in his affirmation of myths and their therapeutic dispensation, ultimately attaining world wide fame as a scientist gone mystic.

By contrast, a new generation of psychoanalysts tends to be frankly embarrassed by the growing popular acceptance of what has become the Freudian myth. Yet we noted that this very fact may presage a turning of the tide and the impending decline of the faddist phase which has been superimposed on the analytic movement. This should by no means detract from the validity of basic psychoanalytic tenets. But it is likely to reduce the popular appeal of psychoanalysis and its reputation as a psychiatric panacea.

Some of the recent extravagant claims of therapeutic results attained with various methods of behavioral therapy have a distinctly faddist quality. Whatever the merits of the procedure used, an obsessive-compulsive neurosis of many years standing which is claimed to be cured in six weeks of conditioning is more likely to have responded to the magic of a newly emerging myth, aided by doctrinal compliance. There is reason to believe that gains of this order will be as short-lived as the myth itself. The same may be true for the striking therapeutic effects attributed to psychedelic drugs. Here too claims of lasting improvements, including "rapid" changes of personality, have been made.[3] However, only time will tell how much of the change is due to the drug itself, how much to the myth shared by patient and therapist, and how much to doctrinal compliance and to particularly impressive placebo effects.

Nevertheless, so far as short-term results are concerned, some drugs do have a greater leverage effect than others. They circumvent the magic of words; they dispense with the paraphernalia of affective overspill or neurohumeral synaptic transmission spreading over the network of the central and vegetative system. Mixing our metaphor, certain pharmacological agents seem to be going straight to the biochemical heart of the gray matter, cortical or subcortical.

Yet myth, in this respect, may well run a close second to drugs. The powerful leverage of the "Faith that Cures"[4] upon psychosomatic or even organic disease have been amply documented. It is illustrated by the testimonial tablets in the shrines of Epidaurus or Ephesus. It has been borne out by the investigations of the Bureau des Constatations Medicales at Lourdes and confirmed by more recent findings. On a more pedestrian plane, the disappearance of warts or the raising of blisters by hypnotic suggestion has been established in a series of well controlled experiments.[5] Whatever be their *modus operandi*, they obviously involve a chain of tangible neurophysiological events triggered off somewhere in the "higher reaches" of the human mind. It is true, changes of this type are of a lesser order of magnitude than those obtained by direct pharmacological action. But they affect more than the biochemical dimension of personality: they affect man as a whole. This is why drugs alone are still less likely to produce the desired results than myth "alone." Myth, in effect, never occurs alone. It articulates with man's total experience, mental and physical, and we have seen that its points of articulation can be traced over the whole expanse of his individual and racial history.

❉   ❉   ❉

What then is the contribution of myth to the process of scientific psychotherapy? First, it sets the stage for the professional encounter of patient and therapist. It is true that under modern conditions, the term ideology may be used in preference to myth. But we emphasized in the introductory chapters that effective ideologies are in fact the latter-day derivatives, or neotypes, of ancient mythical concepts. A patient seeking psychotherapeutic help is steered into treatment by widely held ideologies, and a climate of opinion favoring such a step. In the Soviet Union today psychoanalysis is not likely to get to first base. A Puerto Rican or Haitian patient in New York City, still committed to his native voodoo creed, will have little faith in the analytic couch. But a middle or upper class urban intellectual will take to it like Tarzan to the trees. He is likely to enter the treatment situation with the proper expectations and reasonable confidence in the psychoanalytic approach.

We noted, furthermore, that such attitudes are reinforced by the patient's acceptance of his role as an analytic patient; by his contractual agreement to pay his fee; by his succumbent position; by his ready surrender of conscious control over his associations. All this, coupled with the analyst's silence and his passive, nondirective attitude, may be conducive to what we described as the existential shift. It is true that these paraphernalia of analytic technique are based on thoroughly rational dynamic principles. But they are overdetermined at the same time by vestiges of magic and myth in the analytic approach. As such they give added momentum to the existential shift.

In Chapters V, VI and XIII we reviewed in more detail therapeutic techniques in which magical and mythical elements have remained closer to the surface. Hypnosis, waking suggestion or existential therapy are cases in point. In these examples, we noted, the existential shift is in itself one of the decisive factors in bringing about the desired response. Hypnosis in particular was discussed as a paradigm of magic operating well-nigh undisguised under contemporary conditions. The miracle monger or successful charlatan of our day is on the other end of the continuum. In his case blind faith in his own magic, if not outright madness, may substitute for method. Yet here again the shift from pragmatic, cause-and-effect attitudes to a primitive, prelogical level of functioning is unmistakable. The augur may smile at the thought of his trickery. But he too may occasionally be carried away by it. Once more we are confronted with the principle of dual causality and with man's conflicting loyalty to his two masters.

The neurophysiological concomitants of the existential shift are largely a matter of conjecture. But it is reasonable to assume that the deeper it goes, the more intimate its articulation with the mental, physical and spiritual aspects of personality, the greater is the probability of the shift resulting in an actual change in the existing adaptational state of the individual, including his ego defenses. Given favorable circumstances, the shift may jolt him out from the baseline of an existing pathological homeostasis. It is a matter of clinical experience that such an abrupt change may indeed help the patient break out from the vicious circle of neurotic behavior and lead to an "auspicious" circle operating in the reverse direction. Such authorities as Franz Alexander, Lewis Wolberg, Judd Marmor and others have pointed out that this may in effect be a crucial factor in the dynamics of brief psychotherapy.

All too often the auspicious circle fails, however, to materialize. The existential shift may lead to temporary symptomatic improvement. The patient's doctrinal compliance may persuade him, as well as his therapist, that major progress has been made. A flurry of excitement may greet the advent of an important new departure in therapeutic theory and practice. Short-lived successes based on this chain of events may bring a new crop of equally short-lived therapeutic successes in a growing number of patients. Yet in the absence of basic changes in underlying dynamics, the previous neurotic defense structure is soon reestablished. This may in turn lead once more to a precariously balanced homeostatic adjustment, with either the old or a new set of symptoms making their appearance. Thus the new nostrum, theory or therapeutic technique may prove to be yet another instance of the countless myths that, having outlived their life cycle, fall by the wayside.

It is this disappointing record of the mythical element in the history of psychotherapy—and in the history of ideas at large—that has given rise to the popular representation of myth as a synonym of lie. In the end, scientific psychotherapy has seen no option but to disavow all association with its redoubtable legacy of the past. It proceeded to empty the outgrown, and all but inanimate baby out with the bathwater—regardless of its remaining vitality.

REFERENCES

1. BERNFELD, S. and FEITELBERG, S.: Ueber Psychische Energie, Libido und deren Messbarkeit, Imago, Vienna, XVI, 1930.

2. WHORF, L.: Language, Thought and Reality, The MIT Press, Cambridge, Mass. 1964.
3. COHEN, S.: The Beyond Within, Atheneum, New York 1964.
4. CHARCOT, J. M.: La Foi qui Guerit, Archiv. Neurol. 25, 72-87, 1893.
5. ULLMAN, M.: On the Psyche and Warts, Psychosomat. Med. 21,6. 1959 and 22,1. 1960.

—XVI—

Three Phases of the Therapeutic Process

In the light of the preceding argument, what then is the *modus operandi* of psychotherapy? Can it be summed up in a few descriptive sentences, equally applicable to primitive healing, pre-Freudian psychotherapy, psychoanalysis or other forms of psychological treatment?

We have seen that the opening phase of virtually all forms of psychotherapy is characterized by the existential shift initiated by the patient's expectations and by his response to the external paraphernalia of the treatment situation. This is reinforced by subtle cues emanating from what was described as the analyst's therapeutic presence: by cues signalling his motivation to help; his own therapeutic expectations and his capacity for emphathetic understanding of the patient's plight. These influences are in turn outgrowths of the therapist's personal myth. They are rooted in largely unconscious or preconscious ideas clustered around a nucleus of magic belief and narcissistic phantasy. While phantasies of this order are usually exposed and repudiated during the therapist's training analysis, they are not altogether obliterated but channeled into an elaborate system of emotionally charged convictions regarding the efficacy of his approach. As a general rule, these convictions are not amenable to empirical proof or scientific validation. They are largely due to what we described as the therapist's regression in the service of treatment. Like myths, they may prove highly effective, regardless of their truth value.

It is this quality of the therapist's anticipations, conscious and unconscious, which may make them the vehicles of the patient's doctrinal compliance—with all its implications. One implication is what was termed the myth-induced leverage effect: the psychological leverage of words, symbols and myths, with their attending overspill on various levels of the central nervous system and personality as a whole.

We noted that these features of the first phase of treatment are common to both primitive healing and highly sophisticated methods of psychoanalysis; to "brief" psychotherapy; behavioral therapy; existential analysis; etc. Whatever their avowed purpose or theoretical preconceptions, their opening phase is characterized by the existential shift; by various degrees of the myth-induced leverage effect and the affective overspill, leading to new levels of adaptation. That it is the modern schools of analytic psychotherapy which have developed the rationale, the conceptual tools and the techniques needed to consolidate the gains attained in the first phase is another matter.

Yet for reasons pointed out on an earlier page, psychoanalysis has itself been slow in realizing the part played by this aspect of the therapeutic approach. As a result, the opening phase of analytic treatment has not been altogether exempt from the principle of trial and error. This is illustrated by a problem of therapeutic management Freud had encountered early in his career. He found that one group of patients, the schizophrenics, were not amendable to the analytic approach.[1] By contrast to the neurotics, they were not "analyzable." He tried to account for this difficulty by distinguishing between so-called narcissistic and transference neuroses, that is to say, between patients capable and those incapable of positive transference. We have learned since then that schizophrenics, character neurotics and certain delinquents do respond to modifications of the classical techniques even though this is difficult to reconcile with Freud's early theories.

In the light of the leverage hypothesis the explanation is close at hand. Patients once considered analytically inaccessible are those who fail to respond to the existential shift and the initial leverage effect which should be elicited by the treatment situation. Individuals of this type are not responsive to the analyst's "therapeutic presence." They do not share his personal myth. Their habitual ego defenses prevent the requisite existential shift. For them the analyst's detached, impersonal, nondirective approach merely amounts to a continuation of whatever emotional deprivations and frustrations they had encountered in their formative years. They require a more active, more directive therapeutic "presence"; they need a therapist capable of bringing them back from their state of isolation and withdrawal. On the other hand, the "average" analytic patient, at the turn of the century, had been exposed to a plethora of parental authority and unsolicited guidance by his educators, clergymen or superiors. He must have welcomed the advent of the nonauthoritarian, nondirective analyst with a sigh of relief.

Today's detached, alienated character neurotic poses yet another problem. He is ready to reach out for companionship, guidance and support. Yet on finding himself on the analytic couch, he may respond much like Freud's narcissistic schizophrenic. He may feel once more cast out into a spiritual void, into a vacuum of interpersonal relationships from which he had sought to escape in the first place.

It is characteristic of the tortuous course of the history of psychotherapy—and of the history of ideas in general—that modern existential therapists tend to go all out in the opposite direction. Their approach seems to be geared to the needs of the detached, alienated personality of our time: to Robert Musil's *Man Without Qualities;* to Sartre's *Antoine Roquentin;* to Saul Bellow's *Herzog.* The existentialist therapist renounces analytic detachment and reserve and offers fellowship, togetherness and the healing encounter in their place. This, it should be noted, is quite obviously the treatment of choice in patients suffering from the consequences of up-bringing in a cold, detached, emotionally deprived environment. It may provide the impetus to jolt them out of their pathological level of adaptation and help bring about the desired existential shift. But it may send other patients into headlong flight, looking for the analytic couch as a sanctuary from the after effects of their particular brand of early traumatic experiences.

All this should remind us once more that the problems encountered right in the opening phases of psychotherapy are closely interwoven with the prevailing spirit of the time, with cultural and situational factors. The popular image of psychoanalysis today is changing. The analytic couch, as one of the stage props of the American scene, seems to be losing its magic. The Freudian myth, thanks to mass produced replicas of the original, is being increasingly demythologized and debunked—a victim of its very popularity. We emphasized that this does not detract from the validity of the analytic position. But it is apt to diminish the myth-induced leverage effect of the analytic situation and to generate renewed demands for yet other variations on the Freudian or Jungian or Adlerian theme. Such new departures as the diverse methods of brief psychotherapy or various methods of group therapy, psychodrama, or sociodrama have indeed proved valuable additions to available techniques. Other changes, brought about merely for the sake of change itself and lacking proper appreciation of their underlying dynamics, remain subject to the principle of trial and error. Initial successes in their opening phases are not enough to keep them afloat for any length of time.

As a general rule, however, the myth-induced existential shift and its attending leverage effects are of decisive importance for the patient's response to psychotherapy. By accident or by design, they carry him back to the early stages of his personal development, thus duplicating his experiences in the postnatal period with all it has in store for the unfolding of a person's future life history. For better or for worse, the opening phase may thus determine the subsequent course of the patient's psychotherapy in its entirety.

What has been described as temporary transference cures is in effect due to this state of affairs. Brief psychotherapy, on the other hand, is largely based on the methodical exploitation of the momentum gained by the patient's initial response to the therapist's myth, coupled with his own therapeutic expectations. It is an approach designed to take the best advantage of the opening phase of the treatment. At the same time it seeks to telescope into it some of the therapeutic accomplishments usually reserved for the second and third phase.

*   *   *

In most other forms of analytic psychotherapy the opening phase is usually followed by the unfolding analytic process in a stricter sense. The psychoanalyst, unlike the primitive healer, is not satisfied with using the momentum gained by the existential shift in order to consolidate the treatment relationship and to perpetuate his myth. He seeks to exploit the patient's initial response for the long haul of methodical analysis. In so doing he moves into the second phase of the treatment process. The second phase is concerned with the management of the transference relationship and transference neurosis, with interpreting resistances, dreams and free associations. The goal is to promote understanding, to provide "insight," to fill in amnestic gaps with attending cathartic release and corrective emotional experience.

It is this phase which is generally considered as psychoanalysis *par excellence*. It is in effect outside the province of most nonanalytic methods of psychotherapy, relying as they do either on the accident of myth-induced existential shifts alone, or on diverse methods of suggestion, persuasion, exhortation and reeducation.

On the other hand, psychoanalysis, as well as most other methods of analytic psychotherapy, usually include elements of education and reeducation in their approach. This is done under the heading of psychoanalytic "working through" based on tacitly implied principles of learning theory. Franz Alexander's concept of corrective emotional experiences as part of a process of guided emotional maturation;[2] S. Rado's emphasis on imparting on the patient the emotional skills needed to cope on the level of "self-reliant cooperation" with his problems is specifically geared to this principle.[3] In a similar vein, Judd Marmor has rightly pointed out that reeducation is an integral aspect of the analytic process and may be involved in it right from the outset.[4] He also noted that even the detached, nondirective psychoanalyst cannot help but influence his patient by serving as a model or ideal figure after whom he tends to fashion himself.

The period of "working through," of guidance and reeducation is the third phase of the psychoanalytic process. It is in effect closely interwoven with every aspect of the second, the psychodynamic, phase and overlaps with it. Making allowance for this tendency to overlapping, a parallel between later stages of the child-parent relationship and the patient's experience in the ongoing treatment situation suggests itself. While the existential shift triggered off in the first phase carried him back to the early infantile stage, the analyst, acting *in loco parentis*, now carries him through an abridged—or not quite abridged—phase of learning, of methodical re-education. It is the phase of labor following the phase of love and its tempering effect in the transference relationship. It is the stage of optional guidance, available for the asking; of the drawing up of blueprints for a future no longer dependent on parents or parental figures.

We noted that the three phases do not necessarily follow one another in the described sequence. We have seen in Chapter XIII and XIV that the phase of the myth-induced existential shift may come into the picture late in the day and that, on the other hand, one or the other of the three phases may be skipped or remain in abeyance. In effect, Phase I has been con-spicuously absent, or at least ignored, in classical psychoanalysis. Pre-scientific psychotherapy, on the other hand, tends to rely exclusively on the first phase. In the absence of dynamic insight, concepts and formulations, it is governed by the principle of trial and error. By contrast, such scientific approaches as Pavlovian conditioning, various types of behavioral or de-sensitization therapy, dispense with myth and its latter-day derivatives. Behavioral therapists, like modern mystics, tend to close their eyes to its operation.

❋   ❋   ❋

Psychoanalysis, as it is conceived here, utilizes the myth shared by therapist and patient in a methodical way. It permits, and indeed en-courages, both the patient's and the therapist's regression in the service of the treatment, much in the same way that it has recognized its importance in the creative artist's approach to his work. Viewed in this light, Phase I can indeed be compared with the gestation or early postnatal period of the child. But the momentum gained from the creative impulse is not enough to bring it to fruition. It must be channelled into the dynamics of the unfolding doctor-patient relationship in the second phase. It must be re-captured and deployed in an interpersonal situation geared to the *un-learning* of old and to the *learning* of new behavioral patterns and ad-justments in Phase III. Psychoanalysis, in its revised and expanded form, is neither a breeding ground of myth, an exercise in psychodynamics nor a substitute for parental or postparental education alone. It is the proper blend of the three ingredients.

If this is true, each generation of psychoanalysts, indeed every individual therapist, will have to do more than acquire the professional skills and ex-periences required by his academic curriculum. He will have to devote equal attention to acquiring the spiritual discipline, to develop the cultural awareness and the sense of values which forms the matrix of his evolving personal myth and therapeutic presence. The gift of intuition may be one of the by-products of this development. Yet it is more than an added frill of his growing professional proficiency. It is the learned capacity to mar-shall, at a moment's notice, the cumulative store of data that has accrued to him in his lifetime, enabling him to come up with the assurance of an electronic computer, with the therapeutic response appropriate to a given situation. Here, again, relying on myth, on dynamic understanding or on the mere accumulation of knowledge is not enough. Nor is the analyst's training or training analysis. Indeed, undue emphasis on his formal educa-tion may easily lead to loss of spontaneity, to the stifling of his personal myth and to the irretrievable restriction and demythologization of his whole mode of existence.

The drawbacks attending a swing to the opposite extreme should be equally guarded against. The mystic, the Zen master, even an occasional existential analyst, may insist on giving both the first and the last word to myth. Turning the table on Freud, he may leave analytic therapy—like the swordplay of the Samurai, or the art of the Sumiye painter—to intuition alone. He may try to make the *conscious unconscious*, instead of the other way around. —

The psychoanalyst, as he is conceived here, is guided by scientific pre-cepts and principles. He is committed to the supremacy of reason. But he is also aware of the principle of dual causality. He affirms the continuity of his professional heritage with magic and myth. Yet, in contrast to his predecessors, he knows that he is doing so. He is aware of the historic antecedents—of the multiple stratifications (or *Geschichte*)—of his disci-pline. He is cognizant of the many imponderables of his therapeutic "presence." But he will not acknowledge defeat in coming to grips with both the rational and the irrational aspects of his personality structure and in mobilizing them for the purpose of treatment.

Psychotherapy is in effect the consistent application of techniques that aim at integrating conflicting levels of the patient's personality. The patient seeks to retrieve—or to regain—that measure of freedom and mastery which he had lost to his illness. The therapist's job is to help him in this pursuit. But he can do so only to the extent that he is capable of combining his command of technical skills with a modicum of control over his deepest motivations to help. He must be able to "regress" in the service of treat-ment. But while in the state of purported regression, he must never lose sight of the goal toward which he wants to progress.

Put in psychoanalytic terms, extending conscious controls over those areas of the ego which have been lagging in its maturational sequence or which have regressed to more primitive adaptive solutions is one of the major objectives of analytic treatment and of personal growth in general. It is the hallmark of the synthetic functions of the ego, holding its own against the threat of disorganization and entropic decay. The psychoanalyst, joining hands in this venture with his patient, may profess to be merely engaged in the pursuit of his professional routine. But if this is true, part of his professional routine may consist in glossing over, ignoring or camouflaging his personal myth. The fact is that trying to strengthen the ego's synthetic function is merely a demythologized version of Plato's fable of the Two Horses, with a view of putting the Charioteer back in the driver's seat, or of St. Augustine's doctrine of restoring disjointed parts of the soul so as to make it whole again.

REFERENCES

1. FREUD, S.: c.f. Chapter VIII (2a).
2. ALEXANDER, F.: c.f. Chapter XI(22).
3. RADO, S.: c.f. Chapter XIII (11).
4. MARMOR, J.: c.f. Chapter VIII (15).
      ―――――― Psychoanalytic Therapy and Theories of Learning, in: Science and Psychoanalysis, ed. J. Masserman, Vol. VII, Grune & Stratton, New York 1964.

— XVII —

Psychotherapy: Short Term or Long Term?
Illustrative Case Histories

What is the relevance of our three phases of the therapeutic process to the practice of psychotherapy? How do our formulations affect one of the major decisions confronting the therapist at the beginning of treatment: his choice between short-term versus long-term therapy or "classical" analysis?

The question itself implies that the therapist (or the patient) are in a position to make the choice. Unfortunately, this is rarely the case. A therapist lacking proper psychoanalytic training will of necessity resort to one of the briefer forms of treatment—analytic or otherwise. On the other hand, a duly trained psychoanalyst may be led to ignore the possibility of brief therapy in preference to what Jules Masserman called "long term medical tax reduction until 'insight' is achieved."[1]

Practical limitations or financial considerations of this order must not tip the balance in favor of one decision or the other. Unfortunately, more compelling clinical criteria to determine the therapist's course of action are difficult to formulate. The story of the 17th century general exhorting his troops to put up a good fight since it marked the beginning of the Thirty Years' War is apocryphal. Nor is it a case of self-fulfilling prophesy. But Franz Alexander may have had just this contingency in mind when he cautioned his fellow analysts against routinely preparing their patients for years of hard labor on the analytic couch.[2] Such a prediction may indeed lead to the expected results. A judicious decision can only be based on a tentative appraisal of the patient's personality; of his ego resources or ego strength; on the evaluation of his capacity to cope with stress; and on his response to what Alexander called trial interpretations. In short, the decision requires a preliminary "trial analysis"—to say nothing of making allowance for the patient's social class, solvency or income bracket.[3,4]

According to Lewis Wolberg, the best strategy is "to assume that every patient, irrespective of diagnosis, will respond to short-term treatment, unless he proves himself refractory to it.[5] The difference between Wolberg's and Alexander's positions is perhaps merely one of semantics, but it may well affect the ratio of patients chosen for either one or the other form of treatment.

Put in our terms, the decision should be contingent on the patient's capacity to derive more than temporary benefits from the existential shift

179

effected in the opening phase of the treatment. The question, to quote Wolberg again, is whether the shift is capable of liberating constructive forces in the individual, propelling him towards further spontaneous growth; whether it succeeds in setting up chain reactions that become self-perpetuating. The question is, whether the shift jolts the patient out of what Raymond Waggoner called a *regressive* form of adaptation or to a more *progressive* adaptational pattern.[6]

As pointed out in the preceding chapter, proper evaluation of the patient's response in the opening phase usually provides the answer to these questions. This is illustrated by the following case history:

Charlie B. is a man of 23 who was referred to me by Dr. W., his general practitioner. Dr. W. is a "graduate" of one of my post-graduate courses in psychiatry offered to general practitioners. He was therefore well aware of the existing psychiatric problem. Charlie had been married for 1½ years yet he stayed away from his wife for several nights a week to drink and play cards with his buddies. He was a law student but got hopelessly bogged down in his academic work and admitted that he had only "stuck it out" because of pressure from his father. The older Mr. B. is a self-made man who wanted his son to have a better start in life than he himself had in his youth. He managed to get Charlie admitted to college, financed his studies, paid for his apartment, etc. He was a controlling, authoritarian person, trying to run the family with an iron hand. Charlie never dared to rebel openly against him, and his drinking was a substitute for his subdued rebelliousness. At the same time it expressed his protest against his wife who, he felt, had likewise become a demanding and controlling figure in his life. Charlie felt guilty for his misdemeanor, drank more to allay his guilt feelings, and became increasingly contrite and depressed.

He was sullen and uncommunicative during his first interview. Faced with a new doctor with a properly beefed-up reputation, he took it for granted that he would once more be put through the third degree of harangues and exhortations, followed by an ultimatum to mend his ways or lose his father's financial support.

The therapist's unexpectedly permissive, nonauthoritarian, *laissez-faire* attitude took Charlie by complete surprise. Instead of trying to cash in on the reputation carefully built up by the referring physician, the new doctor met the patient in terms of what can be described as his "anti-myth"—or rather, he adjusted his myth to the patient's needs at a moment's notice, as it were. Like the sailor mentioned in the Preface, the therapist changed the position of his sail and turned his craft at a sharp angle so as to make the best use of the prevailing wind pattern—or of the patient's expectations and responsiveness to his therapeutic "presence." Apparently this alone sufficed to bring about the existential shift. Charlie was visibly relaxed by the end of the session. We agreed to discuss plans for the future the next time.

The plan was simple: it was to meet the patient's, and not his father's, needs for a future career. Evidently, Charlie had been forced all along to live beyond his intellectual means. He was unfit for academic studies, bored by books and unable to concentrate on his courses. He wanted to work as a carpenter, to tinker about the house and have a good time with his buddies. In addition, he obviously had an unresolved Oedipal conflict and problems of latent homosexuality. Yet his whole background, his low intelligence and lack of motivation, made him ineligible for psychoanalysis.

Nevertheless, the initial momentum gained by the existential shift, and the explicit approval of his plan to drop out of law school brought about a prompt improvement of the clinical picture. His depression lifted; he stopped drinking and spending long hours playing cards with his friends. Dr. W. patiently explained to Charlie's father why his son would be better off in a more menial occupation. The plan was ultimately adopted by the family. Treatment was terminated after the fourth weekly session. Subsequently Charlie was admitted as an apprentice to a trade union. He is now doing well on what for him is a more congenial level of adaptation. That this adaptation includes occasional prolonged sessions of drinking and a game of cards should be mentioned by way of a footnote only.

It should also be noted, however, that Charlie's favorable response to brief psychotherapy was by no means due to the myth-induced existential shift alone, characteristic of the opening phase of the treatment. It was based on the proper dynamic understanding of his problem. This served as a guide for the therapist's active intervention—without the need for deeper analytic interpretations, which would at any rate have gone beyond the patient's comprehension. Nevertheless, reeducation in a minor key was an important feature of our brief contact. The patient's quick response to this procedure was in turn due to the limited goals he had set for himself and to the relative low intensity of his intrapsychic conflict.

Our next patient, Miss Herma B., was already mentioned in Chapter XIV. She too responded favorably to the first phase of the therapeutic process. But in her case the myth-induced existential shift fell short of both the patient's and the therapist's goals of successful treatment. It will be recalled that after three months of hedging and maneuvering Herma confessed that for the past three years she had been addicted to Dexedrine and other amphetamine derivatives. Three weeks after her confession she made a complete break with her addiction and consented to a symbolic auto-da-fé of her remaining store of drugs. This dramatice turn of events was followed by a marked letup of her pattern of compulsive hoarding, obsessive rumination, and endless dawdling in the bathroom. Her erratic sleeping habits were normalized, she went to bed and got up at ordinary hours. After three years of idleness she found employment in her previous line of work and soon reached the salary she had prior to her illness. Thus Herma became a graduate of the first phase of treatment. But from then on therapy remained stalemated. She was analytically unproductive. She remembered nothing from her childhood, had no dreams to report and tried to fill the hour with small talk about her job, about babysitting with her nephews and nieces, about an old girl friend whom she planned to contact again, etc. There were no men on the horizon. A former boy friend, Bob, the jazz musician and first supplier of her "happy pills," had phoned her but she had given him the brushoff. She was satisfied with continuing to live in her parents' house and to babysit for her sister on weekends.

How did Herma's initial improvement come about? We noted that it was largely due to an existential shift triggered by the analyst's therapeutic presence and "personal myth." Put in the simplest terms, and at the risk of being repetitive, the myth sprang from the therapist's belief that, against all odds, he would ultimately be able to help the patient. He knew that in Herma's eyes he had been, from the outset, surrounded by the aura of the "healer." Even before she met the therapist in person, he had become her father substitute in two ways: first he had been her sister-rival's analyst, glamorized in the afterglow of a successful treatment. Now it was Herma's turn to take possession of her sister's doctor and to live with him happily ever after. Unfortunately, Herma had also been only too glad to take her rival's place in the parental home and to establish herself as their "only" daughter. Her emotional immaturity, her infantile behavior, and her lack of motivation to assume more than a minimum of adult responsibilities pointed in the same direction. In these circumstances the rewards of methodical analysis could not possibly compete with her continued need for childish dependence on her family and with her thinly veiled homosexual attachment to her sister. Analytically speaking, Herma's improvement was thus largely due to positive transference on her therapist, aided by identification with her hated and beloved sister. She chose "flight into health" instead of coming to grips with her unresolved Oedipal and homosexual problems.

Our interpretation adds, however, a new dimension to this picture. The circular process of feedback touched off by the meeting of the therapist and the patient's dovetailing myths and expectations, provided the leverage for the ensuing existential shift. The associated affective overspill made it then possible for the patient to give up her drug and to attain a new baseline of homeostatic adaptation, mental and physical. At this point, however, the effected leverage lost its momentum. In the absence of deeper dynamic changes in her drive pattern and personality structure, she fell back on a new set of defenses, bringing out her underlying character neurosis which had temporarily assumed the dimensions of a full-fledged obsessive-compulsive trend.

*   *   *

On the face of it, Herma's case is an example of an essentially myth-induced existential shift leading to symptomatic improvement. In this respect it resembles results achieved by various pre-Freudian schools of psychotherapy, with all their attending shortcomings. There are, however, points of difference. First, the therapist was aware of the dynamics involved in both his and the patient's expectations. Consequently he was in a position to exploit their respective myths in the service of the treatment. Secondly, the proper evaluation of the limitations of the existential shift as well as of the limiting factors in the existing pathology and personality structure made a rational therapeutic management of the problem possible. Thus, instead of relying on the principle of trial and error, the treatment was guided by essentially dynamic considerations.

Our next case, Mrs. Florence G., aged 29, was discussed before in Chapter XII to illustrate the part played by doctrinal compliance in the patient's therapeutic response. Prior to consulting me, Florence had been undergoing treatment with another therapist whom she left "in a huff," without having resolved her hostile transference upon him. She was a detached, alienated type of personality and her previous analyst's conventional approach had been unable to break through her defenses. In the light of these antecedents I decided against continuing her treatment along classical psychoanalytic lines and told her so.

Abandoning the couch and the traditional nondirective, impersonal approach, was in itself sufficient to initiate the existential shift in this case. The ensuing changes in the transference relationship have been described on page 125. They were ushered in by a dream featuring a "change in the North American climate"; an "inner upheaval or flood" from which the dreamer emerged as a new person. Florence herself interpreted this dream as a dream of birth or rebirth, comparable to *satori* of the Zen masters or to a veritable "peak experience."

It should be noted, however, that in this case the existential shift occurred at an advanced stage of the treatment, not in the opening phase. Nor was it an isolated incident unrelated to the dynamics of analytic therapy. On he contrary, it was in the wake of the patient's realization of her newly attained personal identity, through her experience of birth or rebirth, that all her previous analytic insight fell into place. She realized the part played in her neurosis by continued attachment to her father and by her unresolved transference to the previous analyst. But she also felt that the time had come when she could no longer be satisfied with looking for father substitutes in the analytic relationship or in short-lived extramarital affairs. At the same time forgotten memories emerged from the past. She reached a new understanding of what she had learned in her preceding analysis, facilitating the process of corrective emotional experience.

Eleven months after starting therapy with me and five months following her dream of rebirth, Florence declared: "No, let's not talk about dreams any more. I feel everything is settled and finished. I do feel differently now. I don't know how it happened; all I know is my marriage is more pleasant than before. Things bother me less. What on earth did I complain about? I was so detached from it all . . . It's true this has not changed much. But strangely enough—I don't·mind. My husband isn't the one exciting man in my life; but he no longer just takes me for granted. Also, I no longer need him to *define* me . . . to understand me—with a capital U! I have a sense of myself, of my own . . . I was always looking for outside definition of myself . . . of who I am—what I should do or be. Whether I am wonderful or not wonderful . . . Sex? I think it is a sort of technical thing now . . . That has not changed much . . but this has something to do with my feeling for Toni, not with sex itself."

A number of similar observations could be quoted from my practice and from reports in current neo-Freudian literature. Yet here again, the new departure lies in the inclusion of the myth-induced existential shift into the analytic frame of reference and its exploitation for the goals of treatment.

The case of Florence G. brings out yet another point. By contrast to our previous examples of limited therapeutic goals, it underscores the crucial importance of coordinating and integrating the myth-induced (or drug-conditioned) existential shift and its attending affective overspill with the methodical analytic approach, with the management and interpretation of the transference neurosis, supplemented by the requisite period of "working-through" and reeducation.

On the other hand, it goes without saying that in the absence of myth and methodical dynamic interventions, all attempts at reeducation, persuasion and exhortation are apt to scrape the surface only. Like myth- or drug-induced existential shifts alone, they are unlikely to bring about lasting changes in the existing psychopathology or in the patient's personality structure.

Our fourth illustrative case history is of an altogether different order. It is the history of a paranoid schizophrenic who was referred to me for treatment at the age of 29. George M. is the only son of an obsessive-compulsive mother and of a weak, ineffectual father who tried to maintain his status in the family by occasional temperamental outbursts directed against his wife and his son. Throughout George's childhood and adolescent years, Mrs. M. had maintained her compulsive grip over the youngster, making him the victim of a prolonged symbiotic relationship, as described in several chapters of my book *Neurosis in the Family*.[7] The result was a boy with severely stunted ego development, caught in a robotlike dependent relationship with his mother. George shared his mother's obsessive cleanliness, coupled with disgust by his father's crude, brutish and generally "anal" behavior. He became obsessively concerned with men spitting, sneezing or clearing their throats in his presence. These morbid preoccupations gradually assumed delusional proportions. George felt he had become the target of a homosexual conspiracy against him. Yet he was equally afraid of women. In his dreams and phantasies they sapped his energies, or masturbated him while he was tied to a pole. The vagina was a dark cave into which he might fall and in whose poisonous fumes he might perish. Like with many other schizophrenics, "love" was a deadly peril to him, a revival of the stifling symbiotic bond with mother—or rather the danger of his return to symbiotic bondage with her.

It is needless to say that in this patient long-term analytic psychotherapy was the treatment of choice. It was predicated on our sketchy description of the underlying psychodynamics. His case was taken as yet another confirmation of the part played by early emotional deprivations and a severely disturbed family constellation in the making of the schizophrenic. His ultimate breakdown was viewed in terms of total defeat of his attempts to assert his male identity against the overpowering symbiotic mother. This in turn made him the helpless victim of anal-sadistic persecutors of the male sex, fashioned after the distorted image of father foisted upon him by his obsessive-compulsive mother.

Psychotherapy proceeded along the lines indicated by this interpretation of personal and interpersonal dynamics.[7] For the record, it should be noted that George's internist had found evidence of thyroid hyperfunction in his case and prescribed a thiouracil preparation for its treatment. His analytic therapy took more than four years, with two to three sessions per week. It was punctuated by occasional hostile outbursts, including the upsurge of murderous impulses against the therapist whenever he was not careful enough to refrain from sneezing or clearing his throat in the patient's presence. It is not necessary to go into details in the present context. Be it sufficient to note that the focus was largely on reviving and unmasking George's early symbiotic relationship with his mother; on encouraging his belated rebellion against her; and on trying to exorcise what G. Bychowski called, the maternal introject from his personality structure.[8] At the same time interpretations of men spitting, blowing their noses, or otherwise "misbehaving" in his presence as symbolic of sexual or anal-sadistic aggressions had a markedly cathartic effect upon the patient.

In the end, George succeeded in making the break from his mother. He began to see himself, as well as his father, in a new light: as fellow victims of his mother's neurotic illness. His paranoid delusions and ideas of reference receded. To the relief of the therapist he was no longer troubled by people coughing or sneezing around him. He met a shy, passive-compliant girl, two years his senior, and married her a year after terminating analysis. He is now father of two children. Ten years after our first contact his referring physician informs me that George has maintained his gains. His marriage is satisfactory; his children are doing well and he has made steady progress in his career.

This condensed report of the history and therapeutic management of George M. is in close concordance with widely accepted modifications of the analytic approach to schizophrenia. The only significant departure from current practice may· be the author's emphasis on interpersonal dynamics, on the patient's symbiotic bondage to his mother and active encouragement of his rebellion against it. In short, George's therapy was essentially psychoanalytic, based on establishing a working transference relationship; on more or less specific interpretations of his transference and transference resistances; on using various methods of ego-strengthening in his struggle with the maternal introject and with his instinctual drives, followed by systematic "working through" and reeducation. Apart from the existential shift involved in the newly formed transference relationship there was no apparent evidence, throughout the course of therapy, of the operation of the therapist's myth. Nor was the therapist aware of more than the usual share of his emotionally charged interest in schizophrenia and of his habitual therapeutic motivations in the patient's treatment.

❖   ❖   ❖

But one qualification has to be made at this point. On July 23, 1957, about two years after George's initial contact with me, he reported a dream which was strongly suggestive of a telepathic element involved in its manifest content. The dream was as follows: "I was talking to you. You said you will become a professor of engineering—to teach an engineering subject in my college. You were lecturing about a technical subject— it was totally different from what you are doing here. I thought: Why does he give up what he is doing? Must be a pretty smart guy to switch like that to something new."

His associations were unrevealing and merely expressed his profound ambivalence towards the therapist. The latter, he felt, tried once more to beat him and to outsmart him in his own specialty. At the same time, however, he was impressed by the therapist's competence and versatility which, he hoped, would ultimately effect some magic cure of his illness.

As mentioned in Chapter VII more light can be thrown on the dynamics underlying dreams of this order when we turn our attention to what happened in the therapist's life on the night the dream occurred. On that particular night, between 10 and 11 p.m., I had been engaged in a lively exchange with a friend, an optical engineer and inventor, who described to me in great detail a new anamorphic optical lens which he had helped to develop. He showed me a recent issue of the *Journal of the Society of Motion Picture and Television Engineers* containing an article about the invention. I leafed through the pages of the journal and dwelt at some length on my interest in communication theory, on the connection between neurophysiology and cybernetics, etc. I have to add that my friend had not been familiar with the term cybernetics, and that I may have taken some narcissistic pride in turning the tables and explaining a technological subject to him.

Viewed against this background, the correspondence between dream and actual event is highly suggestive of telepathy. The correspondence involves (1) my "switching" from psychiatry to an altogether different field; (2) my "lecturing" on the subject "like a professor"; (3) my delivering a "lecture" to an engineer—which happens to be the patient's profession. To the three points of correspondence we have to add the exact temporal coincidence between the two purportedly corresponding mental events.

A further criterion which lends added support to the telepathic interpretation of the dream is what I described as the *psychological significance* of such a reading. Failing to introduce the telepathic factor, the dream would have many gaps to our understanding. On the other hand, on taking its telepathic implications for granted, the deeper meaning of the dream is readily understood. The patient projects himself into the place of my friend the engineer. He is in fact my interlocutor. He expresses admiration for the wisdom of his therapist—and identifies with him. But at the same time he resents what appears to him one more instance of being outsmarted by a rival father figure. His very telepathic performance may well be interpreted as an attempt on the patient's part to restore the balance between himself and his rival. It is as though the patient were saying in his dream: "You may think, Doctor, that you are a smart guy and know all the answers in the field of both psychiatry and science. But I, the dreamer, know all about you—and here I am, pitting my own claim for omniscience against yours."

One more detail concerning the transference-counter-transference situation may be mentioned by way of a footnote only. The patient reported his dream on his last session prior to the therapist's departure for Zurich,

Switzerland, where he planned to present a paper to the Second International Psychiatric Congress dealing with the problem of schizophrenia.[7a] To be more specific, the paper dealt with schizophrenia and the telepathy hypothesis. Jule Eisenbud,[9] Montague Ullman[10] and myself,[7b] have pointed out that apparent coincidences of this kind are themselves psychologically significant. They are, in part, determined by the therapist's own preconscious needs to have his pet scientific hypotheses confirmed by the patients' productions. In short, on accepting a telepathic interpretation, the dream can readily be identified as yet another example of doctrinal compliance, this time of compliance with the therapist's emotionally charged views concerning the part played by telepathy in our mental organization, and in particular in schizophrenic patients. Brief mention was made in Chapter XI of a minor epidemic of similar incidents in analytic patients treated by colleagues interested in the same line of research.

❖ ❖ ❖

Political expedience of the kind advocated by Ernest Jones (see Chapter XI) should counsel against introducing this seemingly extraneous subject into our discussion. Why, one may ask, should an argument, primarily devoted as it is to matters of clinical interest, and already burdened by its recurrent emphasis on magic and myth, be further compromised by another digression into parapsychology? The answer is that, like Sir Edmond Hillary's Mount Everest, "It is there." It is there, even though the mountain, in our case, could better be compared to an iceberg, with only a small portion sticking out above the water line. Nevertheless, its "being there" has to be acknowledged as one of the facts of our mental life. More than that. Once we are satisfied with the *prima facie* evidence of what may amount· to telepathically induced doctrinal compliance we must realize that it is not likely to be confined to freakish occurrences of the order of George's telepathic dream. It may well have its impact upon the patient on a broader front.

The dream occurred after two years of analysis, at a time when first signs of improvement had already become discernible in the clinical picture. It was a time when the patient seemed to have become responsive not only to the therapist's fleeting preoccupation with the subject of telepathy but also to his overriding therapeutic motivations. If so, George's response to his therapist was a repetition of the way he had responded to his mother's verbal, preverbal and nonverbal influences in his childhood years. But there is a difference. *Then* he had "obliged" by acting the part allotted to him by his mother's script; *now* it was a new parent figure who wrote the scenario and whose therapeutically more desirable motivations called the tune. That the patient's response to the therapist had been a mixture of compliance and resistance, as illustrated by his associations to the dream, was in itself a sign of progress. It adumbrated his growing capacity to assert himself against parental control and to pit his will against "father" in a more realistic and less explosive manner than he had before.

If this is true, the patient's apparent telepathic dream is indeed more than a freakish incident unrelated to the existing analytic situation. Apart from its far-reaching theoretical implications touching upon the pathology of the schizophrenic process, it suggests that, unknown to the therapist himself, his therapeutic presence—or his personal myth—did have a discernible influence upon the patient after all. The unintended telepathic element contained in the dream was in fact a faint echo from the unconscious, signalling the operation of an effective myth in the doctor-patient relationship. If so, it may well be considered an index of its "effectiveness."

At the same time, the incident highlights a new aspect of what we described as both the patient's and the therapist's regression in the service of treatment. We noted that the regression, in this case, was not merely confined to the patient's doctrinal compliance; to the therapist's empathetic "fusion" with the patient or to a temporary reenactment in the treatment situation of a symbiotic pattern, duplicating the early mother-child relationship. The "regression" seemed to be conducive to a fleeting existential shift going beyond the bounds of a purely subjective experience. It suggests an actual breakthrough to an unusual level of psychological functioning of those involved in the incident.

Whether or not it is still legitimate to attach a regressive label to such an event must remain an open question. What has originally been described as the creative artist's regression in the service of the ego may just as well be regarded as a shift to a higher plane of self-expression and self-actualization. By the same token the emergence—or reactivation—of myth in the treatment situation may be indicative of a trend to progressive rather than to regressive adaptations.

Determining the proper place of psi phenomena in the broader evolutionary scheme of things is still more problematical. Is psi a throwback to a primitive, archaic pattern of communication between person and person? Is it a faltering attempt to establish, at least temporarily, a more "perfect" union between them than that attainable by verbal communication? Do psi phenomena open up new avenues in the course of the growing diversification of the evolutionary process, or are they merely leading into a blind alley?

Only time—time viewed in the evolutionary perspective—will tell.

REFERENCES

1. MASSERMAN, J.: Historical-Comparative and Experimental Roots of Short-Term Therapy, in: Short-Term Psychotherapy, ed. L. R. Wolberg, Grune & Stratton, New York 1965.
2. ALEXANDER, F.: c.f. Chapter XI (22).
3. HOLLINGSHEAD, A. B. and REDLICH, F. C.: Social Class a Mental Illness, Wiley & Sons, New York 1958, 1960.
4. KAHN, R. L. and POLLACK, M.: Sociopsychological Factors Affecting Therapist-Patient Relationships, in: Psychoanalysis and Human Values, ed. J. Masserman, Grune & Stratton, New York 1960.
5. WOLBERG, L. R.: The Technique of Short-Term Therapy, c.f. (1).
6. WAGGONER, R. W.: The Integration of Therapy, in: Progress in Psychotherapy, Vol. IV, ed. J. Masserman and J. L. Moreno, Grune & Stratton, New York 1959.
7. EHRENWALD, J.: c.f. Chapter XII (12).
———— The Telepathy Hypothesis and Schizophrenia, 2nd Internat. Congress for Psychiatry, Zurich, Vol. III, p. 186, 1957.
———— c.f. Chapter VII (2).
8. BYCHOWSKI, G.: The Ego and the Introjects, Psychoanal. Quart. 23, 11, 1956.
9. EISENBUD, J.: c.f. Chapter VII (3).
10. ULLMAN, M.: On the Occurrence of Telepathic Dreams, Journ. Amer. Soc. Psychic. Res. April 1959.

— XVIII —

Psychotherapy: Models and Metadynamics

The case histories reviewed in the preceding chapters illustrate three major phases of the therapeutic process: (1) the phase of the myth-induced existential shift; (2) the didactic phase, concerned with education and reeducation; overlapping with, or followed by, (3) the psychodynamic phase, represented in "pure culture" by Freudian analysis. At the same time, however, the three phases are paradigmatic of three different models of psychotherapy.

The primitive healer attributes sickness, mental or physical, to supernatural influences brought to bear upon the patient. He believes he is capable of curing him by the proper use of magic rituals, spells and incantations. It should be noted, however, that as a general rule he makes no claims of enduring therapeutic results. For obvious reasons, they are at best confined to symptom removal. Yet this primitive concept of sickness and cure by the magician's myth is readily accepted by both sufferer and healer. In fact, their shared belief tends to reinforce the affective leverage of their myth and to assure its efficacy in the group at large.

Faith healing by a priestly healer is based on much the same principles. The difference is that in this case divine revelation or diverse articles of faith substitute for myth; that the healer's omnipotence is displaced to the divinity, and that in addition to mere symptom removal, lasting cure or salvation is promised in the hereafter.

Healing by magic, myth or faith is in effect the earliest prototype of psychotherapy (see Table I). It was undoubtedly governed by the principle of trial and error. But while apparent cures were there for everyone to see, the magician's failures and errors were taken as part of the natural order of things, and the efficacy of salvation was luckily exempt from the test of pragmatic experience. Within these limitations primitive healing obviously met existing social, cultural and spiritual needs. This may account for its stubborn survival over the millennia. Indeed we have seen that the belief in miraculous cures by faith or myth-induced affective leverage—and by this alone—is still widely held in our culture. As can be seen in our Table, it usually dispenses with rational guidance, education or reeducation, to say nothing of psychodynamics in the modern sense.

Our second prototype stands for a didactic approach, including diverse rational interventions of the traditional kind. They range from persuasion, admonition and exhortation to suggestion, moral therapy and spiritual

TABLE I

Four Models of Psychotherapy

Models	I	II	III	IV
Guiding principles	Primitive healing	Guidance, persuasion, conditioning	Analytic psychother-apies	Psychoanalysis, revised and expanded
Myth, therapist's motiv.; pat. expectat.	+ + +	Ø	Ø	+
Reeducation, "working through" learning theory	Ø	+ + +	+ +	+ +
Psychodynamics	Ø	Ø	+ + +	+ + +

The vertical columns indicate four models of psychotherapy evolved from a primitive prototype based on magic and myth. As shown in the horizontal column, the mythical element has been purged by most "scientific" models. On the other hand, all models except primitive healing, include a didactic purpose, overt or covert, in their approach. Model III stands for various schools of psychoanalysis, Freudian and neo-Freudian. They are all based on psychodynamic principles but ignore myth. Model IV stands for a revised and expanded version of psychoanalysis advocated by the author. It includes dynamic as well as metadynamic principles and aims at their integration with myth and principles of learning theory.

guidance, as it was provided through the ages from the Yellow Emperor's Classic on Internal Medicine, 1060 B.C., to the stoic philosophers of antiquity; to the French Encyclopedists; to Alfred Adler's individual psychology; to Rank's will therapy or Viktor Frankl's "logotherapy." Its latest version includes the more recent methods of systematic reeducation, conditioned reflex and reciprocal inhibition therapy developed by Eysenck,[1] Salter,[2] Wolpe,[3] and their associates. Despite wide divergencies, all these methods have one thing in common: they are confident that man, at least potentially, is amenable to reasoning, that he can learn from experience and that developing proper techniques to bring these lessons home to him, should enable the patient to see his erring ways, to give up faulty habits of perception, action or reasoning and to free himself from false beliefs, baseless anxieties or phobias. Once this is accomplished, the patient is considered cured and there is no reason to probe into psychodynamics of transference, countertransference and related problems. In short, representatives of this approach are satisfied with "symptom removal." Such subjective aspects as the patient's sense of self-fulfillment, his quest for happiness and self-realization are ignored, to say nothing of the therapist's personal myth or motivations.

Our third model can be described as the psychodynamic, Freudian or neo-Freudian model. In this model psychodynamic principles have the pride of place. The goal is to provide insight, manage the transference relationship, interpret resistances, fill in amnestic gaps; achieve cathartic release, etc. However, psychoanalysis also places considerable emphasis on "working through," on methodical reeducation, depending on the patient's age, personality and the nature of his problems. Implicitly or explicitly, it includes established principles of learning theory in its approach. Indeed, Franz Alexander,[4] Judd Marmor,[5] Joost Meerloo,[6] and other analysts have rightly pointed out that following the example set by the therapist's personality, assimilating his values and responding to subtle cues in his behavior is an important aspect of every form of psychotherapy, including psychoanalysis.

The psychodynamic model has no use, however, for the therapist's personal myth. It considers vestiges of myth and magic in his personality as symptoms of narcissism, of the infantile quest for magic omnipotence. What is left of them is subjected to strict analytic scrutiny and interpreted out of existence. "Cure" is achieved by rational, psychodynamic interventions. It aims at more than mere symptom removal. It seeks to eradicate the roots of conflict from which the patient's illness has sprung. The ultimate aim is reconstruction of personality and attainment of maturity.

It will be noted that these three models give a reasonable account of the three principal aspects of the therapeutic approach. But they fail to make allowance for a fourth version: for a model encompassing and integrating the main features of the first three models.

Our fourth model stands for such an attempt at integration. Like a three-color print, it results from superimposing the plates reserved for the three colors. It is a diagrammatic representation of a revised and expanded system of psychoanalysis as it is conceived here. It is based on such principles of psychodynamics as have stood the test of contamination-proof analytic fact-finding, unadulterated by observer bias and doctrinal compliance. Like the Freudian model, it includes principles of learning theory in its frame of reference. But it also makes allowance for the mythical factor which is disregarded in the classical model. It integrates myth shared by therapist and patient with the scientific approach. It fully endorses the incorporation of modern ego psychology into Freudian theory. But it also calls for its extension into largely neglected, ignored, or "repressed" mythical dimensions.

It is needless to say that our four models portray the real thing on a high level of abstraction. Like a non-objective image of the human face, they bear no resemblance to any particular case in point. In order to

do justice to special characteristics of a given school, or to individual contributions of its originator, more elaborate models would be called for,
embracing more than the three major variables presented in our Table.

We have to realize, furthermore, that our portrayals are based on publicly
stated propositions and guiding principles of the diverse schools. They
take their authorized self-image at its face value, as it were. Yet it goes
without saying that a model confined to registering such surface markings
only, is apt to leave us in the dark as to what is hidden under the surface.
In order to arrive at useful generalizations about the rationale, the dynamics and the presumed *modus operandi* of a given school, we must therefore extend our inquiry into a study in depth: we must look for what
can be described as their underlying *metadynamics*.

Metadynamics is that aspect of a particular psychotherapeutic school of
thought which is generally ignored in its public pronouncements but is
tacitly implied and utilized in its practice. Metadynamics views public
pronouncements and even dynamic formulations of this order as "manifest contents" whose latent meaning has yet to be explored. It is the
dynamics underlying diverse, seemingly conflicting, systems of psychodynamic thought, and it applies with equal strength to those schools
which claim they have nothing to learn from psychodynamics and which
have a blind spot preventing them from seeing its operation in their own
approach.

                    ❁   ❁   ❁

What, then, can we learn from applying the principles of metadynamics
to the four models of psychotherapy outlined here? How do they apply
to the diverse subclasses of the didactic and psychoanalytic models current
in our day?

We noted that in our first model the magician's myth is the key factor.
There is no conscious purpose to apply psychodynamic principles, to en-
lighten, to teach. But even here the practitioner's words and acts are
predicated on his groping attempts at making sense, at shedding light into
darkness, at serving as a guide to the perplexed. The word *educate*, it
will be recalled, is derived from *educere*, leading forth. Even the magician
acts as an educator, without meaning to do so. At the same time he knows
how to manipulate the leverage effects of his personal myth and to use its
dynamics—or metadynamics—to its best advantage.

Our second model is based on guidance, persuasion, exhortation and
ultimately on diverse means of reconditioning and reeducation developed by
the behavioral therapists. The "moral therapists" of a past age have carried
the methods of classroom and pulpit to the patient's bedside. The modern
behavioral therapists have put them to the test of animal experiments
and seek to apply to their therapeutic approach what they have learned in

the laboratory. They focus on readily discernible external behavior and virtually ignore inner experiences. They are not interested in psychodynamics and scoff at the emphasis on interpretation and analytic insight. Their therapeutic goal is removal of symptoms and they do not set their sights on such lofty or ill-defined goals as making the unconscious conscious, integrating personality structure or helping a person towards maturity or self-realization. Their model of psychotherapy is derived from learning theory, not from Freud's metapsychological concepts. To Eysenck, Wolpe, Salter and their associates, libido theory is a myth—and taking myth seriously would be more objectionable than even Freud's theory of libido.

Yet it is readily understood that the behavioral therapist, despite his avowed purpose of functioning as what Krasner called a "social reinforcement machine" (see Chapter XI), is bound to affect his patient's behavior in keeping with the patient's expectations of help, sympathy and understanding—to say nothing of the therapist's own motivations to help. Recent literature of conditioned reflex therapy, reciprocal inhibition, or desensitization treatment testifies to the therapeutic zeal and crusading spirit of their originators. We noted that even Wolpe's critics are impressed with his dynamic personality and persuasiveness.[7] This is reinforced by the behavioral therapist's widely publicized challenges to the psychoanalytic "establishment," and by the ever-present restlessness of the *Zeitgeist* for which there is always "time for a change." This very insistence on change; on ever repeated swings of the pendulum from one extreme to the other; on recurrent existential shifts, may be an added factor in favor of both the merits and the myth of behavioral therapy.

Thus, despite the deceptively simple surface appearance of the behavioral approach, it cannot conceal altogether its underlying metadynamics. The behavioral therapist, despite his protestations, cannot dispense with what we called his therapeutic "presence," his personal myth. The spoken or unspoken promise of help is an integral aspect of his approach. Nor can he suppress his patient's doctrinal compliance and its attending leverage effects. He is also likely to have a hard time in sorting out responses of this order from the effects of behavioral therapy in a stricter sense.

Turning our attention to the third—the Freudian—model, we have to realize that it is in effect a composite picture of several consecutive stages of the spiritual growth—and growing pains—of their originator. Its latest version goes far beyond what J. G. Miller described as Freud's early Neurological, Reflex Arc, or Hydraulic Models.[8] It includes more recent contributions to ego psychology. It makes allowance for the principles of learning theory. It is committed to an essentially causal-deterministic outlook;

to a naturalistic, biological orientation. It pays less attention to cultural and situational factors or interpersonal dynamics, but it is greatly concerned with problems of adaptation. Through Hartmann's formulations of the conflict-free zone of the ego, it has even admitted a measure of freedom into its frame of reference.

But we noted that one thing is missing from the Freudian model: any reference to the therapist's myth. Freud himself, we stated, had an attitude bordering on reaction formation against surviving vestiges from the discredited past. He looked with suspicion at "Oceanic" feelings and was wary of existential shifts. Although he was fully aware of what we described as doctrinal compliance as a potential source of error in the analytic situation, he failed to make allowance for its metadynamics in his system of thought.

It is these three more or less neglected ingredients of the psychoanalytic situations: the therapist's personal myth, myth-induced existential shifts, and the patient's doctrinal compliance which fall within the purview of metadynamics. In effect, it is their hidden metadynamics which accounts for their conspicuous—or inconspicuous—absence from the classical model.

Despite differences, Alfred Adler's individual psychology ranks as one of the major subclasses of the Freudian model.[9] Thus it is not by coincidence that it purged itself with equal zeal of all remaining vestiges of magic and myth. Even more than the Freudian system, it has aspired to become a therapy of "pure reason"—if not of ordinary common sense. Individual psychology has a frankly didactic purpose. At the same time it has substituted Freudian determinism with a consistently teleological, Thomistic system of explanations. It maintains its link with biological aspects by calling attention to the part played by organ inferiority and its compensation. By contrast to Freud's libido theory, it minimizes the importance of sexuality in the origin of neuroses. If Freud tends to sexualize the individual's quest for power, Adler reduces the power of sex to the point of insignificance or turns it into one of the tools in the quest for power. Thus Individual psychology has developed an explanatory system essentially based on one single variable. Nevertheless, some of its propositions can easily be converted into Freudian terms. Adler's inferiority feeling bears close resemblance to Freud's concept of castration anxiety. His "masculine protest" can roughly be translated into Freud's penis envy; the Oedipal conflict is viewed as the pampered child's need to vie for or to monopolize father's or mother's love and attention. The Freudian unconscious, on the other hand, is turned into the stepchild of Adler's psychology: it is simply that part of a person's mental content which he does not care to recall or to look at. Dreams, slips of the tongue and neurotic symptoms reflect a person's "style of life." The Freudian superego, instead of being derived from introjected authority, is projected back into the outside world and designated as the feeling of social responsibility or *Gemeinschaftsgefuehl*.

Based on these more or less loosely knit general propositions, Adlerian therapy aims at reducing inferiority feelings, at correcting faulty habits of thinking and increasing social cooperation. Thus Adlerian therapists specifically subscribe to the principles of learning theory but have no use for psychodynamics in the Freudian sense. That they ignore the metadynamics of myth, doctrinal compliance and the myth-induced existential shift goes without saying.

Jung's system of thought is in effect a concatenation of many systems. Like the Freudian model, it is a blend of several consecutive stages of Jung's thinking. But the concepts of a more or less thoroughly desexualized libido; of the individual versus the collective unconscious; of diverse psychological types; of the mythical powers of the archetypes have remained recurrent themes in his doctrine. We noted, however, in Chapter IX that in the end Jung attributed to myth decisive importance in shaping the destiny of man. For him myths and archetypal symbols are at the root of organic or spiritual growth and development. They are timeless, immutable, but at the same time the fount and origin of change, the repositories of purpose and value in the universe.

We also noted that the principles of symbolic representation, of transference, resistance, repression can all be found in Jung, though less consistently so than in the Freudian system. The concept of reaction-formation and other defenses seems to be substituted—or blurred—by the principle of complementarity, e.g., in dreams versus the waking experience—in extraversion versus intraversion. There is no Jungian equivalent of Freud's topographical, genetic or economic principles. Personality tends to be broken up into a cluster of such mythical entities as the Anima, the Animus, the Shadow, the Persona, the Soul and the Self.

By contrast to Freud, Jung explicitly advocates the use of both causal-deterministic and teleological explanatory principles. His subsequent introduction of the concept of synchronicity made his epistemology even more inclusive, though at the same time less "systematic." In effect, we have seen that his approach ranges from the scientific to the frankly mystical. It includes Freudian, Adlerian as well as existentialistic principles. At the same time Jung did not hesitate to serve as a mentor and spiritual guide for his patients, trying to steer them towards the goal of ever higher planes of individuation.

Yet as pointed out in Chapter IX, his thinking was vitiated by his unconscious reaction formations against what to him had become intolerable "Freudian" truths and by his need to explain away or to rationalize, in parapsychological terms, some of his hallucinatory and delusional experiences. Thus his system of thought was wide open to the dynamics of myth but had no methodological safeguards to protect him from the pitfalls of delusion. Despite his penetrating vision and profound insights, Jung remained unaware of some of his own "complexes" and, by implication, of the metadynamics involved in his approach.

H. S. Sullivan's formulation of interpersonal relationships[10] focuses on yet another aspect of dynamic psychiatry. It is true that psychoanalysis was fully aware of the part played by parental influence in the growing child. This is what elsewhere I described as primary environmentalism.[11] But Sullivan and the diverse culturalist schools which he inspired attribute prime importance to *inter*personal as opposed to *intra*personal or intra-psychic conflict in the etiology of neuroses. They stand for what can be termed as *secondary environmentalism*.

Still, Sullivan did not neglect such biological variables as physiological "deficits" or needs and their satisfaction, and paid careful attention to the developmental and maturational sequence of growth. At the same time he had a sharp eye for the wide variety of security operations used by the individual to reduce or control anxiety, for the patient's tendency to selec-tive inattention and for his diverse patterns of avoidances. Thus Sullivan includes both biological, cultural and situational factors in his frame of reference. His approach too is essentially psychodynamic and he too uses methods of reward and punishment as guiding principles in psycho-therapeutic practice.

His concept of the therapist's participant observation in the treatment situation strikes a new chord. In effect, it adumbrates the existentialist emphasis on personal involvement, commitment and encounter. The same is true for the formulation of diverse modes of experience, ranging from the earliest "prototaxic" to the "parataxic" and ultimately the "syntaxic" modes. However, despite his marked intuitive gifts and empathic under-standing of patients—especially schizophrenics—Sullivan left no place for the part played by myth and myth-induced leverage effects in his system. The goals of Sullivan's therapy are thoroughly rational in their planning and execution. The Sullivanian therapist aims at arriving at an acceptable compromise with his patient. Whatever therapeutic results he achieves is a "function of negotiation" as Ford and Urban put it.[12] Sullivan's system is, in effect, just as mythophobic as Freud's was.

Karen Horney's contribution to psychotherapy could be described as a creative blend of Freudian, Adlerian and Sullivanian precepts.[13] Perhaps she will be less noted for her gifts as a systematizer than for her illuminat-ing impressionistic descriptions of various "trends" or "patterns" of neurotic behavior. Equally important are her holistic concepts of personality structure and her clear formulations of the part played by cultural factors as opposed to innate biological determinants.

Horney remained close to Freud in subscribing to basic psychodynamic principles. She adopted some of Adler's contributions in her theory of neuroses. But by contrast to other neo-Freudians she was well aware of the mythical implications of psychotherapy. Towards the end of her career she became increasingly interested in Far Eastern thinking and existential philosophy. Since her death this trend has been further developed by Harold Kelman and his associates.[14] But for the absence of anything resembling such an "establishment," Kelman would perhaps be in the existentialist camp. Similar considerations apply to Erich Fromm's brilliant contributions to the field. He has in effect gone far in trying to reconcile the existentialist and psychoanalytic approach.

We have seen in Chapter X that with the advent of existential analysis the pendulum has swung all the way from Freud's mythophobic to the frankly mythophilic side of the scale. The existentialist position, we stated, is primarily rooted in myth. Although essentially eclectic and ready to employ psychodynamic principles in their practice, many existentialists are just as critical of Freud as are the behavioral therapists on the other end of the spectrum. Yet the existentialists object to Freud for the opposite reasons. They object to his overemphasis on biological factors; to his strictly deterministic, causal-reductive reasoning and to his avowed materialistic orientation. At the same time it should be noted that the existentialist, placing as he does, *value* at the center of his universe, cannot help but serve as a model and spiritual guide for his patients. In spite of his protestations, he too smuggles the contraband of reeducation, guidance and teaching by example into his therapeutic armamentarium.

There is another gap in the existential analyst's self-image and analytic self-appraisal. Although myth, in many layers and at many stages of its life-cycle is one of the guiding principles of his therapeutic approach, he seems to recoil from its deeper dynamic evaluation. He is largely unaware of the metadynamics of myth and, consequently, of the nature of his own impact upon his patients.

*   *   *

What, in the light of this condensed review of diverse schools of contemporary psychotherapy, and of their underlying metadynamics—is the key factor in the patient's therapeutic response? What is the common denominator in their respective therapeutic approaches? The reader who has followed the argument pursued in the preceding pages and has glanced at the Table at the beginning of this chapter will not be surprised when he is led to the conclusion that the element common to all is myth—even though the conclusion itself may not necessarily be his own.

Indeed it may be well to recall at this point that other authorities in search of the common denominator have come to different conclusions. There is Jules Masserman whose caustic criticism of diverse mythical concepts surviving in psychoanalytic theory was quoted in Chapter VIII. Masserman holds that man has to defend himself at all costs against the danger of being overwhelmed by the "uncontrollable immensity of the universe." Man cannot tolerate the thought of his mortality, of his physical impotence and of the coldness of his fellow human beings. To counter his anxieties, he develops certain Ur-defenses, delusions or myths: the myth of personal invulnerability and immortality; the delusion of omnipotence and omniscience; the illusion of amity and fraternity of men. In Masserman's view, psychotherapy does not aim at providing insights or "putative truths." It consists in the "reestablishment of certain delusions necessary to all mankind." Meeting these needs, however fantastic or unrealistic they may be, seems to lie "at the very core of all therapy."[15]

Perhaps such a formulation sounds more cynical than it is meant to be. Masserman emphatically endorses the reality of the patient's need and the necessity of giving him what he is looking for. The cleavage between Masserman's conclusions and the views presented here thus lies in the fact that he abhors myths, denounces them as delusions and deplores that they are "at the core of the psychotherapeutic process," while I have arrived at diametrically opposite conclusions as to the intrinsic value or the merits of myth. Nevertheless, I am perhaps more inclined to agree with Masserman's position than he is likely to agree with me.

J. D. Frank has pointed to yet another common denominator in various types of psychotherapy.[16] Working at the Phipps Clinic in Baltimore, he has adduced impressive evidence that the principal factor, at least in symptom removal, is the mobilization of the patient's expectancy of help. This is equally true for situations of primitive or religious healing as for the Western patient attending a psychiatric outpatients' department. The beneficial effect may well be mediated by a placebo. Indeed Frank suggests that the common factor in all psychotherapy may conceivably be nothing but a placebo effect. He qualifies this statement, however, by adding that other methods of treatment are needed in order to consolidate the gains achieved and to improve the patient's personal functioning.

In this case the difference between Frank's and my formulations is only apparent. Frank would presumably concur that usually the patient's attitude of trust and expectancy is met halfway by the therapist's unspoken but tacitly implied promise of help. In effect, this unspoken promise, interlocking with the patient's attitude of expectancy forms a mutually reinforcing system of circular feedback, characteristic of myth in the making.

Perhaps Frank would also agree that the patient's attitude of expectancy is of a special kind. When I see the flash of lightning in the sky I expect it to be followed by thunder. The subsequent thunder crash will occur regardless of my attitude of expectancy—or its absence. This is in contrast to the pattern of feedback involving the therapist's and the patient's emotionally charged attitudes. Such attitudes, we stated, may be instrumental in bringing about the desired results. It is this quality of effectiveness which distinguishes patient expectations in particular from expectations pertaining to strictly mechanical, causal-deterministic sequences of events. Frank's notion of *expectancy* is thus a concept *sui generis*, calling for a special appellation. Considerations of historic continuity, coupled with its effectiveness and propensity to circular feedback, make it indeed barely distinguishable from myth.

On the basis of his rich clinical experience, Judd Marmor has arrived at yet another conclusion.[5] Analyzing the therapeutic approaches of the various schools, he too is struck by the patients' tendency to validate their therapist's theories with their productions; he too points to the decisive importance of what we described as doctrinal compliance. But Marmor concludes from his observations that the patient's response to therapy, psychoanalytic or otherwise, is essentially a learning process. The dynamics of insight, abreaction and positive transference notwithstanding, the patient inevitably takes the therapist as a model with whom he identifies and whose behavior he copies. Conversely, "whether or not the analyst is consciously tempted to act as a teacher, model or ideal to his patient, he inevitably does so to a greater or lesser extent." This, in Marmor's view, is "the central aspect of the treatment process." Put in our terms, the learning process, even though it is by no means the stated purpose of the analytic approach, nevertheless is an integral part of its metadynamics.

Marmor's argument certainly carries conviction as far as the familiar methods of a scientific psychotherapy are concerned. It applies to Model II of our Table, with its main emphasis on Guidance, Persuasion and Conditioning. It is an unavoidable ingredient of the psychodynamic model—of Model III. But it does not apply to Model I: to Primitive Healing with its direct appeal to the patient's magical needs and expectations.

A fourth factor that might conceivably qualify as a common denominator was touched upon in Chapter VII: the part played by telepathy in the therapeutic situation. The problem was recently discussed by Emilio Servadio,[17] Joost Meerloo[6a] and other psychoanalysts. Yet we noted that at the present stage of our knowledge considerations of this order go beyond the testable limits of myth. In the absence of more substantial experimental evidence, the potential part played by the psi factor in psychotherapy must remain a matter of conjecture.

❊   ❊   ❊

If these considerations lead us back to myth as the common denominator, it is necessary to qualify such a broad generalization. It may be true that myth in the open, or myth in disguise, is a virtually ubiquitous ingredient in all schools of psychotherapy. However, this does not mean that it is also an effective therapeutic agent.

Fish breathe through gills. Human embryos, at an early stage of their development, show the same structures in their anatomy. Rudimentary vestiges of gills can still be found in the adult. This does not indicate, however, that man, in a pinch, can fall back on atavistic methods of underwater breathing. Still, we have seen that myth and magic, the lowly hand-maiden of myth, are more than mere atavistic remnants of our mental equipment. They may become reactivated in precisely such psychological emergencies as the psychotherapist is called upon to deal with.

To change our metaphor, checkmarks, positive or negative, entered in the appropriate boxes of our synoptic table of psychotherapies, are not enough to do justice to the complexities of life. For months or years, myth may lie dormant in a stalemated analytic situation. Like Sleeping Beauty of the fairy tale, it has to be aroused by a properly motivated suitor in order to be brought back to life. Nor does its absence from the stated premises—from the "manifest" content—of a given psychotherapeutic system of thought indicate that the mythical element is altogether missing from the metadynamics of its latent content. This is true for the psychodynamics of the doctor-patient relationship under both modern and primitive conditions. It is there, even without a Geiger counter ticking away to indicate its presence. In a similar vein, a didactic slant is an intrinsic feature of the therapeutic situation regardless of its stated objective and avowed principles.

The case histories discussed in the preceding chapters have to be viewed with these complexities in mind. They suggest that the therapeutic process is in effect a recapitulation, or rerun, in abridged historical sequence, of the four models of psychotherapy featured in our Table. At the beginning there was myth. The therapist's personal myth and the myth-induced leverage effect is a throw-back, as it were, to a past developmental stage of psychotherapy. It is a regressive feature "in the service of treatment." At the same time it represents the opening phase of every psychotherapeutic approach: from faith healing to psychoanalysis or conditioned reflex therapy. It sets the stage for the unfolding, in the second phase, of the dynamics of the doctor-patient relationship, with its attending aspects of learning, education and reeducation. In psychoanalysis proper it overlaps—or is blended with—the third, the psychodynamic phase, aiming at insight, cathartic release, or "working through."

It is readily understood that it is the judicious combination and integration of the three phases—and therapeutic approaches—represented by our models which is likely to yield optimal results. Whether or not this goal will be consummated does not depend on the formal technique applied, on the use of couch or easychair, or on the length of the treatment alone. It depends on mobilizing in the treatment situation of all the personality resources of both patient and therapist. It requires both method *and* myth—therapeutic motivation *and* technical skills of the highest order.

On the other hand, confining attention to one single aspect of the therapeutic process cannot possibly do justice to the wholeness of man. St. Augustine has stated some 1500 years ago that the essence of illness is the lack of wholeness or completeness of man. This is just as true today as it was then. "Cure," as it is conceived here, presupposes more than symptom removal, more than the individual's adjustment to cultural demands and societal requirements. Ideally it includes all of these accomplishments. But at the same time it aims at enabling man to break out of his precarious adaptation to a single rigidly maintained level of functioning. It sets its sights at freeing him to move from one mode of existence to another.

Trying to extend control over existential shifts of this order is in effect an example of modern man's quest for ever-increasing degrees of personal freedom and self-fulfillment. Potentially, man is a citizen of many worlds and many modes of existence. His home is a pluralistic universe, as William James put it. We have seen that it ranges from Western man's standard, technological, mode of experience, to the satori of the Zen masters; from dreaming to wakefulness; from the normal to the paranormal; from the sacred to the profane; from primary process functioning to the artist's creative self-expression and the therapist's regression in the service of treatment; from compulsive rigidity to the schizophrenic's headlong plunge into darkness and insanity and, hopefully, to his reemergence to sanity again.

Our argument has tried to arrive at least at a tentative understanding of the dynamics and metadynamics involved in these existential shifts. It is perhaps not too presumptuous to expect that such an understanding should bring man closer to the broader objectives of psychotherapy: the integration and reconciliation of conflicting aspects of his personality, enabling him to live in a modicum of peace with himself and with his society.

REFERENCES

1. EYSENCK, H. J.: c.f. Chapter VIII (8) and (8a).
2. SALTER, A.: c.f. Chapter XII (15).
3. WOLPE, J.: Psychotherapy by Reciprocal Inhibition, Stanford Univ. Press, 1958.
4. ALEXANDER, F.: c.f. Chapter XI (22).
5. MARMOR, J.: c.f. Chapter VIII (15) and Chapter XVI (4a).
6. MEERLOO, J.: Illness and Cure, Grune & Stratton, New York 1964.
   ———— Hidden Communion, Garrett Publications, New York 1964.
7. THIGPEN, C. H. and CLECKLEY, H. M.: c.f. Chapter XII (16).
8. MILLER, J. G.: Psychoanalysis and Systems Theory, in: Science and Psychoanalysis, ed. J. Masserman, Grune & Stratton, New York 1958.
9. ADLER, A.: The Practice and Theory of Individual Psychology, Harcourt Brace, New York 1924.
10. SULLIVAN, H. S.: c.f. Chapter XI (1).
11. EHRENWALD, J.: c.f. Chapter XII (12).
12. FORD, D. H. and URBAN, H. B.: Systems of Psychotherapy, Wiley and Sons, New York 1964.
13. HORNEY, K.: New Ways in Psychoanalysis, Norton, New York 1939.
14. KELMAN, H.: c.f. Chapter XII (9) and Chapter XIV (18a).
15. MASSERMAN, J.: c.f. Chapter VIII (11).
16. FRANK, J. D.: c.f. Chapter IV (5).
17. SERVADIO, E.: Unconscious and Paranormal Factors in Healing and Recovery, The 15th F. W. H. Myers Memorial Lecture, Soc. Psychic, Research, London 1963.

Index

[library stamp]

WIDENER COLLEGE
WOLFGRAM
LIBRARY
CHESTER, PA.

DATE DUE

DATE DUE			
DEC 1 8 1978			
DEC 1 0 1980			
AUG 1 8 1982			
NOV 1 0 1982			
AUG 2 6 1994			
NOV 1 2 1997			
MAY 1 0 2000			
DEC 1 7 2009			
GAYLORD			PRINTED IN U.S.A